Bumper PUB QUIZ BOOK

OVER **5000** QUESTIONS
TO MAKE YOU THE MASTER
OF PUB QUIZZES

Bath · New York · Cologne · Melbourne · Delhi
Hong Kong · Shenzhen · Singapore · Amsterdam

This edition published by Parragon Books Ltd in 2015

Parragon Books Ltd
Chartist House
15–17 Trim Street
Bath BA1 1HA, UK
www.parragon.com

ISBN 978-1-4723-8050-0

Printed in China

Contents

Introduction

This quiz book contains over 5,000 quiz questions, with a range of difficulties and topics to ensure there is something suitable for everyone, no matter their quizzing ability. As such, they would make great source material for a pub quiz.

There are 314 separate quizzes, one per page, and full solutions are given at the back of the book so that you can check your answers.

For some of the quirkier questions that ask for numerical answers, it's up to you how accurate you require yourself to be. It's not expected that you will get the precise answer at the back, but instead to see how close you can get! For a pub quiz, they would work well for 'closest team wins' style questions.

Good luck, and have fun!

The Bumper *PUB* Quiz Book

Quiz 1

1. What is the weight of the men's Olympic discus?

2. In which country did the torte originate?

3. *Rain Man* won the Academy Award for Best Picture in which year?

4. Which desert is located in the west of India?

5. What continent did break-dancing originate in?

6. In 1996, militant Taliban leaders seized the capital of which country?

7. What does a caterpillar morph into?

8. What type of computer document is a 'WAV' file?

9. What is the name of Jerry's best friend in *Seinfeld*?

10. Why should you not feed chocolate to a dog?

11. In which city will you find the Brandenburg Gate?

12. What country announced that it had nuclear weapons on February 10, 2005?

13. At what age did Tiger Woods become the youngest Masters Champion?

14. What is a 'julep'?

15. Which of the following people created a cosmetics empire: Gloria Vanderbilt, Mary Kay Ash or Warren Buffet?

16. In what year was the sci-fi book *Starship Troopers* published?

The Bumper *PUB* Quiz Book
Quiz 2

① Which ancient civilization invented the clock?

② What is a 'goa'?

③ What kind of animal is a Sea Monkey?

④ In the movie *Ghost*, who plays the murdered Sam Wheat?

⑤ Syria is located on which continent?

⑥ Which one of these drinks contains no alcohol: Cherry Bang, Pink Lady or Shirley Temple?

⑦ Which nationality does chorizo belong to?

⑧ Other than a dance, what can the word 'mambo' mean?

⑨ What modern-day African country was home to the kingdoms of Ile-Ife and Benin?

⑩ Golfer Rory McIlroy is a native of which country?

⑪ What was the name of the first major Japanese vessel, a heavy cruiser, sunk by a US submarine in World War 2?

⑫ Which Cambridge comedy group has alumni including Hugh Laurie, David Mitchell and Simon Bird?

⑬ Which of these planets is not one of the inner planets of our solar system: Earth, Mars, Mercury or Saturn?

⑭ What is a neuron?

⑮ The electron flow in a circuit passes through an NPN transistor from ___ to ___?

⑯ The Wombats' song *Kill the Director* is about what film starring Cameron Diaz and Kate Winslet?

The Bumper *PUB* Quiz Book
Quiz 3

1. What is the capital of Djibouti?

2. What position did soccer player Ronaldo play?

3. Batrachophobia is the fear of what?

4. What is the term for synchronizing the refresh cycle of video cameras?

5. The UN's 'Trafficking Protocol' refers to the trafficking of what?

6. What does a curved line beneath a series of notes indicate in music?

7. Who plays the wife of Will Ferrell's character in *The Other Guys*?

8. Who was the first Norman King of England?

9. How many astronauts manned each Apollo mission?

10. What Japanese spirit is served warm?

11. What Nigerian dictator died on June 8th, 1998?

12. The Fray is a rock band based out of which major US city?

13. Prince Charles became the Prince of Wales and the Earl of Chester at what age?

14. Beijing is the capital of what country?

15. Who wrote the 1962 book *The Golden Notebook*?

16. Which is an erythrocyte?

The Bumper *PUB* Quiz Book
Quiz 4

1. Which Italian region is the town of Assisi situated in?

2. Which English monarch faced the Gunpowder Plot in 1605?

3. How many teeth do African elephants have to chew their food with?

4. Who was the eldest son of Saddam Hussein?

5. Which major river is associated with Cairo?

6. Who composed the scores for both *Fletch* and *Beverly Hills Cop*?

7. The airport code ROM designates which European airport?

8. In ballet, as well as in French, what is another term for 'arms'?

9. How many years are in a decade?

10. What is the process of adding young fermented beer to a finished beer called?

11. At what age did Kelly Holmes start to get involved in running: 8, 10, 12 or 14?

12. If you 'lour', what are you doing?

13. What is the name for the branch-like tube that makes up the body of a fungus?

14. What muscle does a 'barbell sumo deadlift' exercise target?

15. Which country's flag does not have the same pattern on both sides?

16. How many 'takes' were used by The Beatles to record 'Twist and Shout'?

The Bumper *PUB* Quiz Book
Quiz 5

1. The members of the UK cabinet must be members of one of which two institutions?

2. What number is equal to the Roman numeral MDCXVI?

3. The Louvre is located in what country?

4. To the nearest 5 per cent, how many of Indonesia's 17,000 islands are permanently inhabited?

5. If you ordered 'uni' in a Japanese restaurant, what would you get served?

6. Who became UK Poet Laureate in 1972?

7. What pungent vegetable should you not feed a dog?

8. Which British rider won the Tour de France yellow jersey 13 times in 2013?

9. What is glucose?

10. Who played the lead role in *The Wolf of Wall Street*

11. What was the fate of Mao Zedong's widow Jiang Qing?

12. What is a 'phantasm'?

13. A great egret is which type of animal?

14. In geology, what is a 'serac'?

15. In what year was Leon Trotsky expelled from Russia?

16. What is energy generated by falling or flowing water called?

The Bumper *PUB* Quiz Book
Quiz 6

1. Which London theatre was known as 'The Globe' until 1994?

2. With a population of around 15 million, what is the capital of Bangladesh?

3. What is the name of the campground at the Walt Disney World Resort in Florida?

4. 'Esmerelda' is a Spanish word for the green colour of what gemstone?

5. On a book, what is an EAN?

6. About what percentage of solar radiation is absorbed by the Earth's atmosphere, oceans and land masses?

7. Which John Cusack film, set in New York at Christmas, follows two people destined to be together?

8. Who was the first UK Prime Minister?

9. Which actor plays the main character, Ou-yang Feng, in the 2008 film *Ashes of Time (Redux)*?

10. Who was the creator of *Babylon 5*?

11. Which track was a hit ballad for Lita Ford with Ozzy Osbourne?

12. What are Doc Martens?

13. The Mediterranean island of Cyprus claims which capital city?

14. What is the term for the taste of a white wine with a too-high acid level?

15. What co-founder of *National Geographic* was better known for his work in telephony?

16. At which age did Maria Sharapova begin to play tennis?

Quiz 7

1. In medicine, what do the letters 'EEG' stand for?

2. What war was said at the time to be 'the war to end all wars'?

3. What gives a 'brain' cocktail its blood vessels?

4. What is the delusion of being an animal called?

5. Which tennis term is defined as 'a shot that is hit in a high arc'?

6. What is Hamlet's mother called?

7. Who plays the title role in US comedy *Ugly Betty*?

8. How did the name *Audi* originate?

9. What currency is used in Tonga?

10. Beyonce's 2009 release *Halo* was written by Ryan Tedder of which band?

11. What type of animal is a puffin?

12. During World War 1, Germany tried to get which nation to declare war on its neighbouring country, the US?

13. In music, what speed is 'lento'?

14. In Russian history, who were the Oprichniki?

15. Which continent has the lowest average GDP per capita in the world?

16. What was Giorgio Armani originally trained in?

The Bumper PUB Quiz Book
Quiz 8

1. What is the meaning of the medical term 'emesis'?

2. How many fights did boxer Miguel Cotto win in 2011?

3. How many honorary doctorates were awarded to Albert Einstein?

4. Which river in Amsterdam was used to make an Amsterdam beer named for it?

5. 'The inability to digest the predominant sugar of milk' best fits which medical term?

6. In what year was boxer O'Neil Bell born?

7. Which royal couple is credited with forming the nation of Spain?

8. The book *The Greatest Generation* was penned by whom?

9. In a north-west English dialect, what is a 'seg'?

10. What film starring Kevin Dunn as Colonel Hicks was released in 1998?

11. Which country was the first created with the help of the United Nations?

12. Nelson Mandela's third wife was the widow of the former President of what country?

13. What was the third most-visited website in 2014, according to Alexa?

14. What is the name of the Google blog service?

15. What does 'Comun' mean when seen on a bottle of Brazilian wine?

16. What planet in our solar system has the most liquid water on its surface?

Quiz 9

① The Rialto Bridge is one of the four bridges spanning the Grand Canal in which Italian city?

② Which Queen song has the lyric 'Mama, just killed a man, put a gun against his head.'?

③ In what country will Liberian President Charles Taylor serve his jail sentence for war crimes?

④ What type of software program is used to look at web pages?

⑤ A ganache is a combination of cream and what?

⑥ Farfalle is a food item of what type of cuisine?

⑦ From what country does tennis player Richard Gasquet hail?

⑧ What is halitosis?

⑨ Which of these is not an African language family: Afro-Asiatic, Bantu-Hamitic or Niger-Congo?

⑩ What animals does the word 'lagomorph' refer to?

⑪ What character does Robert Pattinson play in the 2008 film *Twilight*?

⑫ What was 'Cambria'?

⑬ Which Central American British territory's highest elevation point is The Bluff at 43m (141ft)?

⑭ Which two letters traditionally follow years that occurred after the birth of Jesus?

⑮ What Arctic sea whale has one long horn on its head?

⑯ Which painting is said to have hung in Sigmund Freud's office?

The Bumper *PUB* Quiz Book
Quiz 10

1. What is the capital of the former protectorate of Sikkim, now a state of India?

2. The Crown Jewels are kept in what part of the Tower of London?

3. In what year did Henry II become King of England?

4. Swollen gums or gums that are tender and bleeding are signs of what disease?

5. Who was the grandson of Genghis Khan?

6. Which 2011 film is named for the day on which Julius Caesar was killed?

7. Renault painted a Formula One chassis what colours to celebrate its 30th anniversary?

8. What bone in the body is often referred to as the 'collar bone'?

9. In the *Twilight* books, what is the name of Bella's mother?

10. What are the two types of cubism?

11. How many chambers does a fish heart have?

12. The 'crepe' originated in what area of France?

13. Which sea lies at one end of the Great Wall of China?

14. What did an 'ell' used to measure?

15. Who wrote the play *A Few Good Men*?

16. What song got the tiger away from Ringo Starr in The Beatles' film *Help!*?

Quiz 11

1. Krueger Beer introduced canned beer in what year: 1925, 1935, 1946 or 1953?

2. In which country would you find the city of Aden?

3. What animal has a baby born at about one inch long and a name that literally means 'I don't know'?

4. In the 1999 film *The Mummy*, what key destination was burned off the map?

5. Who was the first African-American to win the Nobel Peace Prize?

6. What does the literary term 'rident' mean?

7. Who designed the SS uniforms and insignia worn by the military in Nazi Germany?

8. Who won the Booker Prize in 2006 for *The Inheritance of Loss*?

9. What, in Athens, were the Propylaea?

10. What was Wembley Stadium originally known as?

11. What is a 'desmid'?

12. Which Swede won the Boys' Singles event at the 2009 French Open?

13. What is an espresso con panna?

14. What was the Russian-language equivalent of USSR?

15. Who was Alexander the Great's father?

16. What is the fastest-moving insect in the world?

The Bumper *PUB* Quiz Book
Quiz 12

1. Robert Wyatt released what acclaimed album in 2003?

2. Where did Muhammad Ali fight his last fight?

3. How many teeth does a honey badger have?

4. In what year did *Gigi* win the Academy Award for Best Picture?

5. What imprinted German biscuits originated in Baden-Wuttemberg?

6. What tiny island to the east of Australia was named by Lieutenant Henry Lidgbird Ball in 1788?

7. How fast can a leopard run?

8. Why has the zebra never been domesticated and used as a regular means of riding?

9. On maps, what colour is usually used for the London overground network?

10. What meat is the primary ingredient in the US soup 'booyah'?

11. How many sailors survived Ferdinand Magellan's voyage around the world?

12. What year was the Second Temple in Jerusalem destroyed?

13. Who wrote the 1925 classic *Mrs Dalloway*?

14. The Battle of Waterloo was fought 12 miles outside which city?

15. What process does a starfish use to grow a new organism when it is cut into pieces?

16. What term describes a mineral or combination mined for the production of metals?

The Bumper *PUB* Quiz Book
Quiz 13

1. How many internationally recognized time zones does the earth have?

2. Which film won the Best Picture Oscar for 2004?

3. What is considered a normal body temperature for humans?

4. What beauty gadget is used to pluck stray eyebrow hairs?

5. What is the imaginary vertical line that divides the Earth into East and West Hemispheres?

6. How many yards is the penalty mark from the goal line on a standard soccer field?

7. What country completely surrounds The Gambia, except for its coast?

8. What is the first track on The Fray's *How To Save A Life*?

9. What type of creature is a 'thorny devil'?

10. For how long did Rome burn in 64 AD?

11. On what date were the Channel Islands captured by Germany in World War 2?

12. Which of the following brews is not native to Ireland: Guinness, Murphy's or Tetley's?

13. What is the name of the main body of water in the Australian Capital Territory?

14. Which Italian style of art used soil, cement, twigs and newspapers?

15. Which month comes immediately before June?

16. In which layer of the atmosphere does all weather occur?

The Bumper **PUB** Quiz Book
Quiz 14

① Who won the men's singles at the 2014 French Open?

② What is the archipelago of 7,107 islands in the South China Sea known as?

③ Which country considers itself European even though its capital is in Asia?

④ Which painter entitled one of his works 'Where Do We Come From? Who are We? Where Are We Going?'?

⑤ For what branch of physics did Einstein say 'God does not play dice'?

⑥ What bay does water from the River Ganges ultimately discharge into?

⑦ What was the first endangered species to be successfully cloned?

⑧ In 1994, Caleb Carr wrote which classic?

⑨ What is lymphadenopathy a medical term for?

⑩ In what year did William I become King of England?

⑪ What is the cooking technique where you ignite a sauce or other liquid so that it flames?

⑫ Madonna released which album in 2012?

⑬ What does the GQ in GQ Magazine stand for?

⑭ Who was the leading ace for Norway in World War 2?

⑮ Which 2011 film directed by Steven Soderbergh examines the potential repercussions of a pandemic?

⑯ Who crowned Napoleon emperor of France in December 1804?

The Bumper *PUB* Quiz Book
Quiz 15

1. Which writer famously killed his wife while trying to shoot a glass off her head?

2. What botanic name do we give to the petals of a flower?

3. What year was the box-office-bomb *Cutthroat Island* released?

4. Which British island's capital city is Douglas?

5. Which scientific term is defined as a physical particle with a negative charge?

6. What country in South America, with Bogota as its capital, uses the peso as its currency?

7. What kind of weapon is an 'assegai'?

8. Alex Arthur won his first fight by beating Dariusz Snarski in what round in 2002?

9. What is the name of OPI's most popular shade of red nail varnish?

10. What performance gave Irish dance international fame?

11. Who was the father of Muhammad Ali Pasha?

12. 'Bearbrass' was once considered as an alternative name for the capital city today known as what?

13. When was the first commercial short text message (SMS) sent?

14. In what modern-day country did the dog called the Rhodesian Ridgeback originate?

15. Nelson Mandela joined the African National Congress in what year?

16. Which green-skinned fruit is sometimes called the 'chocolate pudding fruit'?

The Bumper *PUB* Quiz Book
Quiz 16

1. What word is used to mean 'stopping' in a medical context?

2. Rastafarians and dreadlocks are associated with which island's culture?

3. Who preceded Fidel Castro as political leader of Cuba?

4. Which Greek mathematician first calculated the value of pi?

5. Kirin is a brewing company found mainly on what continent?

6. What is the largest body of fresh water in Britain?

7. For which film did Christian Bale famously lose almost 30kg (66lb)?

8. Which Spanish King sent the Armada to attack England?

9. What was the first human-made object to break the sound barrier?

10. What London institution is built around the 1857 Round Reading Room?

11. In which country are the majority of homes heated by geothermal energy?

12. Which Dave Matthews song names the official fan club?

13. Which fighter was forced to retire after eight rounds against Felix Sturm in 2012?

14. Which gender of person did Edgar Degas most commonly paint?

15. In what location is the 1997 film *Life is Beautiful* set?

16. What do you traditionally give for a fiftieth anniversary?

The Bumper *PUB* Quiz Book
Quiz 17

① What country in Europe with Sarajevo as its capital uses marka as its currency?

② As of 2014, how many times have FC Barcelona won the European Cup / UEFA Champions League?

③ What are the top growths of a mature tea plant called?

④ Who played Lucy Harmon in the 1996 film *Stealing Beauty*?

⑤ Coulrophobia is the fear of what?

⑥ Doha is the capital of what country?

⑦ Who won the 1998 FIFA World Cup?

⑧ What South American country has Montevideo as its capital?

⑨ Which UK bank is with you 'For the journey'?

⑩ The giant African land snail can grow to be roughly how long?

⑪ After the Battle of Hastings, what did William become known as?

⑫ In what year did Henry VI ascend the English throne?

⑬ What is an 'adze'?

⑭ What is the main energy molecule for the human body?

⑮ What did the Ancient Sumerians add to their calendar every few years to keep it accurate?

⑯ Who wrote the novel *One Flew Over The Cuckoo's Nest*?

The Bumper *PUB* Quiz Book
Quiz 18

1. What is the generic term for very small loose particles of hard, broken rock or minerals?

2. 'Someday love will finally be enough' comes from what Anna Nalick song?

3. In which city did the Thirty Years' War both begin and end?

4. Matt Biondi won seven medals at the 1988 Olympics in which sport?

5. What kind of medical condition is 'alopecia'?

6. Pollo rostizado is a food item of what type of cuisine?

7. In what city was the 2007 film, *The Last Mimzy*, set?

8. A ramp is an example of which of these simple machines: inclined plane, lever or pulley?

9. In which country is Copenhagen Airport located?

10. How many Nazis were convicted at the main trial of the Nuremberg War Crimes Trial?

11. What is the capital city of Lebanon, which borders the Mediterranean Sea?

12. How many title defences did Muhammad Ali make?

13. Where is the Thar Desert?

14. How many countries border Iraq?

15. What hero of an American tall tale was the engineer of the *Cannonball*?

16. Which country's subway system was paralysed by a deadly nerve gas attack in 1995?

The Bumper *PUB* Quiz Book
Quiz 19

1. Which of these factors is in the equation for Newton's Second Law: Acceleration, length, time or volume?

2. What is the name of the Amsterdam version of Gothic architecture?

3. Which African country's highest elevation point is Jabal ash Shanabi?

4. Who was the first sovereign of the United Kingdom, following the 1707 Act of Union?

5. Which musical theatre show features characters Grizabella and Rum Tum Tugger?

6. Which aeronautical term is an aeroplane with a pair of similar-sized wings in vertical alignment?

7. Who directed and starred in *Life Is Beautiful*?

8. What word describes a dance that follows a story line?

9. 'BVD' underwear is short for what name?

10. Which CEO of Apple succeeded Steve Jobs?

11. What World War 1 German fighter pilot was nicknamed 'The Eagle of Lille'?

12. Which *Friends* character got a spin-off series of their own?

13. What is a 'Tortilla'?

14. Who launched the first liquid-propelled rocket?

15. Who founded the United National Independence Party in British-controlled Northern Rhodesia?

16. In what year did the Eastern Bloc nations refuse to participate in the World Cup?

The Bumper *PUB* Quiz Book
Quiz 20

1. What is the primary method of movement for a jerboa?

2. What is the deepest freshwater lake on Earth?

3. What, in science, is a 'petri dish'?

4. What is another name for the Queensland nut or bush nut?

5. *Tonight* was a popular song in 2012 for whom?

6. Which one of Justinian's generals defeated the Persians at the Battle of Dara?

7. Who won the 1996 French Singles Championship?

8. Who was King during the 'Eleven Years' Tyranny' of 1629-40?

9. What is the literal translation of 'caliph'?

10. In 1335, what portion of the world's grain harvests were used to make beer?

11. Which is the most common cross-blade type of screwdriver?

12. On which American television series did *Sons of Anarchy* creator Kurt Sutter begin his writing career?

13. What is the title character's last name in the film *Hugo*?

14. What type of metal is used to produce a daguerreotype photograph?

15. Which country has Singapore as its capital city?

16. In science, what is a 'porro'?

Quiz 21

1. Who was the President of France from 1969 until his death?

2. Which Swedish actor had starring roles in both *Masters of the Universe* and *Rocky IV*?

3. Why was Italian leader Giulio Andreotti pardoned from his jail sentence in 2002?

4. What is mysophobia?

5. Which vegetable would not be out of place on a pizza or in a burrito: cabbage, pepper, radish or spinach?

6. In February 2013, what country announced its third underground nuclear test in seven years?

7. What year did the first woman go into orbit?

8. What is the capital of Central America's Costa Rica?

9. Who played the goalkeeper in the film *Escape to Victory*?

10. Which supermodel got their big break on the cover of French *Elle*: Amber Valletta or Heidi Klum?

11. What was the O2 Arena in London originally known as when it opened in 2000?

12. Who wrote the thriller *The Runaway Jury*?

13. Approximately how long can a sperm whale stay underwater on a single breath?

14. At what London underground station do the Jubilee, Piccadilly and Victoria lines cross?

15. What is the name of Beth Gibbons' debut solo album?

16. Which of the following is not a Canadian beer: Carling Black Label, Molson Golden or Tuborg?

The Bumper *PUB* Quiz Book
Quiz 22

1. Titian most commonly painted pieces for display in what type of building?

2. What region did James Cook explore in the 1700s?

3. What relation was the Green Goblin in the *Spider-Man* film?

4. What is the liquid in your mouth that helps soften food called?

5. Which of these is an overseas territory of Chile: Easter Island, New Caledonia or Vanuatu?

6. On which continent is India located?

7. What type of compression is used in an 'mp3' file?

8. In what year was Michele Piccirillo born?

9. Which of Aristophanes' plays is set in the Greek underworld?

10. Which fashionista is encouraging an eco-friendly approach to traditional red carpet fashion?

11. Which animal is genetically closest to humans?

12. The book *Bujold Barrayar* was written by whom?

13. Who was Elizabeth Cochrane Seaman better known as?

14. What cheese can be substituted for ricotta in lasagna: cheddar or cottage cheese?

15. The speed of light is what, in miles per second? 152,000, 173,000, 186,000 or 194,000

16. Which country did NATO bomb in 1999 to try to end the war in Kosovo?

The Bumper *PUB* Quiz Book
Quiz 23

1. How are British pop duo Katie White and Jules de Martino better known?

2. Who wrote the *South Beach Diet* book?

3. Luigi Villoresi, the winner of the first race at Silverstone, drove what type of car?

4. How many times was Elizabeth Taylor married?

5. What is the national flower of Belgium?

6. What substance spilled from the Exxon Valdez?

7. What else generally goes on 'cinnamon toast' besides cinnamon and butter?

8. What is the capital city of the most easterly Caribbean island in the West Indies, Barbados?

9. What city was China's first capital?

10. Which French photographer founded 'Magnum Photos'?

11. What is 'unction'?

12. What is the process of joining the male and female sex cells of a plant called?

13. Which Caribbean nation gained its independence from the UK in 1979?

14. Sperm whales swim at top speeds of approximately what speed?

15. What country did General Manuel Noriega run in the 1980s?

16. What was the most important celestial object for the Aztecs?

The Bumper *PUB* Quiz Book
Quiz 24

1. What is the surname of the first female Chancellor of Germany?

2. On the Internet, what would you fetch from a POP or IMAP server?

3. Who is the original creator of the *Spider-Man* comic books?

4. Which country was once known as Northern Rhodesia?

5. In what world capital will you find Ho Hoan Kiem, the Lake of the Restored Sword?

6. Which popstar died in August 2001 when their plane crashed on take-off?

7. Thabana Ntlenyana is the highest peak in which African country?

8. Who remixed The Streets' song *Weak Become Heroes*: Basement Jaxx or Royksopp?

9. Which animal has a gestation period of only 13 days: hamster, mink, opossum or squirrel?

10. India's wine-grape harvest season takes place during which months?

11. Which of the following fish can adapt to both salt water and freshwater: shark, salmon or tuna?

12. Which of these historic figures died first: Abraham Lincoln, Albert Einstein, Theodore Roosevelt or Winston Churchill?

13. In text, what does 'supra' indicate?

14. Graymalkin in Shakespeare's *Macbeth* refers to what: a Scottish thane, a witch's familiar or an English nobleman?

15. What sport was Michael Owen encouraged to take up in his boyhood by his father?

16. To what islands was French emperor Napoleon Bonaparte exiled?

The Bumper *PUB* Quiz Book
Quiz 25

① Which is the largest subspecies of brown bear?

② Who is the sun goddess of Japan?

③ Which Shakespeare play features the characters Bottom and Puck?

④ Who played sax on The Beatles' *You Know My Name (Look Up The Number)*?

⑤ From which European country did New Zealand's name originate?

⑥ What is the technology which allows video to be viewed while it downloads called?

⑦ What country hosted the 1964 UEFA European Football Championship?

⑧ If nitrous oxide is added to an engine, what will the effect be?

⑨ English local elections are typically held in what month?

⑩ Which people launched the only successful winter campaign in history against Russia?

⑪ In what year was the Norman invasion of England?

⑫ In music, what does 'fortissimo' mean?

⑬ Which 2005 film is about a werewolf changing the lives of three young adults?

⑭ As of 2014, who is President of the Royal Academy of Arts?

⑮ The official currency of Iran is what?

⑯ What are the two main ingredients in the Scottish dish 'stovies'?

The Bumper *PUB* Quiz Book
Quiz 26

1. What does a seismologist study?

2. What was the name of Tupac's first solo album?

3. In which 2001 film did Gary Oldman play the vicious character Mason Verger?

4. What is the currency of Fiji called?

5. Which country is most associated with blood diamonds?

6. Which planet is 483,000,000 miles from the sun?

7. What food was known as 'liberty cabbage' during World War 1?

8. In art, what is 'sfumato'?

9. What is the unit of currency in Pakistan?

10. Who is Shiva's wife?

11. What length is the typical human oesophagus?

12. Who wrote the sci-fi book *Stand on Zanzibar*?

13. Where did pita bread originate?

14. British sitcom *Vicious* features which two knighted actors?

15. In 1992, Michael Schumacher won his first Formula One race driving for whom?

16. What did the ruler of Egypt and Sudan gift to the United Kingdom in 1819?

Quiz 27

1. Flexibility is enhanced by the daily performance of?

2. What family do dolphins, porpoises and whales belong to?

3. Which General Assembly dedicated 18th July as 'Nelson Mandela International Day'?

4. At what family event was Philip II of Macedon assassinated?

5. What sort of boat is a 'scow'?

6. Who is Guanyin in Chinese mythology?

7. Why was Hugh Grant arrested in the US in 1995?

8. When blood becomes more acid than normal, what is the condition called?

9. What official web browser plug-in allows you to view a PDF file?

10. Why is it wise to decant most commercial brands of wine prior to consuming?

11. What did a US company dump into Lake Managua in the 1950s that caused considerable pollution?

12. What country touches the Indian Ocean, the Arabian Sea and the Bay of Bengal?

13. What is the name of the submerged fringe of a continent?

14. In *The Rock*, which actor said 'Gentlemen, welcome to the Rock'?

15. The eastern half of Colombia is made up of which two types of terrain?

16. What kind of animal is a 'pika'?

The Bumper *PUB* Quiz Book
Quiz 28

1. Which two countries both claim the right to the Falkland Islands?

2. What year was cyberpunk novel *Neuromancer* first published?

3. What vegetable is the main ingredient in salsa?

4. Composer Gunther Schuller honoured Paul Klee by writing what about him?

5. What is a group of bears called?

6. The International Red Cross was founded in what European country?

7. Which planet is known as 'the red planet'?

8. Who preceded Edward Heath as UK Prime Minister?

9. What type of vehicle is a 'landau'?

10. What would you most likely find in a French person's 'estomac'?

11. In what year did McDonald's start publishing the calorie counts for its items on the menu?

12. In which country did the Akita breed of dog originate?

13. What is the capital of Paraguay?

14. A Spanish Gran Reservas wine is how many years old?

15. Who did Chardonnay marry in the first season of *Footballers' Wives*?

16. What is the maximum width of a British Formula Three car?

Quiz 29

1. Nelson Mandela celebrated his 90th birthday in which year?

2. Which chemical is added to toothpaste to reduce tooth decay?

3. What collection of small dishes, often including dumplings, is served for snack or lunch in China?

4. The northernmost point in Scandinavia is in which country?

5. Which is the only country to end with the letter 'K'?

6. Lake Parano is located in which capital city?

7. Who is the founder of Rational Emotive Behaviour Therapy?

8. What were the two sides in World War 2 known as?

9. What branch of science deals with fossils?

10. What meat is traditionally used in a shepherd's pie?

11. What is 'humiture'?

12. Sofia is the capital of which country?

13. What two RAM sizes of Sinclair Spectrum were originally sold?

14. Which Australian Prime Minister mysteriously disappeared while swimming?

15. What was the derisive nickname of former England soccer manager Graham Taylor?

16. In which city is *Ghostbusters* set?

Quiz 30

1. How many bytes are there in four kilobytes of memory?

2. Which South American country's highest elevation point is Nevado Sajama?

3. What is the capital city of Zimbabwe?

4. Camels are known to drink up to 150 litres (40 gallons) of water in a single drink – true or false?

5. According to the Ancient Greeks and Romans, which mineral prevents drunkenness?

6. Where was Henry VIII buried?

7. In 1879, the world's first psychology lab was established by Wilhelm Wundt in which country?

8. Who resigned as British Prime Minister on November 22, 1990?

9. Which fruit's name is derived from its colour?

10. In which Aristophanes play do the women go on a sex strike?

11. What is Adele *Crazy for* in a 2008 song title?

12. How many points is a red ball worth in snooker?

13. Who was 'pichichi' (top soccer scorer) in the 2009-10 season in the Spanish La Liga?

14. In *Romancing the Stone*, what does Jack name his boat?

15. In maths, what is 'sec'?

16. What country in Africa with Lilongwe as its capital uses kwacha as its currency?

Quiz 31

1. In what year did UK footballer Colin Bell lead his team to a league championship?

2. Which cyclist won BBC Sports Personality of the Year in 2012?

3. Which Caribbean island in the Lesser Antilles is shared by France and the Netherlands?

4. What city is the capital of Greenland?

5. What is NASA's Mars rover called?

6. Which of these best describes the literary category of *Catch-22*: biography, crime, dark comedy or mystery?

7. In the INXS song *Original Sin*, what do they suggest when they say 'dream on'?

8. Who founded Western Europe's first empire after the fall of Rome?

9. What powdery substance contains the male sex cells of a flower?

10. Which religion is most dominant in Bosnia-Herzegovina?

11. Which probe took the first photo of the hidden side of the moon?

12. Who was the creator of G-Unit clothing?

13. What is the most populous city in Saskatchewan?

14. Who voiced Lino in *Shark Tale*?

15. What is the nonsense word in *Mary Poppins*?

16. What was the original meaning of the phrase 'shish kebab'?

The Bumper *PUB* Quiz Book
Quiz 32

1. What is the literal translation of the Malay word 'orangutan'?

2. Which condiment, named after an English county, has anchovies in it?

3. Where did the first major battle of the Hundred Years' War take place?

4. What are animals that have no backbones called?

5. Which character is 'axed' in *The Other Boleyn Girl*?

6. In heraldry, what do you call a shield divided into two horizontal stripes?

7. If I step in a 'sop', what have I trodden in?

8. Which European country's highest elevation point is Kekes?

9. Where was the 2006 World Cup final played?

10. Who did Adele tour with in 2006?

11. What is the capital city of Martinique, the West Indies island?

12. Which is the highest mountain in England?

13. What process produces a duplicate of the original cell?

14. Which form of Buddhism stresses meditation as a means to enlightenment?

15. Which Spanish Surrealist lived from 1904-1989?

16. In the *Harry Potter* books, which house was Cedric Diggory a member of?

The Bumper *PUB* Quiz Book
Quiz 33

1. Which was the first website to feature a banner advertisement?

2. Which world leader was nicknamed 'The Iron Lady'?

3. The granddaughter of which war leader abandoned her plans to have and film her plastic surgery?

4. What mountain range divides northern England into eastern and western regions?

5. How many European countries have adopted the Euro, as of 2014?

6. Nigeria beat what team to win the African Cup of Nations in 2013?

7. What is the name for the point at the top of an opened umbrella?

8. Which country was invaded in 1956 when it nationalized the Suez Canal?

9. What is the pulling force that the Earth exerts on every object near it?

10. The cities of Alexandria and Luxor are popular tourist spots in which Arab country?

11. In text, what is 'kerning'?

12. What name do the French use for a pastry shop?

13. How tall is actor Warwick Davis?

14. Which star portrayed Lt. Ben Gannon in the film *Stealth*?

15. In what city is the UK's National Gallery?

16. What word is given to sounds that are too high for humans to hear?

Quiz 34

1. Which British island is Saint Helier the capital of?

2. What is Apple's high-end audio editing software called?

3. How many kilometres of blood vessels and veins are in the typical adult's body: 54,000, 86,000 or 97,000?

4. Bab El Mandeb, a strategic shipping lane, links the Red Sea to what body of water?

5. What are the three main ingredients in a 'Dublin coddle'?

6. In which country does the Alcantara Bridge cross the Tagus river?

7. Which royal dynasty succeeded the Stuarts?

8. In which city is the Prado Art Gallery?

9. Which star of *Wedding Crashers* appeared alongside Kevin James in the 2011 comedy *The Dilemma*?

10. What is the gestation period of the giraffe?

11. Kaluza-Klein Theory is an early version of which physics theory?

12. Thor is the Norse god of what?

13. What year did Hungary lose in the World Cup Final?

14. Which musical duo created *Les Miserables*, *Miss Saigon* and *Martin Guerre*?

15. In what year did the post-World War 2 Berlin Airlift begin?

16. In a church, what is an 'ambo'?

Quiz 35

1. What is another term for the genetic disorder Trisomy 18?

2. Which atom consists of a single proton?

3. In *Friends*, who plays Rachel's sister, Jill?

4. What is the monetary unit of the Maldives?

5. What is the longest river in Australia?

6. Who, as of 2014, has won 42 PGA Tour events including 3 Masters?

7. Who succeeded Margaret Thatcher as UK Prime Minister?

8. Who played Robert de Niro's doctor in *Awakenings*?

9. What sort of animal is an 'agouti'?

10. What was the name of the town in Tim Burton's *The Nightmare Before Christmas*?

11. A stock losing value might be called a what?

12. Jack McManus sings 'You're the last shade of red that I'll' what?

13. Where are half of the world's apples grown?

14. What name is given to a ring-shaped coral island?

15. How long did Roman consuls rule?

16. What insect carries the parasite that causes malaria?

Quiz 36

① What type of drink is vermouth?

② What is the science of the origin, history, and structure of the Earth called?

③ Cuba is often in the path of what type of storm?

④ Amelia Earhart was the first woman to do what?

⑤ What are the 'good guys' called in the 2007 film *Transformers*?

⑥ Which animal does Carlos Moya have tattooed on his right bicep?

⑦ Which country has Cairo as its capital city?

⑧ Who wrote the song *Free Nelson Mandela* released in 1984?

⑨ A nanny is an adult female animal of what sort?

⑩ What is the Russian word for the best grade of caviar?

⑪ What did Starburst sweets used to be called?

⑫ Which immersive theatre company performed *The Drowned Man* in London in 2013?

⑬ Who was the last Stuart monarch?

⑭ What is the name of the sugary substance that many insects get from flowers?

⑮ What was boxer Marco Huck's birth name?

⑯ Where is Gatwick Airport?

The Bumper *PUB* Quiz Book
Quiz 37

1. What country's Formula One circuit was built on a man-made island in the St. Lawrence River?

2. Out of what material would a scabbard likely have been made in the Middle Ages?

3. If you have a pain in 'la dent' or 'el diente', who should you go see?

4. What is the largest religious group in Poland?

5. Which planet is not named after a god from classical mythology?

6. Who was the creator of the original ASCII emoticons?

7. Who played the Tenth Doctor?

8. Where in Canada is Barton Street located?

9. What do you use to make the 'V' in a 'V-Up' exercise?

10. Wiley is a founding member of what musical group?

11. What can you measure in units of Pascal, Torr or Bar?

12. In archaeology, what is an 'eolith'?

13. Which film won the Best Picture Oscar for 2006?

14. In what country would you buy a serape to keep you warm?

15. In astronomy, what is a 'nebula'?

16. Who is 'The Naked Chef'?

The Bumper *PUB* Quiz Book
Quiz 38

1. What was the head of state in Iran called before the revolution of 1979?

2. What is the giant Rub al-Khali in Saudi Arabia?

3. Botswana shares its southern border with what African country?

4. What is the smallest type of horse?

5. What song did Gareth Gates release as his debut single?

6. Which Greek gorgon had snakes in her hair?

7. Which English novelist wrote *Pride and Prejudice*?

8. Which Flemish artist often painted only the finishing touches on his pictures?

9. What garden creature is known in France as 'escargot'?

10. In Haiti, what is a 'loa'?

11. Which Italian biscuit literally means 'twice-baked'?

12. What is the name of the Russian ballet that the characters go to see in *Anastasia*?

13. What colour is 'cerise'?

14. In which Mexican city did boxer Erik Morales grow up?

15. Which of these living things has been called a 'living fossil': ginkgo, soft-shelled crab or thistle?

16. In what year did Richard I become King of England?

Quiz 39

1. Which tennis star won consecutive Wimbledon singles titles in 2000 and 2001, and in 2007 and 2008?

2. In 1947, Margaret Thatcher graduated from Oxford University with a Bachelor's degree in what subject?

3. What is the colour of the emerald birthstone?

4. Who took office on November 12, 2003 as Palestinian Prime Minister?

5. Who was the ninth Prime Minister of Canada?

6. Which female artist has won the most Grammy Awards, as of 2014?

7. Which country has pyramids that are thousands of years old?

8. Elurophobia is the fear of what?

9. Which hotel was favoured by westerners after the 2003 invasion of Iraq?

10. What is a downburst covering an area smaller than 2.5 miles in diameter called?

11. Who was the lead male actor in *Dallas Buyers Club*?

12. Who is the Roman god of wine?

13. What film starring Jeff Bridges as Jack Lucas was released in 1991?

14. Who did Amy Macdonald tour with early in her musical career?

15. What is the original meaning of the word 'Woolloomoolloo', the name of an inner Sydney suburb?

16. What does 'laudatory' mean?

The Bumper *PUB* Quiz Book
Quiz 40

① How many nations joined the coalition forces in 'Operation Desert Shield'?

② What kind of scientist would study rocks, minerals and mountains?

③ Most varieties of which fruit do not ripen during the summer: cherry, orange or strawberry?

④ What religion was Nobel Prize-winner Jean-Paul Sarte?

⑤ How many laps do drivers race in the French Grand Prix at Magny-Cours?

⑥ The airport code JKT designates which international airport?

⑦ Which soft drink company used the slogan 'Be a Pepper'?

⑧ What does 'DVD' stand for?

⑨ If you are eating a cookie in the US, what exactly are you eating?

⑩ In Judaism, what ceremony do 13-year-old boys receive to mark the start of adulthood?

⑪ 'Victory Day' in Malta commemorates military victory in 1565 over what force?

⑫ What superstar won the FIFA World Player of the Year in both 2004 and 2005?

⑬ Which sea creature has an eye the size of a basketball?

⑭ In what year did the original Woodstock music festival take place?

⑮ What country in Africa, with Nouakchott as its capital, uses ouguiya as its currency?

⑯ In the movie *Ghost*, what is Demi Moore's character called?

The Bumper *PUB* Quiz Book

Quiz 41

1. What colour, besides white, is a STOP sign?

2. What is the opening track on the Roots Manuva album *Run Come Save Me*?

3. Who is credited for discovering the Pacific Ocean?

4. Which fictional town is home to the characters of the animated series *The Flintstones*?

5. What does the hard disc acronym 'SCSI' stand for?

6. Who did Russian President Boris Yeltsin name as his successor in 1999?

7. Which animal product does an ovo-vegetarian eat?

8. Where are the Lewis Chessmen likely to have been made, around AD 1150-1200?

9. How many points are on the leaf on the Canadian flag?

10. Who played General Medrano in *Quantum of Solace*?

11. Which Iraq weapons investigator resigned in 2004, stating that there was no evidence of weapons?

12. What was the second most-visited website in 2014, according to Alexa?

13. A 'philatelist' is a what?

14. In Greek mythology, who did Athena turn into a spider?

15. Which fighter was known as 'The Body Snatcher'?

16. Which Rene Magritte item was stolen from a London storeroom in 2006?

Quiz 42

1. Who set a record for the longest solo space flight, in 1963?

2. Medically, what is 'infarct'?

3. Drinking sea water causes what ironic effect in humans?

4. In medicine, what is a 'styptic' substance?

5. What does a human adult do about 23,000 times a day?

6. Arthur Miller was known for what artistic profession?

7. In what film did Tom Hanks play Joe Fox?

8. How many cantons does Switzerland consist of?

9. Three of the Quad Cities are in which US state?

10. In what year was the World Cup held in Spain?

11. A picture condition in which horizontal lines are displaced in an irregular manner, fits which audio/video term?

12. Which country speaks Spanish as its main language: Mexico, Singapore or South Africa?

13. What is the name of the scale used to measure the 'heat' of chillies?

14. What is the capital of Pitcairn Island?

15. What type of computer document is a 'GIF' file?

16. Which is the highest mountain in Wales?

The Bumper *PUB* Quiz Book
Quiz 43

1. Vanuatu, a group of islands in the South-West Pacific, has what capital city?

2. Dimitri Shostakovich is known for being what?

3. Cephalgia is a medical term for what malady?

4. Which character in Greek mythology was granted eternal sleep?

5. In heraldry, what colour is 'tawny'?

6. How many gold medals did Carl Lewis win in the 1984 Summer Olympics?

7. If you order white wine in a French restaurant, how will it probably be kept at the table?

8. Which planet orbits at approximately 150 million miles from the sun?

9. Where did the Romans go to socialize and bathe?

10. What is Evelyn's brother's name in the film *The Mummy*?

11. How many Earth days does it take Mercury to orbit the sun?

12. Who of these is a principal deity in Chinese mythology: Gold Emperor or Jade Emperor?

13. What is a 'rondeau'?

14. In what year did the US begin work on the Panama Canal?

15. In Spain, what is a 'toro'?

16. What Irish-English actor of stage and screen died on December 14, 2013?

The Bumper *PUB* Quiz Book
Quiz 44

1. Which Open junior title in tennis did Andy Murray win in 2003?

2. How many of the world's countries are landlocked?

3. What is the official residence of the President of Russia?

4. Where is the United Nations building?

5. What is the Greek alphabet equivalent of the letter 'm'?

6. In 1956, Colin Wilson wrote which classic about social outcasts?

7. The digital release of which 2011 Radiohead album preceded the CD by more than a month?

8. Which Chinese drama saw a worldwide release thanks to a personal intervention by Rupert Murdoch?

9. What was the infamous Bloody Mary's occupation?

10. Which of these animals might use a coral reef for hiding and protection: giant squid, moray eel or whale shark?

11. 'The School of Athens' was painted by which Renaissance artist?

12. Under Elizabeth I's rule, what happened to people who did not attend the Anglican Church?

13. Which Roman emperor succeeded Caligula in 41AD?

14. What food group is yoghurt part of?

15. How many European countries formed the European Space Agency in 1962?

16. Complete the *Alien* tagline: 'In space, no one can...'

The Bumper *PUB* Quiz Book
Quiz 45

1. The island of Kiritimati is also known by what name?

2. In a room, what is a 'dado'?

3. Who was the co-author of Karl Marx's *The Communist Manifesto*?

4. In *The Taming of the Shrew*, who is Petruchio's long-suffering servant?

5. What takes up 50-70 per cent of a whale's weight?

6. What is the name of Justin Timberlake's character in *Bad Teacher*?

7. Who is the Greek goddess of wisdom, skill, peace and war?

8. What animal is classified as the only marsupial in the United States?

9. 'Bonjour' is French for what greeting?

10. Which aeronautical term refers to the dimension of a wing parallel to the direction of motion?

11. In what year did the BBC 'April Fool' the nation with a Panorama report on spaghetti crops?

12. Piet Mondrian once stated that what type of line was 'so emotional'?

13. What kind of juice goes in a 'Salty Dog' cocktail?

14. *It's All Coming Back To Me Now* was recorded by which female artist?

15. Which golfer pulled off a single-stroke win at the 2012 US Open?

16. What year were the first students selected as Mandela Rhodes Scholars?

The Bumper PUB Quiz Book
Quiz 46

① What football club does Roman Abramovich own?

② The 'Luftwaffe' was the name given to the air force of which country during World War 2?

③ What animal has the largest brain compared to the size of its body?

④ The Italian dish 'polenta' is made of what main ingredient?

⑤ In which year was the world's first test-tube baby born?

⑥ Grey, blue, bowhead and finback are varieties of what?

⑦ Where do the 'Mon' people come from?

⑧ Who did the Byzantines fight a war with over trade in 1171?

⑨ What is the approximate size of the Amazon rainforest?

⑩ Which European explorer discovered the Pacific Ocean?

⑪ Who wrote *The Catcher in the Rye*?

⑫ Finnish blacksmith Kai finds love with Chinese maiden Pin Yu in what 2006 film by A.J. Annila?

⑬ Brazil is extensively covered by what terrain?

⑭ What is 'ceviche'?

⑮ To the nearest 10 million, what was the population of Canada as the 21st century began?

⑯ In *The Muppet Christmas Carol*, which muppet told the story?

The Bumper *PUB* Quiz Book
Quiz 47

1. What year was *Ringworld* published?

2. What do conifers use to hold seeds?

3. On the London Underground system, what station is situated directly between Leicester Square and Holborn?

4. What was the name of the atomic bomb dropped at Hiroshima?

5. What is the capital city of Yemen, on the shores of the Red Sea?

6. In the film *Hellraiser*, who says, 'We have such sights to show you'?

7. What is the basic difference between spices and herbs?

8. Where were Nirvana next scheduled to play when they found Kurt Cobain dead?

9. 'Pop Art' got its name from its depiction of what?

10. After winning in 2014, how many World Cup championships does Germany hold?

11. Who was the winner of the Presidential election in Mexico in 2006?

12. In what year did Hitler's Germany invade Poland?

13. Approximately where is the blowhole located on the head of a sperm whale?

14. Tau is the Greek alphabet equivalent of which English letter?

15. What do you traditionally give for a sixty-fifth anniversary?

16. What country borders Kuwait, Saudi Arabia, Jordan, Syria, Turkey and Iran?

Quiz 48

1. What are the principle ingredients of a caponata?

2. Who starred in both the 1998 film *Affliction* and the 1991 film *JFK*?

3. Mafadi is the highest peak in which African country?

4. What does the song by The Streets 'turn the page' on?

5. Which Queen was crowned at Westminster Abbey in 1689?

6. Which is not an official language of Switzerland: German, Italian, Romansch or Swedish?

7. What did computer keypunch operators do?

8. Which prominent American tennis player refused to join the ATP when it was founded?

9. As well as in paint, what other medium did Edvard Munch create 'The Scream' in?

10. Which Spanish artist painted 'Persistence of Memory'?

11. What is a female turkey called?

12. Archaically, who was an 'eme'?

13. What shoe does the name 'Ojibwe' in the Anishinaabe language refer to?

14. Which Queen introduced the Pomeranian breed to England?

15. What is required in order to make stir fried food: a deep pan, high heat or lots of water?

16. The 1974 book titled *The Killer, Angels* was written by?

The Bumper *PUB* Quiz Book
Quiz 49

1. What is the name of the comic book store in *Mallrats*?

2. Anders Jarryd won his only Olympic medal in which year?

3. Did Columbus know the world was round?

4. What principle states that no two electrons in an atom can occupy the same state simultaneously?

5. What was the pre-Islamic religion of Persia?

6. What type of food is the German speciality 'bratwurst'?

7. Which branch of science did young Carl Sagan tell his grandfather he wanted to practise?

8. Whose avant-garde and Space Age clothing designs often ignore the female form?

9. Who wrote the series of fantasy novels *A Song of Ice and Fire*?

10. You can visit Alcatraz prison in which US state?

11. What year did the League of Nations first meet?

12. What colour boots does 'Wonder Woman' wear?

13. Which country's highest point is Mount Olympus?

14. Formula Three racing cars were originally powered by engines made for what?

15. In *Friends*, which English actor sat next to Rachel on the plane to London?

16. Which microstate used the French franc and Spanish peseta as its two currencies prior to 2000?

Quiz 50

1. What is the middle name of former Australian Prime Minister John Howard?

2. The U-Boat models used in the 1981 film *Das Boot* were later re-used in which action film?

3. What does the Fujita scale measure?

4. Which chocolate bar has the same name as the galaxy?

5. Canned food was invented for what Navy in 1813?

6. What Coca-Cola diet cola first appeared in 1963?

7. Which type of animal is a tarantula?

8. Which of the following is a cat in a T.S. Eliot poem: Belinda, Macavity or Bojangles?

9. What does 'xeric' mean?

10. Which general led the American forces in North Africa during World War 2?

11. The earliest surviving man-made sculptures are made of what?

12. Nearly 40% of Mauritania's exports consist of what metal?

13. In September 2013 for Barcelona, against what club did Pedro score a hat-trick?

14. Which was the first London hotel with en-suite bathrooms in every room?

15. What seaside resort neighbours the English town of Hove?

16. In what year was the Bolshoi Theatre founded in Moscow?

Quiz 51

① Which central-east African nation disintegrated into a violent civil war in 1990?

② What is it called in the US when the electricity power supply drops below acceptable voltage levels?

③ How many official languages does Canada have?

④ Which country did St. Patrick help convert to Christianity?

⑤ A 'Pit Bull on Crack' consists of tequila, whisky, rum and what?

⑥ Who is the father of the modern system for naming organisms that uses a genus and a species name?

⑦ What is the first name of boxing's Bowe?

⑧ Which supermodel was married to 'Elite' President Gerald Marie?

⑨ What kind of cake is traditionally used for a wedding cake in England?

⑩ Who captures the title character at the beginning of *Finding Nemo*?

⑪ The airport code FCO designates which European airport?

⑫ What 'language' does Koko the gorilla use to communicate?

⑬ What is the strongest muscle in the human body?

⑭ Machu Picchu is an Inca city in what country?

⑮ How many countries participated in World War 2?

⑯ Which is the second-highest mountain in Scotland?

The Bumper *PUB* Quiz Book

Quiz 52

1. What is the total voltage of a series circuit using 5 AA batteries?

2. How many foci does an ellipse have?

3. What is the capital city of Macedonia?

4. In 1896, what did James Boyle's 'automatic hat' do?

5. What is an aardvark's primary source of food?

6. Which of these is not a command from the toy 'Bop It!': bop it, hit it, pull it or twist it?

7. What company's stock ticker is BID?

8. In what year did the Nuremberg Trials condemn twelve Nazis?

9. Who was the head vampire in the film *The Lost Boys*?

10. Who played Frasier Crane's brother Niles?

11. Which woman won the 2014 Australian Open singles championship?

12. What do you traditionally give for a tenth anniversary?

13. What was the capital of Jamaica until the capital was changed to Kingston in 1872?

14. Which former Soviet Foreign Minister became the leader of the Republic of Georgia?

15. Which type of pie is traditional at British Christmas feasts?

16. What vegetable usually surrounds the steak in a beef wellington?

Quiz 53

① What are the ingredients of a Black Russian cocktail?

② When parking a car facing uphill, which way should you turn the front of the wheels?

③ What is necrosis?

④ When and where was the term 'birdie' first used in golf?

⑤ Which film featured the line 'When you get caught between the moon and New York City'?

⑥ What is a female cat called?

⑦ What is the science of raising plants and animals called?

⑧ Bridgetown is the capital of which country?

⑨ In art, what is a 'relievo'?

⑩ Which species of otter shares much of its range with the spotted-necked otter: African clawless otter, giant otter, hairy-nosed otter or sea otter?

⑪ Kingston is the capital of which country?

⑫ What is the name of the traditional form of female clothing in India?

⑬ The film, *The English Patient*, was directed by whom?

⑭ Which brew is nicknamed *The Cream of Manchester*?

⑮ Which Canadian province was formerly known as Upper Canada?

⑯ Which famous British battlecruiser did the *Bismarck* sink?

The Bumper *PUB* Quiz Book
Quiz 54

1. Which jockey won BBC Sports Personality of the Year in 2010?

2. What city was the film *The Exorcist* set in?

3. The 1961 book, *The Moviegoer*, was written by whom?

4. Where is Red Stripe beer brewed?

5. Who painted 'The Virgin' in 1913?

6. What is the fin on the backs of fish, some whales and dolphins called?

7. Hidden Valley Raceway is located in which Australian city?

8. Which is part of the Solomon Islands: Barbados or Guadalcanal?

9. In what year did Alexander the Great conquer Egypt?

10. Who was the first African-American female astronaut?

11. In which country might you eat 'shabu shabu nabe'?

12. Which Nazi prisoner of war camp was near the River Mulde?

13. A Spanish wine cellar might also be referred to as what?

14. Which country seized the USS *Pueblo* and held Americans captive for 11 months?

15. What did an 'oka' used to be, in Turkey?

16. A pyramid with a square base has four edges at its base and a total of how many edges overall?

The Bumper *PUB* Quiz Book
Quiz 55

① Which tennis player won BBC Sports Personality of the Year in 2013?

② The fossil *Australopithecus afarensis* gets the nickname 'Lucy' from what musical source?

③ What type of government ruled Italy during World War 2?

④ What was Acorn's proprietary network technology called?

⑤ What is the only Portuguese-speaking country in the Americas?

⑥ Which is a 2005 album by the Super Furry Animals: *Guerilla*, *Love Kraft* or *Radiator*?

⑦ Which space agency launches *Ariane* rockets?

⑧ Edouard Manet once said that what was the greatest type of painting?

⑨ Which primary painting colour is not also a primary colour of light?

⑩ Who wrote *Crime and Punishment*?

⑪ In which year did Mao Zedong die?

⑫ In what country is there a town called Monkey's Eyebrow?

⑬ In the 1985 film *Clue*, who plays Wadsworth the butler?

⑭ Which of these films featured Michael Caine: *Batman Begins* or *Hitch*?

⑮ Curaçao is made from what dried fruit peel?

⑯ The 'Australian Open' is a Grand Slam tournament in which sport?

The Bumper *PUB* Quiz Book
Quiz 56

① How many points is a black ball worth in snooker?

② The official church of which country voted to allow women to become priests in November of 1992?

③ What is the most-eaten food in China?

④ Which was the first original *Zelda* game released for the 3DS?

⑤ What chamber do divers go into to prevent a diving sickness called 'the bends'?

⑥ Frida Kahlo was married to which famous muralist?

⑦ Which supervillain was the first to defeat Spider-Man?

⑧ The Dominican Republic uses up 66% of the island of Hispaniola. What is its capital city?

⑨ What was Emily Bronte's only novel?

⑩ In which century did the black plague kill as many as half the people of Europe?

⑪ What instrument do you use to measure wind speed?

⑫ A kimono would be worn by a person from where?

⑬ The Nile River enters the sea on the coast of which country?

⑭ Who is the Roman messenger god?

⑮ When was the Asprey of London store founded?

⑯ Which actor plays the LA fixer, *Ray Donovan*?

Quiz 57

1. You can find St. Peter's Basilica in which city?

2. How many spectators could watch an event at the Circus Maximus in Rome?

3. Which is the US name for a courgette?

4. In what year did Nintendo first sell handheld electronic games?

5. When William becomes King of England, what number William will he be?

6. What is the name of the former royal residence on the Isle of Wight where Queen Victoria died?

7. What drink uses the slogan 'It gives you wings'?

8. Which religious film was directed by Mel Gibson?

9. Which scientific term means 'resistance to flow in a liquid'?

10. Who was the first golfer to win US $1 million in a PGA Tour season?

11. What is the German treat *Apfelpfannkuchen*?

12. England, Scotland, Wales and Northern Ireland all qualified for which year's World Cup?

13. What animal has two humps and originates in the deserts and steppes of Asia?

14. What does the 'T' in the acronym TASER stand for?

15. What country was number one in the UN 2013 Human Development Index?

16. For what characteristic is the Falabella horse best known?

The Bumper *PUB* Quiz Book
Quiz 58

1. From which country does arabica coffee originate?

2. How long can a snail sleep?

3. How many traditional counties are there in Ireland?

4. In Ancient Rome, what was the 'fisc'?

5. Which icy continent has no permanent human residents?

6. Which national side won the 1986 World Cup?

7. Which element has the atomic number 8?

8. What were the names of William Shakespeare's parents?

9. In a Roman army, what image did the 'imaginifer' carry on his standard?

10. Sali Berisha was the first Albanian President since World War 2 who was not of what party?

11. Who provided the voice of the diner cook in the 2007 film *TMNT*?

12. Which defunct British computer manufacturer created the original ARM chip?

13. Which famous family is Kendall Jenner related to?

14. How else could you say 'alternately ceasing and beginning' in a medical context?

15. Bassenthwaite Lake in England is considered a shallow lake at what depth?

16. What word is traditionally chanted at the beginning and end of a yoga session?

The Bumper *PUB* Quiz Book
Quiz 59

1. What is halite another name for?

2. How many years is a half century plus 15 years?

3. Who created the fictional detective Sherlock Holmes?

4. Colombia shares a border with which central American country?

5. Who is the Roman God of War?

6. How does Harry run away in *Prisoner of Azkaban*?

7. What do the French use to make 'pain perdu'?

8. Where did the first successful 'flash mob' meet in New York?

9. What animal is considered to be the first non-human to acquire human language?

10. Who was elected President of the Philippines in 2010?

11. What was the title of Portishead's 1994 debut record?

12. Which of these English kings came into power at the youngest age: William I, Richard II or Henry III?

13. What would police use a 'caltrop' for?

14. What is the official language of Swaziland?

15. Which artist painted 'The Night Watch'?

16. Formula One driver Valtteri Bottas drove for which Formula One team in 2014?

The Bumper *PUB* Quiz Book
Quiz 60

1. How many eyes do most spiders have?

2. Sally Field won Academy Awards for Best Actress in which two years?

3. What is the name of the castle fortress in Scotland built atop the volcanic Castle Rock?

4. In 1973, Jody Scheckter caused a pile-up of how many cars at Silverstone?

5. Is pasta an ingredient in antipasti?

6. Who wrote the book *Mommie Dearest*?

7. How many cards are in the Major Arcana of a standard tarot deck?

8. A study of the psychological effects of imprisonment was conducted in 1971 at what university?

9. In what year did comet Hale-Bopp last pass by Earth?

10. In ecology, what does 'xeric' mean?

11. What is the area, in square miles, of England: 25,120, 50,346, or 75,940?

12. What was Mahatma Gandhi's actual first name?

13. Which monarch was born in St James's Palace in October 1633?

14. Which country is home to the holy city of Medina?

15. In Spanish, when you mix the colours 'blanco' and 'negro' you get what?

16. What country's cuisine offers Dim Sum?

The Bumper *PUB* Quiz Book
Quiz 61

1. What kind of tree loses all its leaves during a dormant period like winter?

2. What type of boundary is displayed at the Mid-Atlantic Ridge?

3. Where is the basilar artery located?

4. St. Mark's Cathedral in Venice is associated with which of these composers: Berg, Brahms or Monteverdi?

5. Who is the Greek goddess of night?

6. What was the last year of Bobby Charlton's professional playing career?

7. Who has been President of Nicaragua since 2007?

8. Where did the Japanese submarine I-30 unload supplies on August 6, 1942?

9. Which film won the Best Picture Oscar for 2003?

10. What is the capital of Queensland, Australia?

11. Which play was written by Eugene O'Neill: *Death Of A Salesman* or *The Iceman Cometh*?

12. Which composer holds the most Tony Awards?

13. Who was Time's Person of the Year in 2013?

14. What is the most westerly country in continental Europe?

15. Peter Paul Rubens' works were made famous by the use of his images on what?

16. What are the ingredients of the Scottish dessert, cranachan?

The Bumper *PUB* Quiz Book
Quiz 62

① What is considered the smallest independent country in the world?

② In electronics, the term rectification refers to the process of changing an alternating current (AC) to what?

③ What do many types of birds, such as geese, do just before the season begins to get colder?

④ What is the London street address of fictional detective Sherlock Holmes?

⑤ With which club did Diego Maradona make his professional soccer début?

⑥ In what year did Egypt and Israel sign their peace treaty?

⑦ Complete the Nelson Mandela quote, 'Money won't create success...'.

⑧ What potion did Harry Potter use to change his appearance?

⑨ How many goals did France score during the World Cup 2002?

⑩ In 2011, Alan Ferguson directed the video for which Beyonce track?

⑪ In 2012, Daniel Day Lewis starred in a major film about which US President?

⑫ Which fruit used to be referred to as the 'love apple'?

⑬ Which of the following is a white wine: Beaujolais Nouveau, Chianti, Pinot Grigio or Pinot Noir?

⑭ Which quality in people was valued most by the Spartans?

⑮ In music, how is 'rubato' music played?

⑯ How long did Russia's war with Sweden, which began in 1700, last?

Quiz 63

① What is another word for a champagne glass?

② What Kung Fu artist co-stars with Brendan Fraser in *The Mummy 3*?

③ What is the name of the breakaway state on the eastern Moldova border with Ukraine?

④ Colombia is often affected by which meteorological water phenomenon?

⑤ In which year did the Japanese army invade Manchuria?

⑥ What Formula One champion was dubbed 'Son of the Wind', 'Big John' and 'John the Great'?

⑦ In which country did golfer Karrie Webb grow up?

⑧ Georgia O'Keeffe's flower paintings show the subject at what distance?

⑨ How high up is the ozone layer?

⑩ What does 'vacuous' mean?

⑪ Which Caribbean country's highest elevation point is Pico Turquino?

⑫ Radiated noise that is transmitted through a magnetic field to signal lines is known as what?

⑬ The Sun's mass is approximately how many times as great as Earth's?

⑭ Which was the first former Soviet Republic to have a female President?

⑮ Which New Wave band had the album releases *Manic Pop Thrill* and *Babble*?

⑯ Which word means that something is capable of causing cancer?

The Bumper *PUB* Quiz Book
Quiz 64

① What bird's feathers were used in early golf balls?

② What is the main ingredient in the Indian dish called 'dal'?

③ Where are the mineral-rich Star Mountains?

④ When was the Special Olympics first held?

⑤ Which Oxford-born author wrote *London Fields*?

⑥ What is 'gazpacho'?

⑦ In what year did *The Full Monty* win the BAFTA Award for Best Film?

⑧ *Batman Forever* featured Drew Barrymore as which character?

⑨ Who assassinated the President of the Democratic Republic of the Congo, Laurent Kabila, in 2001?

⑩ What Basement Jaxx song was the theme for the BBC's Euro 2004 coverage?

⑪ Which world river discharges the second-most water of any river?

⑫ What country is bordered by Germany, the Czech Republic, Slovakia and the Ukraine?

⑬ What is the front face of a building called: facade, firewall, screen or showplate?

⑭ How many stomachs does an ant have?

⑮ What type of literature is a 'fabliau'?

⑯ What does the term 'geocentric' mean?

Quiz 65

1. How many valves does a Ferrari F50 engine have?

2. What did the Romans use aqueducts for?

3. What day is ANZAC Day celebrated in Australia?

4. What is Erse?

5. What year was the battle of Bannockburn fought between the English and the Scots?

6. Who won the 1990 FIFA World Cup?

7. Where is the Mato Grosso plateau?

8. Which type of musical instrument is used by flamenco dancers?

9. How many people died in the 2004 Madrid train bombings?

10. Which 1989 film has as its tagline: *Be Very, Very Afraid*?

11. Sigma is the Greek alphabet equivalent of which English letter?

12. Which of these animals is not an amphibian: frog, salamander, snake or toad?

13. What is the capital of Benin, in western Africa?

14. What region of Spain became world famous for its Bordeaux wines in the 19th century?

15. Who teamed up with Maroon 5 to remix *If I Never See Your Face Again*?

16. What is a huge exploding star radiating as much energy as the sun would over about 10 billion years?

The Bumper *PUB* Quiz Book
Quiz 66

1. What type of holidays do people often take in Switzerland?

2. What is the length of the 18th hole at Augusta?

3. Which country was carmaker Simca based in?

4. What is Beyonce's middle name?

5. What is the usual shape of a river delta?

6. What is the Italian dessert 'tartufo' made with?

7. In Brian Cook's 2005 *Colour Me Kubrick: A True...ish Story* the part of Lolita was played by whom?

8. Which blood type is known as the 'universal recipient?'

9. What is a grown male chicken called?

10. What is the average number of times that a person blinks per minute?

11. By what name was Crowded House known when they first started performing?

12. What is the Greek alphabet equivalent of the letter 'o'?

13. Which of the following tribes is not African: Dogon, Hausa, Ojibway or Yoruba?

14. Which element has the atomic number 2?

15. In what year did Edgar Allan Poe die?

16. In which Shakespeare play would you find the mischievous spirit Ariel?

Quiz 67

1. Who designed the Big Ben clock tower in London?

2. What kind of cheese is used in a tiramisu?

3. What was the name of the high school in *Heathers*?

4. In the brain, what is a 'gyrus'?

5. What country is the musical group The Corrs from?

6. In what decade were ground effects banned from Formula Three racing?

7. What is the soft, triangular, fleshy part of the inside of a horse's hoof called?

8. It is said that Shakespeare got his material for *Macbeth* from which British history source?

9. Which parts of a nerve cell send out signals?

10. What is the name of the public art gallery located at Buckingham Palace?

11. What is a 'rishi'?

12. What did King Louis XIV adopt as his personal emblem?

13. Melting butter and removing the milk solids from it is called what?

14. Who did Lucy leave at the altar in the final series of *Footballers' Wives*?

15. Who was elected President of Mexico in 2012?

16. What is the capital city of Chile?

The Bumper *PUB* Quiz Book
Quiz 68

1. Which common tool comes in Phillips and flathead types?

2. What is the lowest common multiple of 12 and 16?

3. One light-year, the distance light travels in a vacuum in one year, is equivalent to how many miles?

4. In what park is North America's highest point, Mount McKinley?

5. Which US city is home to a hotel and casino with a half-scale replica of the Eiffel Tower?

6. Who painted 'The Ship of Fools'?

7. Under what name did Dire Straits perform their original sessions?

8. What is the origin of dinoflagellates?

9. In the film, what is *The Polar Express*?

10. How old was Theo Walcott when Nike started providing his team kit?

11. What number-matching game, still played today, was invented in China over 1000 years ago?

12. What is the most commonly used oil in Chinese cooking?

13. In what year was Heathrow Terminal 1 first opened?

14. Who succeeded Anthony Eden as UK Prime Minister?

15. IBM debuted its first personal computer in August of what year?

16. What food business tycoon began his chicken empire in a petrol station in 1930?

The Bumper *PUB* Quiz Book
Quiz 69

1. Which was the first Grand Slam event that Venus Williams won?

2. What does the medical term 'local anaesthesia' mean?

3. Which country in Oceania has a highest elevation point of just 4.6m (15ft)?

4. On her album *Out of Season*, Beth Gibbons sings 'God knows how I' what?

5. What did the Romans carry away on the Arch of Titus that depicted a Roman victory?

6. What is a 'sinfonietta'?

7. Nikujaga is a combination of meat and what?

8. Where does the Glastonbury festival take place?

9. Santiago is located in which South American country?

10. What are horizontal stabilizers called when in front of the wing of an aeroplane?

11. What do you call someone who studies earthquakes?

12. Diego Rivera's murals often dealt with what type of national themes?

13. Which of these adult females feeds on blood, while the male eats only plant juices: mosquito or piranha?

14. What does 'agley' mean, in Scotland?

15. After the Nile River leaves Cairo, into how many major branches does it break?

16. Which Brazilian President killed himself while in office?

The Bumper *PUB* Quiz Book
Quiz 70

1. What is the main ethnic group in China?

2. What kind of icing traditionally goes on carrot cake?

3. In what year was Ayrton Senna killed at the San Marino Grand Prix?

4. Vitamins are divided into how many categories?

5. Which is the fasting growing plant?

6. Which leader nationalized the Suez Canal in 1956, instigating an international crisis?

7. The Basement Jaxx song *Red Alert* was used in what football film?

8. Who would go to school at the ENA in France?

9. Who played the character Pinhead in Clive Barker's *Hellraiser*?

10. In terms of length from north to south, where does Chile rank among the world's countries?

11. Does an ox eat meat or plants?

12. What does 'cocksure' mean?

13. The first meeting of the United Nations took place in London in what year?

14. If a ballet movement is adagio, what does that mean?

15. What year did Edward VII of Great Britain die?

16. The octal numbering system uses how many digits?

The Bumper *PUB* Quiz Book
Quiz 71

1. Cowboys from Argentina share a name with what type of women's trousers?

2. What would you call the treatment of disease, usually cancer, by chemical agents?

3. In a website URL, what prefix indicates that a connection is encrypted?

4. Which of these is a Chilean desert: Atacama, Mojave or Sahara?

5. Israeli Prime Minister Ariel Sharon called for the exile of which Palestinian leader in 2002?

6. What country did the Soviet Union invade in 1979?

7. On the London Underground, what is the last station on the southbound Northern line?

8. Which Pope moved his headquarters from Rome to France?

9. For how many weeks did Greg Norman hold the number one ranking in golf?

10. What did the Ancient Romans use to clean their skin?

11. What is the capital of the Mexican state of Nuevo Leon?

12. Why can Gueuze (a Belgian beer) only be brewed near Brussels?

13. Who composed the music for *Sweeney Todd: The Demon Barber of Fleet Street*?

14. What do we call the dependable winds that rush towards the equator from the north and south?

15. In *Funny People*, what fatal disease does George find out he has?

16. Tercel is the name for the male of which animal?

The Bumper *PUB* Quiz Book
Quiz 72

1. What active ingredient is commonly used to make bread rise?

2. The most popular baby names in the UK for a boy and a girl in 2013 were Amelia and Oliver or Sofia and Edward?

3. The lines connecting the foci in an ellipse are the major axis or the minor axis?

4. What was 'laudanum' formerly used as?

5. Niagara Falls is located in the United States and what other country?

6. If you 'barrack' someone, what do you do?

7. Where did Pope John Paul II have a menorah lit in 1997 to recognize Hanukkah?

8. What is the fastest recorded speed of a badminton shuttle?

9. Which type of computer input device uses an LED for surface illumination?

10. When are the state rooms of Buckingham Palace open to the public each year?

11. What is the title of the 2007 album by PJ Harvey?

12. Which artist painted 'The Gleaners'?

13. Which German goalkeeper was selected for the 2012 UEFA Euro Team of the Tournament?

14. Who played Forrest Gump's mother in *Forrest Gump*?

15. In which country is the capital city of Managua located?

16. What company created the Thinkpad?

Quiz 73

① In what country did Mao Zedong lead the Communist party?

② In what book did the saying 'by the skin of the teeth' originate?

③ What is the most photographed, painted, and scaled mountain in the world?

④ KLM is the flag-carrier airline of which country?

⑤ Who was *Sober* on the airwaves in 2009?

⑥ Which civilization invented the first known alphabet?

⑦ What year did Malta first enter the Olympics?

⑧ What sort of expression is a 'moue'?

⑨ What is the capital city of Mauritania?

⑩ In Greek mythology, who was the blind prophet of Thebes?

⑪ Which US President's home was called Mount Vernon?

⑫ Who is the Greek god of wine and parties?

⑬ Which of the following brews is native to India: Caledonian, Kingfisher or Tusker?

⑭ In what year did Italy withdraw from the League of Nations?

⑮ What ocean does Peru border?

⑯ What feisty feline does Shrek encounter in 2004's *Shrek 2*?

The Bumper *PUB* Quiz Book
Quiz 74

1. In politics, who was David Ben-Gurion?

2. Which was the first known statue to stand in contrapposto?

3. What does the Internet acronym 'URL' stand for?

4. In a PAL TV, what is the standard framerate?

5. What is the number 4400 rounded to the nearest thousand?

6. In what century were the first Christmas turkeys eaten?

7. What type of clothing is a 'lungi'?

8. On which continent is Saint Kitts and Nevis located?

9. What was the only make of car mentioned in the Elton John hit *Crocodile Rock*?

10. How is the constellation *Canis Minor* known in English?

11. What mythical animal was said to consume itself by fire?

12. What majestic mountain range is found in Switzerland?

13. Who played James Bond's CIA contact in *Goldeneye*?

14. Which number appears opposite '6' on a dartboard?

15. Which vehicle takes about eight minutes to accelerate to a speed of more than 17,000mph (27,358kph)?

16. What is a small stick used to hold foods together while grilling called?

The Bumper *PUB* Quiz Book
Quiz 75

1. What species of equid is identifiable via its bold black and white stripes?

2. In what year did Mexico declare independence from Spain?

3. A firkin holds how many gallons of beer?

4. The survival plight of which animals was made famous by Dian Fossey?

5. In music, what does 'mosso' mean?

6. In which city is the Parthenon located?

7. Which European capital city was mostly destroyed by an earthquake in 1755?

8. What book by Kurt Vonnegut Jr. was published in 1963?

9. A person who specializes in the study of plants is called what?

10. Who became Real Madrid's shirt partner in 2013?

11. Which of the following Italian towns is home to a large-scale chocolate festival: Assisi, Nera or Perugia?

12. Which country surrounds Lesotho?

13. In computing, what is a VDU?

14. William Hurt plays what President in *Vantage Point*?

15. Who was the first African American woman to win Wimbledon?

16. Who developed the BASIC programming language?

The Bumper *PUB* Quiz Book
Quiz 76

① If you are lying supine, which way are you facing?

② What reagent could oxidize an alcohol to a carbonyl?

③ Which two grape varietals constitute Bordeaux's Chateau Cheval Blanc blend?

④ What was the 'sambuca' used for during the Siege of Syracuse in 212 BC?

⑤ Indonesia, the largest archipelago in the world, has what capital city?

⑥ Who wrote *Madam Bovary*?

⑦ Who played the shy nun, Sister Mary Robert, in *Sister Act*?

⑧ Which is the second busiest airport in the world, as of 2014?

⑨ Who was the designer responsible for the shop Biba?

⑩ Located in the South Pacific, what is the capital of Samoa?

⑪ What alcoholic beverages are in a B&B?

⑫ What country celebrates its New Year with people dancing beneath a dragon costume?

⑬ Megadeth recorded the song *Breakpoint* for the soundtrack of which film?

⑭ Which horse won the Grand National in 2007?

⑮ Which French, car-making industrialist was imprisoned for collaborating with the Nazis?

⑯ What is the current era in the geologic time scale?

The Bumper *PUB* Quiz Book
Quiz 77

1. In what year did The Corrs release the compilation *Best Of The Corrs*?

2. How many maids a-milking are there in *The Twelve Days of Christmas*?

3. What breed of dogs originated in Afghanistan: Afghan hounds, Beagles, Dachshunds or St. Bernards?

4. In 1996, 225,000 Hutus fled to Rwanda from which country?

5. Which Chinese site was the fifth most-visited website in 2014, according to Alexa?

6. What spirit often comes with a maguey worm in the bottle?

7. Who would you hire to help you organize and keep track of your money?

8. What is the premier California region famous for its wine production?

9. What does a 'scorched earth' policy refer to?

10. Spaghetti, lasagna, ravioli, and cannelloni are typical foods found in the cuisine of which country?

11. Which African country's highest elevation point is Mont Sokbaro?

12. What is the name of an instrument that records vibrations in the Earth's crust?

13. Who coached the Italian squad during the 1966 World Cup?

14. Medically, which of these would an IVP be used to detect the presence of: kidney stone or pregnancy?

15. What major chemical other than chlorine is used to purify water of microorganisms?

16. What prominently featured Hong Kong business gave its name to the 2006 film *Dragon Tiger Gate*?

The Bumper *PUB* Quiz Book
Quiz 78

1. Which country won the Davis Cup in 2013?

2. What are electrically charged atoms called?

3. Which actor played the title character in 2007's *Ghost Rider*?

4. Whose experiments with inkblots in 1911 led to one of the most widely-used projective tests?

5. Which Irish novelist once employed Samuel Beckett?

6. Which leader said: 'If a man hasn't discovered something he will die for, he isn't fit to live'?

7. Which island city has a public beach, situated within its central business district, called Ela Beach?

8. As of 2014, how many times has Miranda Richardson been nominated for an Academy Award?

9. Which of the following beers is not native to Japan: Asahi, Kirin, Sapporo or Tsingtao?

10. What colour is the 'e' in the Google logo?

11. On which continent is Guinea located?

12. Calabrese is the best known variety of which vegetable?

13. Who is the Greek messenger god?

14. Which British supermodel released her own fashion line in 2007?

15. What does 'YMMV' stand for in text messaging?

16. Which Rwandan leader's plane was shot out of the sky in 1994, triggering atrocious genocide?

Quiz 79

1. After Lenin assumed control of Russia he quickly signed a peace treaty with what nation?

2. What ingredients are in a Fuzzy Navel cocktail?

3. Which South-East Asian country's highest elevation point is Hkakabo Razi?

4. What's the name for the scientific study of bodies of fresh water, like lakes?

5. Which Booker Prize winner wrote *Atonement*?

6. What is the avocado an Aztec symbol of?

7. Which African leader, known as the 'Lion of Judah', was worshipped by Rastafarians?

8. What is an 'aglet'?

9. In which country was Dolly, the first sheep cloned from adult sheep cells, born?

10. What is the outer skeleton of organisms such as spiders and insects called?

11. What colour is a lobster's blood?

12. A molotov cocktail is a type of what?

13. Who did Martha Wainwright perform with on the song *Release the Stars*?

14. Tennis pro Ivan Ljubicic comes from which country?

15. Why did Jade Fox want Jen dead in *Crouching Tiger, Hidden Dragon*?

16. Which artist published *The Philosophy of Andy Warhol* in 1975?

Quiz 80

1. What country is known for hymettus honey?

2. What year did the sci-fi book *1984* come out?

3. What artist was as famous for cutting off his ear as for his art?

4. What is 'blepharoplasty' in plastic surgery?

5. The film, *Moonstruck*, was directed by whom?

6. Which future monarch was born at St James's Palace in February 1665?

7. Which comedian did poker player Victoria Coren marry?

8. Who was Ashoka the Great?

9. What spiritual song did The Chemical Brothers remix in 1998?

10. What is eaten with most German meals but is not considered a side dish?

11. Which animal appears on the UK royal coat of arms?

12. In what year did Geri Halliwell wear 'that' Union Jack dress to the Brit Awards?

13. What insect was sacred in Ancient Egypt?

14. Who was Alexander the Great's role model?

15. On which continent does Monrovia, the capital of Liberia, lie?

16. How many rounds are there in the British Touring Car competition, as of 2014?

The Bumper *PUB* Quiz Book
Quiz 81

1. Floppy hats called 'berets' are associated with which country?

2. Name either university which author Dan Brown graduated from?

3. Who became King when the English monarchy was restored, following the English Civil wars?

4. What processor did the original BBC Micro have?

5. Where was the former Viceroyalty of New Granada situated?

6. What is the second-highest vocal part called?

7. What are the logical separations between data on a CD called?

8. The Jordan River separates Jordan from what nation?

9. In what region is most wine in Brazil produced?

10. What French actress played Camille Montes in *Quantum of Solace*?

11. Who was the first golfer to win over US $1 million in a single year?

12. Which country was formerly known as Persia?

13. In terms of weather, what is the opposite of 'windward'?

14. If you say 'skol!', what are you saying?

15. What is the artist Mase's real name?

16. How many miles per hour has the fastest cheetah been clocked at?

Quiz 82

① What do you call a computer symbol used to convey emotion?

② Which mountain marks the centre of Jamaica?

③ Who was elected President of the Czech Republic in 2013?

④ In 2007, Alan Ferguson directed a video for what Boys Like Girls single?

⑤ Which Asian mountain is revered by locals as 'Goddess Mother of the Earth'?

⑥ In what year was John Lennon shot dead in New York City?

⑦ On the London underground, what colour is the District line?

⑧ Who had the palaces and cathedrals built in the Kremlin?

⑨ Which is the third busiest airport in the world, as of 2014?

⑩ What is the chemical symbol for copper?

⑪ Who played Fred Fenster in the film *The Usual Suspects*?

⑫ Mount Kilimanjaro is the highest mountain in which country?

⑬ When are fortune cookies usually served in Chinese restaurants?

⑭ Which boxer went the 10 round distance with Rocky Marciano twice?

⑮ What size star is the Sun: dwarf, large, medium or small?

⑯ What classic book's original title was *El ingenioso hidalgo don Quixote De la Mancha*?

The Bumper *PUB* Quiz Book
Quiz 83

1. How many days does it take for the Earth to revolve around the sun?

2. Which hotel was former World Bank President, Paul Wolfowitz, at when it was hit by a rocket-propelled grenade?

3. In the film *Couples Retreat*, how many couples holiday together?

4. By what name was Tokyo formerly known?

5. What was the second-processor technology in the BBC Micro called?

6. What museum was the famous Hope Diamond donated to in the 1950s?

7. In which year was Victoria crowned Queen of the United Kingdom?

8. What Rihanna video starts with Jay-Z singing his part in the rain?

9. What is the tallest type of horse?

10. Which English King was born in January 1457?

11. How many singers are there in a 'quintet'?

12. Which famous racecourse is situated in Berkshire and opened in 1711?

13. Tostadas are a food item of what type of cuisine?

14. What Australian sports event was instigated by Captain John Illingsworth?

15. What was Dr Seuss' real last name?

16. Who wrote the book *Designing Great Beers*?

The Bumper *PUB* Quiz Book
Quiz 84

1. What is the general term for gases that cause global warming?

2. Who became Czar of Russia in 1682 at age 10?

3. What do you call a temperature-sensitive switch?

4. What is the state flower of Pennsylvania?

5. On which Maltese Island can you find the oldest free-standing monuments in the world?

6. Who was Greek classical figure Medea married to?

7. What decade is the song *The Way You Look Tonight* by The Lettermen from?

8. What does the ballet term 'plié' mean?

9. If a recipe required you to 'julienne' a carrot, what would you do to it?

10. In what film was actor Antonio Banderas' first English-speaking role?

11. In Aesop's fable, what did Androcles remove from the lion's paw?

12. What bomber, of which only four were built, first flew in 1979?

13. Which Indonesian dictator stepped down in 1998 after 32 years in power?

14. Which geyser-bearing town is a major tourist destination in New Zealand?

15. Which French city is claimed as the most romantic city in the world?

16. What is the first name of Tim Henman's wife?

Quiz 85

1. How many goals did Diego Maradona score in the 1986 World Cup?

2. How many telescopes make up the 'Very Large Array' in New Mexico?

3. Who was the first woman ever to become speaker of the UK House of Commons, in 1992?

4. Andy Warhol was known for his bright hair of which colour?

5. What is the brand name of Amazon's portable reading devices?

6. What is the lowest vocal part called?

7. In what year did George I become King of the United Kingdom?

8. What reedy plant that grew along the Nile became a useful resource?

9. What type of drink is 'retsina'?

10. The arrival of which character marks the start of *A Wrinkle in Time*?

11. How much further from the Sun is Eris compared to Pluto?

12. Herbal medicine that is applied externally with a vegetable-based fat is called what?

13. Which country's highest elevation point is Gunung Kinabalu?

14. In the film *Boogie Nights*, what is Rollergirl's real name?

15. Coriander and what other spice come from the same plant?

16. What dish from Spain consists of saffron rice, shrimp, clams, chicken, sausage and peas?

The Bumper *PUB* Quiz Book
Quiz 86

(1) What do you call a deposit of sediment formed where a stream enters a standing body of water such as a lake?

(2) Economically, what is the opposite of supply?

(3) Who plays the title role in the *Iron Man* films?

(4) What is the measure of the moisture level of air called?

(5) Mixing Scotch whisky and Drambuie will produce which cocktail?

(6) What is the third-best-selling UK Christmas single of all time?

(7) James I ascended the English throne in which year?

(8) What is the part of the sword that goes into the handle?

(9) How many laps is the *V8 Supercar Bathurst 1000*?

(10) On a car, what is a 'spoiler'?

(11) What country in Asia, with Kathmandu as its capital, uses the rupee as its currency?

(12) What was the name of the cut-down BBC Micro, designed to compete with the Spectrum?

(13) Known as Bathurst until 1973, what is the capital of Gambia?

(14) What currency do people use in Vietnam?

(15) Spain is famous for which fortified wine?

(16) The 'G' in actor Edward G. Robinson's name stood for what?

The Bumper *PUB* Quiz Book
Quiz 87

① In Spain, how long must a white wine be aged to qualify for the 'crianza' designation?

② The official name of Cairo is 'al-Qahirah', meaning which: the Sacrifice or the Conqueror?

③ The Lev Yashin Award is given to the World Cup's most outstanding what?

④ Which European country's highest mountain is Grossglockner?

⑤ In what year was the film *ET* originally released?

⑥ What were the series of wars by European Christians to recover the Holy Land from the Muslims?

⑦ Which British group won the MTV Video Music Award for Best New Artist in 2012?

⑧ What year was *Dune* published?

⑨ What are a cat's whiskers for?

⑩ Which of these is true about the Dead Sea: it has no water, it is a salt lake or it is man-made?

⑪ How many train stations were serviced by the Orient Express?

⑫ Which was the subtitle of the first original GameCube *Zelda* game?

⑬ What idea was King Hammurabi's Code based on?

⑭ What does the sea urchin use to help protect itself?

⑮ What was Liberace's first name?

⑯ What are the two main styles of ballroom dancing?

The Bumper *PUB* Quiz Book
Quiz 88

1. 2010 marked what anniversary of the first Earth Day?

2. What Russian mussel, first found in US waters in 1988, has invaded the Great Lakes ecosystem?

3. What is the capital city of the United Arab Emirates?

4. Asian ginseng is native to what countries?

5. Who had Princess Elizabeth imprisoned in the Bell Tower of the Tower of London in 1554?

6. Which film starred James Spader, Kim Richards and Robert Downey Jr.?

7. Who was President of Mexico from 2000-2006?

8. U2's album *Achtung Baby!* was released in what year?

9. Emirates is a flag-carrier airline of which country?

10. How many goals did Zinedine Zidane score in the 2006 World Cup?

11. What is the most prolific wine-making region in France?

12. Name the holiday that celebrates the African harvest?

13. Nelson Mandela's 90th birthday tribute was held where?

14. What famous wine-producing region lies between Napa Valley and the Pacific Ocean?

15. What is the name of the limestone formation that rises from a cave floor?

16. Which Egyptian person's title came from the word for the 'big house' in which they lived?

The Bumper *PUB* Quiz Book
Quiz 89

1. The Rhine River begins in which country?

2. In heraldry, what colour is 'murrey'?

3. Mount Nyangani is the highest point in which African country?

4. Who played Nicolas Cage's wife in *Con Air*?

5. What is histology?

6. About how long does it take for sunlight to reach the Earth from the Sun?

7. Which Middle Eastern country's highest mountain is Mount Damavand?

8. In what year did the French last use the guillotine?

9. What type of art form is 'haiku'?

10. If starving, what could you chew on to sustain life: hand, leather shoes, shirt or tree branch?

11. In what Canadian province would you find Toronto?

12. What was the name of the anti-Castro group at the 'Bay of Pigs'?

13. Where is the Sea of Serenity?

14. What note of the major scale is 'la'?

15. Who officially opened the 1976 Summer Olympics in Montreal, Canada?

16. Which is the most vital type of grain used to make Scotch whisky?

The Bumper *PUB* Quiz Book
Quiz 90

1. Herbal medicine is based on the use of what for medicinal purposes?

2. What Australian sailor was the first woman to sail single-handedly around the world non-stop?

3. Mandela's daughter Makaziwe was named after her older sister, who died at what age?

4. Software giving unauthorized access to a computer they infect are called what?

5. Who had the smallest winning margin in the Tour de France during the 20th century?

6. What volume of sherry is the UK Poet Laureate traditionally given each year?

7. In what century was King's College, Cambridge, founded?

8. In what lake will you find the Ssese Islands?

9. What device regenerates a wireless network signal to extend the range of the network?

10. What does 'lachrymose' mean?

11. What are the three main ingredients in traditional Mexican salsa?

12. What is stored energy called?

13. What is the greatest authenticated age a human being has lived to, as of 2014?

14. In the 1990 World Cup final, winner Germany's shirts were predominately what colour?

15. On which boat did the Pilgrim Fathers sail to New England in 1620?

16. In *A Bug's Life*, what is the name of Princess Atta's sister?

The Bumper *PUB* Quiz Book
Quiz 91

1. Ariel Sharon was Prime Minister of which country?

2. Where was Gianluca Branco born?

3. The Great Barrier Reef is on which continent?

4. What did explorer David Livingstone die of?

5. Which country brews San Miguel beer?

6. What decade is the hit single *Days Of Wine And Roses* by Henry Mancini from?

7. What role does Natalie Portman play in *V for Vendetta*?

8. Who became Romanian President after the 1989 Revolution?

9. The death of which UK Labour Party leader allowed Tony Blair to assume the post?

10. How did Nikita Khrushchev die?

11. In Australia, what is a 'sheila'?

12. What is the final stage of ecological succession called?

13. Belgrade is the capital of what country?

14. What is a 'parvenu'?

15. Who killed Harry Potter's parents?

16. What year did William Fox Talbot invent the modern positive/negative photography process?

1. Which swimmer won BBC Young Sports Personality of the Year in 2010?

2. Which bridge marks the oldest crossing point of the River Thames?

3. What was the birth name of Virginia Woolf?

4. Where is actor Danila Kozlovsky from?

5. What is the main flavouring agent in a Mornay Sauce?

6. Which film marked Robert De Niro's directorial debut?

7. What country does Brie cheese originate from?

8. What type of element is xenon?

9. The country once known as the Union of Soviet Socialist Republics is now called what?

10. In which city was Muhammad Ali Pasha, the founder of modern Egypt, born?

11. In what year was George V crowned King?

12. What is said to be the most sociable of all cats?

13. Which animal can retract its 'horns'?

14. What was Justin Timberlake's debut solo single called?

15. What sea borders Yemen to the west?

16. Andorra la Vella is the capital of which microstate?

Quiz 93

1. What became the world's tallest man-made structure in 1880?

2. How many months are there in five years?

3. What is Sollozzo's first name in *The Godfather*?

4. Who was Suleyman the Magnificent's admiral?

5. The 1927 book, *The Bridge of San Luis Rey*, was written by whom?

6. A former USSR Republic, Armenia has which city as its capital?

7. What might a small room used for storage be called?

8. How many goals did Bobby Charlton score in total for Manchester United?

9. What ocean contains the Gulf Stream?

10. In which country are the large islands New Britain and New Ireland located?

11. What makes a martini 'dirty'?

12. What is a group of rhinoceroses called?

13. Which royal dynasty succeeded the Tudors?

14. What colour is the sole of a Louboutin shoe?

15. What band sings *Yellow*?

16. Which country is the world's leading producer of cocoa beans?

The Bumper *PUB* Quiz Book
Quiz 94

① Jerusalem is within which Middle Eastern country?

② Which Cambridge college did Sue Perkins attend?

③ Scurvy leads to an inadequate production of what?

④ Brazilian food is heavily influenced by that of which European country?

⑤ The Hittites were the first to use which material for weapons?

⑥ In 2012 which popular recording artist had a hit with *Shake It Out*?

⑦ Which real-life figure was the main character in the 2004 Italian film *In The Light Of The Sun*?

⑧ What was the computer mouse called in its original US patent filing?

⑨ What are the three main categories of rock?

⑩ What sports brand uses the slogan 'I am what I am'?

⑪ Which was the largest single-day airborne military operation in history?

⑫ Which is the tallest mountain in Northern Ireland?

⑬ What geographical instrument is used to measure elevation?

⑭ Which British couple won the Olympic gold for ice dancing in 1984?

⑮ Who wrote *The Three Musketeers*?

⑯ Decorating an art piece with paper cutouts is known as what?

The Bumper *PUB* Quiz Book
Quiz 95

(1) What do you call the control for the level of sound coming out of left versus right speakers?

(2) In 1983, Stefan Edberg became the first tennis player to achieve which remarkable feat?

(3) Who was the voice of Mr. Potato Head in *Toy Story*?

(4) What famous author of *Brave New World* died the same day as JFK?

(5) What nickname is Ireland given?

(6) Schooner Maritime Lager is native to which country?

(7) Which UK leader advocated appeasement of Germany and Italy prior to World War 2?

(8) Which goat has horns that resemble cork screws?

(9) What were the names of British General Bernard Montgomery's dogs in World War 2?

(10) In language, what is a 'lexis'?

(11) What type of animal is an 'argali'?

(12) What submersible helped to discover the wreckage of the *Titanic* in 1986?

(13) Which of the following groups are considered micronutrients: fats, fibre, protein or vitamins?

(14) What country in Africa with Luanda as its capital uses kwanza as its currency?

(15) In what year did famed mystery author Agatha Christie die?

(16) What is the base of natural logarithms?

① What animal was *Seabiscuit*?

② Which shortcut key in Windows allows you to display help?

③ How does the radius of a circle relate to its diameter?

④ How many stripes give the striped polecat its name?

⑤ Which of these is not a type of grapefruit: golden, purple, pink or white?

⑥ Rough Trade released what Super Furry Animals album in 2007?

⑦ What does the adjective 'noetic' refer to?

⑧ What British island, accessible by road only at low tide, is also known as Holy Island?

⑨ Who wrote *Tess of the d'Urbervilles*?

⑩ Formula One racing driver Fernando Alonso is of what nationality?

⑪ What Marilyn Monroe film was left uncompleted by her death?

⑫ Which US President said his earliest political activism was on behalf of Mandela?

⑬ A Spartan male began military service at age 20 and remained ready for service until what age?

⑭ What is the name of the capital city of Syria?

⑮ If an Australian says 'arvo' what does he or she mean?

⑯ Atychiphobia is the fear of what?

The Bumper *PUB* Quiz Book
Quiz 97

1. The Cayman Islands, south-west of Cuba, are a territory controlled by which country?

2. Which kind of wine is not chilled before serving?

3. Which group of islands is located to the west of Ecuador?

4. Who was the author of *Tristram Shandy*?

5. In which 2011 superhero film did Chris Hemsworth wield the magical hammer Mjollnir?

6. The first plane belonging to which famous flyer was nicknamed *Canary*?

7. Which cereal grain is the most commonly used in beer?

8. 'Saving Face' was an expose on plastic surgery in what US magazine?

9. Bratislava is the capital of what country?

10. What religious text is 'evangel' an archaic reference to?

11. Which breed of dog is the tallest known breed?

12. Ackee and saltfish is the national dish of which country?

13. What 1997 film chronicled Barry McGuigan's boxing career?

14. What was the real name of the woman known as 'The Black Dahlia'?

15. In what year were Coldplay awarded a Grammy for Song of the Year?

16. What kind of animal is the dhole?

The Bumper **PUB** Quiz Book
Quiz 98

1. Before the introduction of decimal currency, how many pence were there in one pound?

2. What type of dancing was Fred Astaire famous for?

3. A killer whale is not really a whale; what kind of animal is it?

4. What fruit is in Germany's famous 'Black Forest Cake'?

5. What, in the body, is a 'psoas'?

6. How old was Bjorn Borg when he appeared in the Davis Cup in 1972?

7. Which of the following composers was not part of the Second Viennese School: Mozart, Schoenberg or Webern?

8. Which of these is a passage of water located in southern Chile: Dove Passage, Drake Passage or Tern Passage?

9. What does a nephrologist specialize in?

10. In a 1999 crash at the British Grand Prix, Michael Schumacher broke what bone?

11. Which scientist first theorized that the Earth moved around the Sun?

12. What are the Audie awards presented for?

13. Which was the first British submarine to be sunk during action in World War 2?

14. What event ruined the world seen in the Anime film *Nausicaa Of The Valley Of The Wind*?

15. Who played the title role in the film *Erin Brockovich*, about an anti-pollution crusader?

16. Medellín is the second largest city in which South American country?

The Bumper *PUB* Quiz Book
Quiz 99

1. Which female golfer won BBC Young Sports Personality of the Year in 2011?

2. What was the full title of the third *Austin Powers* film?

3. Which volcano erupted from January 18-21, 1951, causing over 3,000 deaths?

4. What currency do the Chinese people use in Taiwan?

5. What organ in the body controls insulin production and secretion?

6. What is an action that one animal uses to influence or inform another animal?

7. How is the constellation *Cancer* known in English?

8. In which country is the Palace of Versailles?

9. What's the dog's name in *How the Grinch Stole Christmas*?

10. What variety of wine is produced by using frozen grapes?

11. What are commonly used to decorate windows?

12. What is the capital of the Czech Republic?

13. A Chinese puzzle made by cutting a square into 7 shapes is called a what?

14. In what year did the original IBM PC launch?

15. Where did 'bachata' dance originate?

16. What Shakespeare play includes the line 'Good night, sweet prince. And flights of angels sing thee to thy rest!'?

Quiz 100

1. What country does Prime Minister Perdana Menteri lead, as of 2014?

2. How long did it take to design and build the world's first privately funded spacecraft, *Spaceship One*?

3. Which tennis sisters presented Mandela with the Arthur Ashe Courage Award?

4. What type of climate word would you use to describe the climate around your house: megaclimate, mesoclimate or microclimate?

5. What is the Islamic holy text called?

6. Which African country has a peak elevation of 53m (174ft) above sea level: Ghana or The Gambia?

7. Ancient Egyptians believed their Pharaohs were the earthly form of what god?

8. Who narrates the 2007 CGI film *TMNT*?

9. On which continent is Azerbaijan located?

10. The song *Don't Speak* was about Gwen Stefani's relationship with whom?

11. What are the first types of organism to return to an area devastated by a major disaster?

12. On the London underground, what colour is the Northern line?

13. On a Heineken label, the star is usually what colour?

14. Who is the evil creature that Beowulf defeats in the epic poem *Beowulf*?

15. What cut of beef is commonly used when making Beef Wellington?

16. In what year was Pele's final World Cup appearance?

The Bumper *PUB* Quiz Book
Quiz 101

1. What is the name given to the largest of all the penguins?

2. Who plays Storm in the *X-Men* trilogy?

3. Who wrote the sci-fi book *Downbelow Station*?

4. What is an 'ambit'?

5. Which country leads the world in beer production?

6. Which was the first British football team to win the European Cup?

7. Which Ed Sheeran song was co-written by Pharrell Williams?

8. The amount of time that a flavour lingers can be described as a wine's what?

9. Jerk chicken, fried plantains and mango ice cream are associated with which country's cuisine?

10. Why did Turkey have to withdraw from the 1950 FIFA World Cup?

11. Into which ocean does the Zambezi River flow?

12. In medical terms, what does the suffix '-asthenia' mean?

13. To the nearest 500 miles, how long is the coastline of India?

14. In religious meaning, what is a 'praxis'?

15. The Baiyoke Tower II, completed in 1997 at a height of 997 feet, is located where?

16. How was the Bubonic Plague more popularly known?

The Bumper *PUB* Quiz Book
Quiz 102

1. Roughly what fraction of the Earth is covered by water?

2. In American folklore, what was the name of Paul Bunyan's legendary blue ox?

3. Which song was on the B-side of Amy Winehouse's single *Take the Box*?

4. What did K.J. Choi do before he was a golfer?

5. What country gets the tropical sea breeze known as 'the Doctor'?

6. Which emperor supposedly tried to murder his mother on a boat?

7. What does 'piscine' mean?

8. Which third film in the *Transformers* series was released in June of 2011?

9. Who will replace the Swedish King Carl XVI Gustaf when he dies or resigns?

10. Which of the following is not an Italian coffee: corretto, demi-tasse, erlingter or ristretto?

11. What was the first turbo-jet-powered commercial aircraft?

12. Which bishop was a good friend of Nelson Mandela and assisted him during his presidency?

13. Which African country's highest elevation point is Soira?

14. Mandela Day was a song written for Mandela's 70th Birthday celebration by what group?

15. What is the first name of golf's Faldo?

16. What is the state flower of Alaska?

The Bumper *PUB* Quiz Book
Quiz 103

1. How many kilobytes are there in 3 megabytes?

2. Who was the FIFA *Ballon d'Or* player of the year in 2013?

3. What is a 'sarangi'?

4. What common Internet term is a technology that transfers multiple signals over a single medium?

5. What style of yoga is practised in a very warm room?

6. What character did Liv Tyler play in *The Lord of the Rings*?

7. Who had a huge hit with *White Christmas*?

8. The airport code CIA designates which European airport?

9. Who was the long-serving President of the World Jewish Congress that died at age 84 in 2013?

10. In medical terminology, what is an immature, embryonic stage in the development of cells or tissues: bam, bard, blast or boom?

11. What is a cryptonym?

12. What is the capital of Jamaica?

13. Which cheese is usually grated and eaten with pasta?

14. How long did the Trojan War last?

15. In what year did Equatorial Guinea gain independence from Spain?

16. Believed to have portals used for solar observations, Hovenweep Castle was built by what indigenous US people?

The Bumper *PUB* Quiz Book
Quiz 104

1. Which country that straddles Europe and the Middle East has its highest elevation point at Mount Ararat?

2. What became the world's tallest man-made structure in 1931?

3. In which capital city would you find the Marley Museum?

4. During which Chinese dynasty was the Great Wall of China built?

5. In the film *Zombieland*, what was Zombieland's original incarnation?

6. What was the number of air-crew for the Nakajima Ki-43 Japanese fighter?

7. What were the main subjects at Wassily Kandinsky's Bauhaus School?

8. What Japanese delicacy can be deadly if not prepared correctly?

9. What famous Ray Bradbury novel was published in 1953?

10. On the London underground, what colour is the Jubilee line?

11. How many goals did China score during the World Cup 2002?

12. What kind of cuisine can you expect to find in a Brazilian 'churrascaria'?

13. What is the name of Othello's wife in Shakespeare's *Othello*?

14. Which major Asian river is known as the Tsangpo in Tibet, where it originates?

15. How long will the average housefly live?

16. What temperature should you not exceed when melting chocolate?

The Bumper *PUB* Quiz Book
Quiz 105

1. What northern marine creature has ivory tusks?

2. What is the only OPEC member state to have ever suspended its membership?

3. In the 2007 film *Stomp The Yard*, where is DJ originally from?

4. The failure of the potato crop led to the Irish Famine, starting in what year?

5. Which element is responsible for poisoning waters around Japan: arsenic, lead, mercury or potassium?

6. Who became the President of South Korea in 1998?

7. Where were the ashes of Nobel Prize winning author, Patrick White, scattered?

8. Which former Chilean dictator was arrested in London in 1998?

9. A 'hoodie' in fashion terms refers to what?

10. Who loans money to Willy Loman in *Death of a Salesman*?

11. What is the process of learning through mistakes called?

12. What is boxer Shane Mosley's nickname?

13. What Norah Jones song is also the name of a country band?

14. How many years did the Hundred Years' War last?

15. What destroyed the Colossus of Rhodes?

16. Which European country has approximately the same population as the UK, but is 2.5 times as large?

The Bumper *PUB* Quiz Book
Quiz 106

1. In which country did the pop art movement originate?

2. Which tennis great, born in 1970, hails from Las Vegas?

3. How many children did composer Johann Sebastian Bach have?

4. Who developed the Second Law of Motion that is described by the equation 'F=ma'?

5. How does Doc Ock look different from normal humans in *Spider-Man 2*?

6. What city is the second largest in area in the USA?

7. In what year did the British officially return the city of Hong Kong to China?

8. What spirit is made from the agave plant?

9. What is electrical current that reverses its direction at a regular interval called?

10. What novel is the film, *Slumdog Millionaire*, based on?

11. Coca-Cola created what type of package in the 1920s?

12. From which country did popcorn originate?

13. What is the name of the protest band in Russia that was arrested and then pardoned by Putin?

14. On which continent is Niger located?

15. Who is the author of the book *Gorky Park*?

16. The Suez Canal flows through which country?

Quiz 107

1. Which organization won the Nobel Peace Prize in 1965?

2. In his paintings, Wassily Kandinsky worked to link colour and what?

3. For what is 'CEO' an acronym?

4. Which US state's flower is the hibiscus?

5. Who wrote *One Hundred Years of Solitude*?

6. What does 'esprit' mean?

7. What was the punishment for a Roman who did not register for the census?

8. What is the female praying mantis noted for doing to its partner while mating?

9. What is the definition of a 'gulf stream'?

10. A 1912 Eleanor Atkinson book featured what famous animal character?

11. What Japanese dumpling dish originated in China?

12. What group performs *Life is a Highway* on the *Cars* soundtrack?

13. In which Australian zoo did the last known Thylacine die in 1936?

14. Who did Mehmet Ali Agca attempt to assassinate in 1981?

15. Who won the 2006 FIFA World Cup?

16. Barbados is considered to be part of which continent?

The Bumper PUB Quiz Book
Quiz 108

1. What are the members of a single type of living organism in an ecosystem called?

2. Which artist became famous for the work 'The Birds of America'?

3. Ethyl pentanoate would be classified as belonging to which derivative group?

4. Mustangs are originally descended from horses brought to America from which country?

5. Which two countries were barred from the 1950 World Cup?

6. What year did the Madrid train bombings take place?

7. In the film *Private Fears In Public Places*, why does Lionel have to put his life on hold?

8. What band is led by original Weezer bass player Matt Sharp?

9. In what year was Edgar Allan Poe born?

10. In Turkey, what is the colour of mourning?

11. Who is Jeremy Piven's character in *Entourage* based on in real life?

12. Which vegetable has the highest sugar content?

13. In what years did the Mariposa War take place?

14. What is the national flower of Portugal?

15. Cuba is located 87 miles (140km) south of which archipelago?

16. Which is the second largest Australian state?

The Bumper *PUB* Quiz Book
Quiz 109

1. To whom did Bradley Manning give leaked documents that led to his arrest?

2. Near which city can you find Merri Creek in Australia?

3. Where are the most expensive shopping stores in New York City located?

4. Herbs are the leaves of what type of low-growing plants?

5. What is the process of taking scrap materials and using them again called?

6. What is the region between the second and sixth cataracts of the Nile known as?

7. What does 'irenic' mean?

8. What term means 'protecting and using a resource wisely'?

9. The 2003 film *Freaky Friday* was a remake of what 1977 film?

10. What is a more common word for 'inheritor'?

11. Which company provides the squash drink for Wimbledon?

12. Which scientist, born 1864, researched alternatives to cotton to help southern US farmers?

13. What was the Flintstones' pet called?

14. A 2002 Sugababes album was entitled *Angels with* what?

15. What is an ailurophile?

16. How many is three and a half dozen?

The Bumper *PUB* Quiz Book
Quiz 110

1. What part of London do Cockneys hail from?

2. Who wrote the gothic tale, *Frankenstein*?

3. Which drummer heavily influenced Led Zeppelin's John Bonham?

4. Which country has Amsterdam as its capital city?

5. What year was the first photo taken with a flash bulb?

6. What are vast amounts of oil that have become trapped in one place called?

7. What is the national flower of the Netherlands?

8. Western Native Americans wore hard-soled moccasins to protect from what?

9. The film, *Gods and Monsters*, was directed by whom?

10. Which is the world's longest river?

11. In what year did Zeppelin fly his first dirigible?

12. What is the South African speciality Koeksister?

13. Acrophobia is the fear of what?

14. What pneumonia-like disease first appeared in 2002 in the Guangdong Province of China?

15. What sort of drink is 'oloroso'?

16. In which year was golfer Trevor Immelman named Rookie of the Year?

The Bumper *PUB* Quiz Book
Quiz 111

1. What was put in a window during the Victorian era to symbolize warmth?

2. What country in Oceania with Port Moresby as its capital uses kina as its currency?

3. If you sit down to dinner in Paris and start with 'pain' and 'fromage', what are you eating?

4. What does Sam I Am eat with his Green Eggs in the famous Dr Seuss book?

5. Which guitar man, singer and songwriter led the highly influential The Jam?

6. Which meat is used for classic Wiener schnitzel?

7. What was Marilyn Monroe's first major movie role, in 1950?

8. What was the name of Australian author Albert Facey's best-selling autobiography?

9. What type of car uses two or more sources of power?

10. The Latin word 'minor', the root of 'minority', means what?

11. What is Britain's oldest remaining overseas territory?

12. In music, what does 'andante' mean?

13. At the beginning of *The Big Lebowski*, what do the thugs ruin?

14. Which adaptation allows an organism to blend in with its surroundings?

15. What is boxer Oliver McCall's nickname?

16. While President of South Africa, Nelson Mandela frequently returned to what home village?

The Bumper *PUB* Quiz Book
Quiz 112

1. Denmark has a land border with which country?

2. How many engines are there on a B-52 aeroplane?

3. What is the national flower of Ireland?

4. Which Hogwarts professor finally got to teach Defence Against the Dark Arts in Harry's sixth year?

5. In *X-Men: First Class*, who plays Professor X?

6. As of 2012, how many of the critically endangered Addax Antelope are estimated to be living in the wild?

7. Which month was once considered by Romans to be unlucky for marriage ceremonies?

8. In what year did Brazil first select Pele for the World Cup?

9. Which country has Algiers as its capital city?

10. Pythagoras was particularly associated with which shape?

11. Beaujolais wine is produced in which French wine region?

12. Which character does Peter Dinklage play in *Game of Thrones*?

13. In fashion, 'faux fur' is what?

14. What do fiddler crabs do with their one large claw?

15. What radioactive metallic element, found in all uranium ores, has an atomic number of 89?

16. What is the capital of the Central African Republic?

The Bumper *PUB* Quiz Book
Quiz 113

1. Who was the 'Lady with the Lamp' who tended soldiers in the Crimean War?

2. In computing, what is the file extension for a compiled Flash file?

3. Which 1995 film has this tagline: *New Animals. New Adventures. Same Hair*?

4. Which star did the Ancient Egyptians closely follow, for agricultural reasons?

5. On which continent is Afghanistan located?

6. To the nearest year, what is the periodicity of Halley's Comet?

7. Who taught Sergio Garcia to play golf?

8. The Ottoman Turks captured Constantinople in what year?

9. Who was the author of *Germinal*?

10. What does the Scots dialect word 'ree' mean?

11. What is a force that resists the separation of two bodies in contact called?

12. What type of clothing does O'Neill specialize in?

13. What number does the Roman numeral 'X' stand for?

14. Which fruit is normally used to make wine?

15. In 1929, Diego Rivera married what famous Mexican artist?

16. Who was Australian Prime Minister from 1996-2007?

The Bumper *PUB* Quiz Book
Quiz 114

1. How many snooker World Championships did Ray Reardon win?

2. In *Aliens*, what was Newt's real name?

3. What is the chemical symbol for iron?

4. Which Arab country suffered a devastating civil war from 1975-1991?

5. What year did Khrushchev visit the United States?

6. What colour is Devil's food cake?

7. What is the typical gestation period for dogs?

8. Who won the Booker Prize in 2007 for *The Gathering*?

9. Which of the following is not a type of Native American tribal dance: war dance, grass dance or step dance?

10. What country in South-East Asia with Bandar Seri Begawan as its capital uses the dollar as its currency?

11. In what year was the Great Fire of Rome?

12. The Spam Museum is located in which US State?

13. What was the capital of India before New Delhi?

14. What is a bitmap?

15. What causes bubbles to appear in beer?

16. What is the name of Othello's advisor in the Shakespeare play *Othello*?

The Bumper *PUB* Quiz Book
Quiz 115

1. Roughly what percentage of an adult human's body weight is taken up by the brain?

2. What nickname are the Royals said to have given to Princess Anne's first husband, Mark Phillips?

3. What do Apple call their tablet computer?

4. Which two countries share Colombia's eastern border?

5. 'The Settlement' is the common name for the capital of what Australian island territory?

6. Complete the song title: 'What does the ___ say'?

7. Who won the 2003 US Open Singles Championship?

8. In 1957-60, Lawrence Durrell wrote which classic?

9. Which element has the chemical symbol Mg?

10. Which coalition defeated Napoleon Bonaparte's forces at Leipzig?

11. The *Surface* is a tablet PC made by what company?

12. Who was President of the Royal Academy of Arts from 2004-2011?

13. What three colours are on the German flag?

14. Which Italian region is the source of Marsala wine?

15. What is your 'noggin'?

16. In what 1987 comedy does Seth Green play a nosy, nerdy younger brother?

The Bumper *PUB* Quiz Book
Quiz 116

1. Why do health-conscious cooks prefer steaming as a food preparation technique over boiling?

2. What kind of anthropology is also known as ethnology?

3. What was The Cure's first number one album in the UK?

4. Who won the duet women synchronized swimming event at the 2012 Olympics?

5. What are the names of the divine twins in Greek mythology?

6. Who plays Arya Stark in *Game of Thrones*?

7. In which year did President Bush and Boris Yeltsin proclaim a formal end to the Cold War?

8. Darwin, Minnesota is home to a 12-foot wide ball of what?

9. Which Australian naturalist led an expedition into the Tasmanian forests to try to find live thylacine?

10. In Greek mythology, who was Hermes?

11. Georgia O'Keefe was married to which famous photographer?

12. Which meat cannot be made kosher?

13. What is the last name of the school guidance counsellor in *Easy A*?

14. In what year did Lloyd-George become UK Prime Minister?

15. How is the remaining wall of Jerusalem's Temple Mount best known?

16. What SI unit was originally defined as one 10-millionth of the distance from the equator to the North Pole?

Quiz 117

1. How long was the first print of the film *Heaven's Gate*?

2. What is it called when current skips part of a circuit?

3. What Italian explorer explored the Mississippi Valley in America?

4. Who wrote the 1905 book *The House of Mirth*?

5. Which river provides the water for Canberra's Lake Burley Griffin?

6. What type of anti-depressant is Prozac?

7. Who designed Fendi's first couture fur collection?

8. Which is the final letter of the Greek alphabet?

9. Which female singer was featured on Eminem's track *Stan*?

10. The Amazon, Brazil's largest river system, originates in which mountain range?

11. Where in Canada was actor Kim Coates born?

12. What is the chemical symbol for zinc?

13. Which English King started the Reformation?

14. Which of these languages is of Latin origin: Hungarian, Polish or Romanian?

15. Mexican ceviche is made by marinating raw fish in what type of liquid?

16. Which country hosted the 13th World Cup in 1986?

The Bumper *PUB* Quiz Book
Quiz 118

1. What do you call a line on a map that joins points of equal temperature?

2. What hot-tasting edible root is often served as a spicy sauce with roast beef?

3. In Canadian politics, what distinction did Prime Minister Sir John Joseph Caldwell Abbott have?

4. *I Want A Famous Face* is a plastic surgery show on which music network?

5. Which element has the chemical symbol N?

6. What number was Gareth Bale assigned at Madrid when he joined the club in 2013?

7. In what year did Queen Victoria die?

8. Who set up Don Corleone for his assassination attempt in the street?

9. In Scottish slang, what is a 'ned'?

10. What body covering do mammals have that other animals do not?

11. Which British territory has The Valley as its capital city?

12. The Central African Republic shares the majority of its southern border with what nation?

13. What was the original name for the Internet?

14. In 'Doctor Who', the 11th Doctor mistakes a group of aliens from Saturnyne for what kind of monster?

15. About how far can a pumping human heart squirt blood?

16. What do the words 'Dalai Lama' mean?

The Bumper *PUB* Quiz Book
Quiz 119

1. How many times in total did footballer George Best play for his national team?

2. In which year did the Arab-Israeli Yom Kippur War occur?

3. What is the name of the home farm in the film *Home on the Range*?

4. Which Canadian won the MTV Video Music Award for Best New Artist in 2010?

5. How old was Queen Anne, who reigned from 1702 until 1714, when she died?

6. Flautas is a food item of what type of cuisine?

7. Which character did Linda Kozlowski play in the original *Crocodile Dundee* film?

8. What gives people 'red eyes' in some photographs?

9. When did the first node go live on what would later be called ARPANET?

10. In Greek mythology, Clotho, Lachesis and Atropos were what famed trio?

11. Which kind of tree is, statistically, the most often struck by lightning?

12. Alexander the Great died of fever in Babylon in what year?

13. In the US, NFPA stands for what?

14. In archaic English, what did 'prithee' mean?

15. Which two cities formed the capitals of the Hapsburg Dual Monarchy that dissolved in World War 1?

16. In India, what is a 'patta'?

The Bumper *PUB* Quiz Book
Quiz 120

1. *Psycho* was remade in 1998, but who directed the original?

2. Which planet takes 165 Earth years to orbit the sun?

3. What gives blue cheese its colour?

4. The art of tattooing is believed to have originated in what country?

5. Elton John has sold many personal items to raise research money for what disease?

6. Who played Solomon Northup in *12 Years a Slave*?

7. What do you call a series of rulers from the same family or ethnic group?

8. What are the smallest bones in the body called?

9. Where was the Minoan civilization founded?

10. In *The Mummy* by Anne Rice, what had Sharples left on Daisy to mark her?

11. Who played the lead female role in the 2004 film, *Wimbledon*?

12. Which Chinese administrative region lies on the west side of the Pearl River Delta?

13. What country is 2650 miles in length but has a width that varies between only 100 and 250 miles?

14. What is a small hole in a tooth known as?

15. What kind of creature is a 'squab'?

16. What was the first ship sunk by the German ship *Graf Spee* during World War 2?

The Bumper *PUB* Quiz Book
Quiz 121

1. How many nations joined the Euro on launch in 1999?

2. In which country do you say 'gamarjoba' when meeting someone for the first time?

3. Which of these rappers was not a member of N.W.A.: Ice Cube, MC Breed or MC Ren?

4. What year did Microsoft release *Windows XP*?

5. Which Tropic passes through northern Argentina?

6. What is the name of Axel Foley's supervisor in *Beverly Hills Cop*?

7. What is 'radar' an abbreviation of?

8. Who was the Confederate spy who became a bodyguard for the Pope at the Vatican?

9. Which shortcut in Windows allows you to move the insertion point to the beginning of the previous word?

10. In the film *Cool Runnings*, four Jamaican athletes compete in what sport?

11. What constant is equivalent to 96,485 coulombs per mole of electrons?

12. Which fighter was the first to defeat Lennox Lewis?

13. What body of water is located directly to the south of India?

14. Who wrote the 1851 book *Moby-Dick; or, The Whale*?

15. A mineral flavour in a wine usually indicates the presence of what in the vineyard's soil?

16. In what year did Maradona score the World Cup's infamous 'Hand Of God' goal?

Quiz 122

1. Where is Disney's newest park due to open in 2015?

2. How many degrees are there in a right-angle?

3. Who is the author of *Chill Factor*?

4. Which animal is notorious for spraying terrible odours?

5. What finishes the song line: 'All I want for Christmas is my two ___ ___'?

6. According to legend, what messenger was sent to Athens from Marathon after the battle?

7. What is the highest mountain in Victoria, Australia?

8. Which actress appeared in both *Clueless* and *Batman & Robin*?

9. What herb's Latin name is *Zingiber officinale*?

10. Under which English King were the first permanent American colonies established?

11. Where is the Sea of Tranquility?

12. Which FC Barcelona player was the top goal scorer for La Liga in 2012-13?

13. What is the longest known palindromic word, coined by James Joyce?

14. What Hungarian red, powdered spice is derived from peppers?

15. From which beach did Australian Prime Minister Harold Holt disappear in 1967?

16. In economics, the number of people who want an item determines its what?

The Bumper PUB Quiz Book
Quiz 123

① Which Nordic country has 'The Little Mermaid' statue that was unveiled in 1913?

② What metals are 'tin cans' typically made from?

③ Which electronic device will cut power if the current gets too high?

④ Who introduced potatoes to Ireland?

⑤ What is a French word that is used to describe a sweet wine?

⑥ Who is credited with creating the World Wide Web?

⑦ What is a 'cyberpunk'?

⑧ Which African country's highest elevation point is Mont Ngaoui?

⑨ In mathematics, Cantor, Zermelo, and Cohen were specialists in which field?

⑩ Vaduz is the capital of which European principality?

⑪ Where is 'Boddington's' beer brewed?

⑫ Which British actor voiced Scar in *The Lion King*?

⑬ In what year was boxer Rodolfo Lopez born?

⑭ Who recorded the 2013 hit *Let Me Love You (Until You Learn To Love Yourself)*?

⑮ In literary terms, what is 'accidie'?

⑯ What year did the *Exxon Valdez* run aground and cause a major oil spill?

The Bumper *PUB* Quiz Book
Quiz 124

1. What does the acronym 'GPS' stand for?

2. Which term describes plastic surgery on a person's chin?

3. What is the maximum number of blowholes a whale can have?

4. In 1980, Vigdis Finnbogadottir was Iceland's first President who was also... what?

5. How many species of tigers are found on the continent of Africa?

6. What is another word for burnt wine: brandy, rum, tequila or vodka?

7. Mark Ronson is the co-founder of what record label?

8. The adventure of Bart, Ladj and Thai begins outside what business in 2006's French film *Sheitan*?

9. Michael Schumacher made a donation of $10 million towards what 2004 disaster?

10. Who invented the mercury thermometer?

11. Which nation in the Middle East gained its independence on the 15th of August, 1971?

12. During the Cold War, which country owned the missiles in Cuba that were aimed at the US?

13. Which two Latin American countries are the only ones more populous than Colombia?

14. What Soviet space dog was the first animal to orbit the Earth?

15. What is the national flower of Scotland?

16. Monet, Renoir and Degas all belonged to which art movement?

The Bumper *PUB* Quiz Book
Quiz 125

1. Which liner was said to be 'unsinkable', but sank during its first voyage?

2. When the Queen is in residence, how many sentries guard the front of the Palace?

3. In addition to mucus, what helps your nose filter out germs and dirt?

4. Ivory Coast is located on which continent?

5. Which is the fastest bird?

6. How would you describe a noisome object?

7. What type of clothing part is a 'bertha'?

8. Whose Formula One disqualification in Canada put him out of title contention in 2007?

9. Tirana is the capital of which country?

10. Which film won the Best Picture Oscar for 2010?

11. In what century was Canute crowned King of England?

12. What does 'ASCII' stand for?

13. What product is rum distilled from?

14. Which country is known for dishes with mozzarella and olive oil?

15. When a dog repeats a learned behaviour and gets a reward, what process is this?

16. Who wrote the one-movement orchestral piece, *Bolero*?

Quiz 126

1. Which European city is known as Auld Reekie?

2. In what year did Christina Aguilera release her self-titled album?

3. Which horse won the Grand National in 2014?

4. Which innovator is credited with inventing Ethernet?

5. In the original version of *The Poseidon Adventure*, which star had a swimming champion medal?

6. In what hotel did delegates meet to draft the United Nations Charter in 1945?

7. What is 'croup'?

8. In the UK, who created the first successful incandescent light bulb?

9. Approximately how many years does a glass bottle take to break down in a landfill?

10. British monarchs stayed in which tower of the Tower of London?

11. Which Ancient Egyptian god had an ibis for a head?

12. Golden Brewery produces which of these beers: Coors, Hamms, Miller or Schiltz?

13. Whose flag has a blue cross on it, Norway's or the United Kingdom's?

14. What is anosmia?

15. Which demi-god was famous for his strength?

16. What is the first phase of cell mitosis?

Quiz 127

1. What Mediterranean punch is made with wine and citrus juices?

2. Which British writer and sailor, born in 1553, spent his life proposing that Britain colonize America?

3. Which country cancelled hosting the FIFA World Cup in 1986?

4. Which of the following regions of Africa is home to wild boars: Atlas Mountains, Great Rift Valley or Kalahari Desert?

5. What was 'ogam'?

6. Who plays the lead role in *Underworld Evolution*?

7. What is the name given to the water-based paint created with egg as a binder?

8. Who was the first female UK Poet Laureate?

9. How old was Mandela when he was removed from the US terror watch list?

10. What is Roger Rabbit's wife called?

11. What is the term for the act of pouring a wine into a special container so that it can breathe?

12. Dromoland Castle is a large hotel found in which country?

13. What heavy element, used in some older types of paint, created a health risk?

14. At which New Zealand beach was the film *The Piano* shot?

15. What decade is the hit single *Gin And Juice* by Snoop Dogg from?

16. What warship hovered off French-controlled Morocco in 1911 during the Moroccan Crisis: *Agadir*, *Bismarck* or *Nimitz*?

The Bumper *PUB* Quiz Book
Quiz 128

1. Which relatives did Harry Potter grow up living with?

2. To what British Prime Minister was Princess Diana related?

3. When looking at a map, which direction typically points to the bottom of the map?

4. Who produced the hit Jay-Z song, 'Dirt Off Your Shoulder'?

5. 'Hawe No Michi' means what in English?

6. Which African country's highest elevation point is Tena Kourou, at 749 metres?

7. What is a long-term rental agreement called?

8. In what year was the UEFA European Football Championship founded?

9. Who was the only American golfer to win a World Golf Championship event in 2011?

10. How many daughters does King Triton have in *The Little Mermaid*?

11. Who sculpted the Statue of Liberty?

12. What note of the major scale is 're'?

13. What type of climate does tea grow in?

14. Which animal is famously slow-moving and hangs upside-down from tree branches?

15. In which country can you find a giant salamander which can grow to 1.5m (5ft) in length?

16. Mitsubishi, Sony and Toyota are all companies with roots in what country?

The Bumper *PUB* Quiz Book
Quiz 129

1. Which tennis term is defined as 'a point that will end the game'?

2. What is the name for the boundary around a black hole, beyond which events cannot affect the observer?

3. Costume jewellery was introduced in the 1920s by what designer?

4. What was Australia's first incorporated municipality?

5. The Dutch East India Company founded a station in what African country, establishing a settlement?

6. What is the Welsh name for Wales?

7. What is a flat surface that goes on and on in all directions?

8. Who played Caesar in the 2014 film *Dawn of the Planet of the Apes*?

9. The first autofocus camera was marketed in what decade?

10. What prion disease broke out in Britain in 1996, leading to widespread concern?

11. Which of the following is not a protective mother: alligator, hyena, komodo dragon or zebra?

12. What is an 'ea'?

13. Which of these Soviet leaders died in the 1980s: Brezhnev, Kruschev or Yeltsin?

14. Who plays the Vice President of the USA in comedy series *Veep*?

15. How many music videos were made for The Fray's 'How To Save A Life'?

16. What kind of beer is made entirely from malt: ale, all-grain, lager or stout?

The Bumper *PUB* Quiz Book
Quiz 130

① Which cyclist won BBC Sports Personality of the Year in 2011?

② In what year was the term 'Internet' used for the first time?

③ Maybelline, Revlon and Cover Girl are all makers of what type of product?

④ Which country's highest elevation point is Mount Kenya?

⑤ Aphenphosmphobia is the fear of what?

⑥ In what year did the first McDonald's restaurant in the world open?

⑦ What is the reason we cannot drink the ocean's waters without purifying it first?

⑧ What country, with Honiara as its capital city, uses dollars as its currency?

⑨ Malcolm X was buried in what year?

⑩ In the USA, what type of meat is traditionally served at Thanksgiving celebrations?

⑪ Who was Time's Person of the Year in 2010?

⑫ Crowded House's lead singer Neil Finn's brother, Tim Finn, is the founder of what successful band?

⑬ What German soldier was called the Desert Fox during World War 2?

⑭ What film bankrupted Carolco Pictures?

⑮ What was the flagship of the First Fleet, which arrived in Port Jackson, Australia, in January, 1788?

⑯ The 1904 book, *Nostromo*, was written by whom?

The Bumper *PUB* Quiz Book
Quiz 131

① In electronics, what does the abbreviation 'EMI' stand for?

② Buenos Aires, which translates to 'fair winds', is the capital of which South American country?

③ What prince follows Prince Charles as heir to the throne?

④ Colin Montgomerie has had how many European Tour wins?

⑤ How much was the prize for winning the first Silverstone Grand Prix in 1948?

⑥ Great Britain signed the Treaty of Sinchulu with what nation?

⑦ The 'W.C.' stood for what in the name of entertainer, W.C. Fields?

⑧ Which wrestler played Thunderlips in *Rocky 3*?

⑨ What kind of dwelling is a 'yurt'?

⑩ *Iron City* beer was the first to use which invention?

⑪ Which European country split into two republics in 1992?

⑫ Fear of the night is known as what?

⑬ Which of the following is not one of the three basic types of economic systems: capitalism, communism, nationalism or socialism?

⑭ Who wrote the 1960s book on the threat of overpopulation, *The Population Bomb*?

⑮ Who commanded the French army in India during the Seven Years War?

⑯ What are the four ingredients in French bread?

The Bumper *PUB* Quiz Book
Quiz 132

1. What is the capital of Honduras?

2. A grown-up male cow is called a what?

3. What turn of the 20th-century killer was known as the 'Vampire of Dusseldorf'?

4. A 2006 single from The Darkness begs the question 'Is it just' what?

5. How many moons does Venus have?

6. What two birds are used to describe pro- and anti-war lobbyists?

7. In the US, what are small outdoor bathrooms called?

8. Which religion has the most members in Italy?

9. What language is most commonly spoken in Afghanistan?

10. Cathay Pacific is the flag-carrier airline of which country?

11. In what year did Panama secede from Colombia?

12. In botany, what does 'obovate' mean?

13. A deficiency of which nutrient can cause rickets?

14. Where do the couples of the 2007 film *Why Did I Get Married?* hold their week-long retreat?

15. What was the most team goals scored in a single game in the 1982 World Cup?

16. A 'coke hat' is another name for what round-topped hat?

The Bumper *PUB* Quiz Book
Quiz 133

1. Mount Meron is which Middle-Eastern country's highest elevation point?

2. Chocolate is made from what type of bean?

3. Around 1530, Titian's work became darker after the death of whom?

4. Which robot befriends a little girl in the opening tale of *I, Robot*?

5. What colour shirt does Tiger Woods wear on the final day of every tournament?

6. People of the Maasai tribe of Kenya traditionally make jewellery and pierce what body parts?

7. Who directed the 1975 film, *Sholay*?

8. Who became the first freely-elected President of the Russian Republic in 1991?

9. What happened to the world's oldest creature, Ming the shellfish, when scientists tried to open it up?

10. Which word means 'hello' in Spanish?

11. Who was the first elected female President of the Republic of Ireland?

12. The Bank of America Plaza, completed in 1985 at a height of 280m (921ft), is located where?

13. Which Prince song starts out with the narrative: 'Dearly Beloved...'?

14. What is the built-in web browser on the iPhone called?

15. What is the rate of change of an object's velocity called?

16. What would you call a statement of expected future occurrences?

The Bumper *PUB* Quiz Book
Quiz 134

1. How long does it take for the Earth to rotate around completely on its axis?

2. Which of these is not a prime number? 31, 71, 97 or 111

3. Where was the Kush civilization located?

4. In what country is the 1997 film *Life is Beautiful* set?

5. What is the main active chemical in marijuana?

6. What continent did the 'waltz' originate on?

7. What sport does Lars Ulrich's father Torben, a jazz musician, play professionally?

8. From whom did Jim Furyk learn the game of golf?

9. Complete the Mandela quote, 'Lead from the back and let others ___'.

10. When did *Doctor Who* originally premiere in the UK?

11. With reference to Japan, what is a 'mon'?

12. What is added to gin to make 'pink gin'?

13. How many wings does a bee have?

14. What philosophical school used reason to support Christian beliefs?

15. In *The Iliad*, what is the name of Hector's wife?

16. What is a unit that measures force?

The Bumper *PUB* Quiz Book
Quiz 135

① What colour are dried orange pekoe tea leaves?

② Traditional Italian menus have how many sections?

③ Which is the only land mammal that cannot jump?

④ King Edward VIII gave up the throne in 1936 in order to do what?

⑤ What type of soldier was a 'kern'?

⑥ What is the capital of Ecuador?

⑦ Which English city calls itself 'The Venice of the North'?

⑧ In what year did William III become King of England?

⑨ What year did Martha Wainwright release her first full-length album?

⑩ Which bird is the best mimic of the human voice and other sounds?

⑪ What area in New York did *The Warriors* call home?

⑫ In which of these World Cup years did Sandor Koscos win a Golden Shoe Award: 1938, 1950, 1954 or 1962?

⑬ Who played Captain Picard in *Star Trek: The Next Generation*?

⑭ By what name was the first Duke of Wellington previously known?

⑮ British athlete Kriss Akabusi's parents were born in which country?

⑯ Who wrote *The Handmaid's Tale*?

The Bumper *PUB* Quiz Book
Quiz 136

① What became the world's tallest man-made structure in 1884?

② 'Apple and pears' is cockney rhyming slang for what?

③ The White Stripes come from what US city?

④ Which war was concluded by the Treaty of Utrecht?

⑤ 'Kombu' is what sort of Japanese food, often used as soup stock?

⑥ Who is revealed to be Luke's father in *The Empire Strikes Back*?

⑦ What was the name of the final Space Shuttle to enter orbit?

⑧ The Cayman Islands' drinking water needs have to be met by rainwater catchments: true or false?

⑨ What are the two major elements making up the sun?

⑩ In 2012, Shanshan Feng became the first LPGA major winner from which country?

⑪ 'Oros Olympos' appears on native-language maps in what country?

⑫ What vegetable family does Calabrese broccoli come from?

⑬ From 1960 to 1965, which African country was a major area of Chinese political influence?

⑭ What is the name of the off-field official that presides over a cricket match?

⑮ What is the state flower of West Virginia?

⑯ How many versions of 'The Scream' did Edvard Munch create?

The Bumper *PUB* Quiz Book
Quiz 137

① What film had the highest worldwide box office receipts in 2013?

② Which African hunting dog is known for yodelling and laughing?

③ Something that is clear enough to allow light to pass is best described by which science term?

④ Bernardo O'Higgins is considered the liberator of which country?

⑤ Who was Time's Person of the Year in 2006?

⑥ What does the term 'au gratin' mean when it comes to cooking?

⑦ Who won the Grammy for Song of the Year in 2014?

⑧ Who became the President of South Korea in 2013?

⑨ How many cards are there in a standard tarot deck?

⑩ Paul Newman played Fast Eddie Felson in which film?

⑪ What were the three colour choices for the first Microsoft Zune MP3 players?

⑫ Vincent Van Gogh's famous painting of a night sky with swirling yellow stars is called what?

⑬ Libya's legislative branch went by what official name?

⑭ Approximately 97% of the population in Iraq are what religion?

⑮ Which city hosted the 2012 Olympic Games?

⑯ Which species is most closely related to humans?

1. In October 1997, *Thrust SSC* was the first car to exceed the speed of sound. How fast did it go?

2. Who has been named Chelsea's Player of the Year three different times?

3. Roman coins carried images of which powerful figures?

4. What currency is used in Saudi Arabia?

5. What forms the largest natural carbon sink on earth?

6. Who is the current UK Poet Laureate, as of 2014?

7. What is Adobe's web graphics creation software called?

8. Which actor voiced *Fantastic Mr Fox* in the 2009 Wes Anderson movie?

9. Which Queen did Julius Caesar help to gain control over her country?

10. What does adding lemon juice to the water when cooking cauliflower help do?

11. Who was the 'waiting' actor Bananarama was referring to in one of their hit songs?

12. In what year were the Hackney Riots in London?

13. Which Academy Award-winning actress played the lead role in the 2011 drama *The Debt*?

14. On which continent is Mali located?

15. What year was the first American female rabbi ordained by a theological seminary: 1966, 1972, 1975 or 1982?

16. What fat is used in place of butter in most Italian food?

The Bumper *PUB* Quiz Book
Quiz 139

① What type of frequencies do bats use for their radar?

② What version of Windows was unveiled and released as a public beta in June 2013?

③ Which nationality is Fidel Castro?

④ On the London underground, at which two stations do the Central and Jubilee lines meet?

⑤ Who played the title role in *Jerry Maguire*?

⑥ In music, what does 'piano' mean?

⑦ What was Muhammad Ali's original name?

⑧ What do you call the made-from-pears counterpart to cider?

⑨ Who was the first supreme ruler of Norway?

⑩ What was the name of All Saints' first hit single?

⑪ What is the layer of gases surrounding a star or planet called?

⑫ Galdhopiggen is the highest mountain in which country?

⑬ What is the name of the broomstick game in *Harry Potter*?

⑭ In ballet, what does the word 'saute' refer to?

⑮ What colour is an adult beluga whale?

⑯ In what Emirate did golfer Vijay Singh buy an island?

The Bumper *PUB* Quiz Book
Quiz 140

1. Nautically, what is the low pressure area along the equator called?

2. In archaic English, what were your 'meed'?

3. Which country first developed the Pilsner style of beer?

4. What country is known as the Republic of China?

5. The 1990 World Cup in Italy featured how many venues?

6. Prussia, Austria and Italy formed what in 1882?

7. In which production did Ruthie Henshall make her West End debut?

8. Michelle Bachelet was sworn in as the first female President of which country in 2006?

9. Who wrote the Booker Prize winner, *Life of Pi*?

10. In 1975, Angola and Mozambique gained independence from which European country?

11. What is a small hairpiece to cover partial baldness?

12. What 1999 film based on a Michael Crichton novel bombed at the box office?

13. Who plays Christopher Turk in *Scrubs*?

14. From what was San Francisco band Y&T's name shortened?

15. What is the common name of the only species in the genus *Amia*?

16. A person with a Ph.D is addressed by what title?

The Bumper *PUB* Quiz Book
Quiz 141

(1) How many pairs of chromosomes do human beings have?

(2) In what year did IBM invent the floppy disc?

(3) The *Star Wars* aliens Klaatu, Barata and Nikto are a homage to what sci-fi film?

(4) What does 'conchiferous' mean?

(5) Which European country lost 68% of its land under the Treaty of Trianon?

(6) Which rapid-winged bird can't walk?

(7) What French heroine was burned at the stake in 1431?

(8) Empanadas are a food item of what type of cuisine?

(9) Which character was filled with guilt in Natsume Soseki's novel *Kokoro*?

(10) What type of folk dancing did 'tap dance' develop from?

(11) In what country will you find the Serengeti Plain?

(12) Who won the 2002 FIFA World Cup?

(13) Which is the only South American country larger than Argentina?

(14) Which animal has the slowest metabolism?

(15) In what year was the former republic of Czechoslovakia formed?

(16) If the first perfect number is 6, what is the next perfect number?

The Bumper *PUB* Quiz Book
Quiz 142

1. Who replaced Tony Blair as British Prime Minister?

2. In which English city did Jane Austen die?

3. What household brand claims to 'Kill germs dead'?

4. What stomach part allows some birds to digest hard materials such as seeds?

5. What 1950s Formula One racer was nicknamed 'Pampas Bull'?

6. What do you call the traditional long and skinny loaf of bread served in France?

7. On the London underground, what colour is the Central line?

8. Which was the first U2 album to reach number one in the UK album chart?

9. Which golf course hosted the first twelve British Opens?

10. How old are most children in Mexico when they begin school?

11. Which of these is not a form of Tap Dance: Fast Step, Soft Shoe or Tap Clogging?

12. What Windows keyboard shortcut will move the insertion point to the beginning of the next word?

13. What was the original name for the twin engine *Beech Travel Air*?

14. Who was the first person to be Governor of Hong Kong?

15. Who was Prime Minister of Great Britain from 1902-05?

16. What film introduced the character Sonny Corleone?

The Bumper *PUB* Quiz Book
Quiz 143

1. What does the acronym CSS stand for in web page technology?

2. In what country would you find a kiwi bird?

3. Who plays Elizabeth Swann in *Pirates of the Caribbean*?

4. Who is the Roman Queen of the Gods?

5. What is the capital of the Isle of Man?

6. Which country is the Ananda Temple located in?

7. If I 'ted' grass, what do I do?

8. Who won the men's singles at Wimbledon in 1975?

9. Which Sinclair machine was the successor to the ZX80?

10. In Japan, what is 'fugu'?

11. Which Italian leader was kidnapped and killed by Communist terrorists in 1978?

12. Who wrote *The Tale of Genji*?

13. What animal can paralyse its prey with a stinger located at the tip of the tail?

14. Charles II first ascended the throne of England in which year?

15. A Japanese preparation of raw fish without rice is called what?

16. Where is the vomer bone located?

The Bumper *PUB* Quiz Book
Quiz 144

1. Gordon Brown was the youngest fresher since 1945 at what university?

2. Which company has a line of fragrances called 'Happy'?

3. Used in home brewing, where does the additive isinglass come from?

4. In what month do Jews celebrate Passover?

5. In which country is it not hot at Christmas time: Australia, Brazil, Canada or South Africa?

6. In *Hamlet*, who called Hamlet to go to a duel with Laertes?

7. If something is 'educed', what is it?

8. What George Michael song's lyrics begin with, 'These are the days of the open hand'?

9. Which brief fraction best represents the number Pi?

10. Which US Presidential wife did Nelson Mandela meet with at his home in South Africa on June 21, 2011?

11. Who is considered the original *Teen Wolf*?

12. What happens to blood vessels in muscles during exercise?

13. The hair of wild boars was often used to make what toiletry product before 1930?

14. In what year was boxer Rico Hoye born?

15. Which Shakespeare play features Mercutio and Tybalt?

16. What does 'acropolis' mean in Greek?

The Bumper *PUB* Quiz Book

Quiz 145

1. What is the maximum number of electrons in the second energy level of an atom?

2. The science and art of making maps and charts is known as what?

3. What was the debut single of Sean 'Puffy' Combs?

4. To whom was Tom Cruise most recently married, as of 2014?

5. Where, in July 1913, was the world's highest-ever air temperature recorded?

6. Approximately how many miles of wire are there in a 737 airliner: 15.5 miles, 31.3 miles or 40.5 miles?

7. Who won the US and British Opens in 1982?

8. Who wrote the film *Ghost*?

9. Which *Friends* actor plays a lead in sitcom *Episodes*?

10. What 64-square strategic board game is believed to have its origins in India?

11. What country was Marco Polo from?

12. What do Adobe call their application subscription service?

13. Szechuan noodles are a food item of what type of cuisine?

14. The word ballet comes from the word for 'dance' in what language?

15. Which of the following was not a real person in feudal Japan: daimyo, samurai, seppuku or shogun?

16. Early women's plimsolls were worn by servants who did not have time for what?

The Bumper *PUB* Quiz Book
Quiz 146

1. Which band sang the theme song to the Bond film *The World Is Not Enough*?

2. In what year was the toy Captain Action created?

3. In which year did Tony Blair become UK Prime Minister?

4. Moral standards of conduct are also known as what?

5. What is the capital city of the US Virgin Islands?

6. Where is halloumi cheese originally from?

7. In what year did Fiji attain independence?

8. What is grape juice that has not been fermented called?

9. Who did Turkey face in their first-ever international football match in 1922?

10. On which continent is China located?

11. Where in the body is blood produced?

12. Who is the main character in *Gone with the Wind*?

13. Who coined the phrase 'junk food'?

14. What does the term myalgia refer to?

15. Which country did the US warn to 'disarm or face serious consequences' in 2002?

16. Which number is equal to the Roman numeral XLIII?

Quiz 147

1. How many pieces are used in a game of chess?

2. Which of these is a lake located in Bolivia: Lake Hooha, Lake Poopo or Lake Woohoo?

3. What ocean did Ferdinand Magellan name?

4. What type of animal is a 'saluki'?

5. In Shakespeare's play *Romeo and Juliet*, Juliet's parents want her to marry which suitor?

6. What is the national flower of India?

7. What volatile gas was responsible for the Hindenburg disaster in 1937?

8. Which city hosted the 1994 Winter Olympic Games?

9. In *Buffy the Vampire Slayer*, what is the name of vampire Angel's dark side?

10. Johann Sebastian Bach was born in the same year as what other famous classical composer?

11. What is the humans' goal in coming to the woods in the 2014 film *Dawn of the Planet of the Apes*?

12. Which female tennis star won the US Open in 1991 and 1992?

13. Famous works of art were the focus of which board game?

14. The term 'pasteurization' is best defined as what?

15. What term indicates the year in which a wine's grapes were harvested?

16. Chandragupta's successor was his grandson Ashoka, whose name meant what?

The Bumper *PUB* Quiz Book
Quiz 148

1. Which vitamin is said to help shorten the duration of colds?

2. What number do you need to add to 128 to equal 200?

3. The word 'geography' is taken from the Greek words meaning what?

4. How many nations share a border with Djibouti?

5. What is the capital of the South American country of Suriname?

6. What is the bassist's real name from the group 311: Aaron Wills, Doug Martinez, Mike Herrera or P-Nut?

7. How many Academy Awards has Woody Allen won?

8. Which horse won the Grand National in 2000?

9. Roughly how many minutes was Mandela's statement from the dock at the opening of the Rivonia Trial: 12, 76, 120 or 176?

10. What is 'rayon'?

11. Whose coronation was in Westminster Abbey in April 1685?

12. Stylish is to Fashionable as Chicanery is to what?

13. What food is known as 'fugu' to the Japanese?

14. What was the original name of Diet Pepsi?

15. Where was the first Academy Awards ceremony held?

16. A whale's 'forelimbs' are known as what?

Quiz 149

1. What colour is 'Leicester Square' in the British version of *Monopoly*?

2. How many London boroughs are there?

3. Which saucer-shaped, tentacled animal depends on ocean currents in order to move?

4. In what year did Michael Jackson and Jarvis Cocker clash on stage at the Brit Awards?

5. Which painter's last words were 'where is my clock'?

6. Which countries does the Black Sea border?

7. Which country was the first to have a female Prime Minister?

8. In what year was Apple Corporation formed?

9. Retired from athletics, Kriss Akabusi now plays what sport as a hobby?

10. In *Garfield*, the film, what makes Garfield jealous?

11. What nickname was given to the Mughal Emperor Akbar?

12. The smallest bones in the body are located where?

13. The 1984 book titled *Cold Sassy Tree* was written by?

14. Who was the original Aunt Jemima?

15. What is the name of Eddy's daughter in *Absolutely Fabulous*?

16. Amsterdam was founded as which type of community in the thirteenth century?

The Bumper *PUB* Quiz Book
Quiz 150

1. Andy Warhol's '100 Cans' was an image of 100 cans of what?

2. What became the world's tallest man-made structure in 2007?

3. In what Tahitian bay did Captain Cook first land?

4. What term describes wine that runs down the side of a wine glass after swirling or sipping?

5. In which of Australia's capital cities is the suburb of Airport West?

6. By what name was Gaius Octavian more commonly known?

7. How long does it take an aardvark to dig a hole two feet deep: 15 seconds, 30 seconds, 45 seconds or 60 seconds?

8. Who was the first President of the Republic of Egypt?

9. What can cause a concussion?

10. Where was the 1962 World Cup held?

11. What are the four stages of metamorphosis in insects?

12. Which of these Baldwins isn't related to the others: Adam, Alec, Billy or Daniel?

13. What university did technology billionaire Michael Dell drop out from?

14. In the film, *The Little Mermaid*, what did Scuttle call a fork?

15. Due to the extreme droughts in some parts of China, what natural weather occurrence is common?

16. The Scouting for Girls song *Elvis Ain't Dead* ends with what line?

The Bumper *PUB* Quiz Book
Quiz 151

1. In medicine, what is the common name for 'varicella'?

2. Which Hollywood actor has piloted three Gulfstream jets and a Learjet and owned a Boeing 707?

3. What is the main component of clay?

4. When was the first golf game televised?

5. In what year was the original BBC Micro released?

6. Kangaroos live in what social group?

7. What was the name of the first Japanese Aircraft Carrier sunk by a US submarine in World War 2?

8. What was Leona Lewis' debut solo hit?

9. Who wrote the science fiction book *Stranger in a Strange Land*?

10. What city received the greatest number of V1 and V2 bombings in World War 2?

11. In which Marvel film did Clark Gregg first appear as Agent Phil Coulson?

12. One of Brazil's most popular dishes is Picadinho de Jacare, made of what?

13. What lobe of the brain is primarily responsible for vision: frontal, occipital, parietal or temporal?

14. What London monument is directly opposite the Royal Albert Hall?

15. Which country has Funafuti as its capital?

16. What is the alternative name of the Scottish Parliament Building?

The Bumper *PUB* Quiz Book
Quiz 152

1. What genre of writing is Stephen King most known for?

2. Where is Britain's Royal Observatory?

3. What is 3/4 expressed as a percentage?

4. In what year did Italy join the Germany-Japan Pact?

5. Which fruit is grenadine made from?

6. An isogeotherm is an imaginary line connecting points of equal temperature where?

7. Skin grafts most commonly use skin taken from what part of the body?

8. The art of Marc Chagall was inspired largely by images from what stage of his life?

9. What does 'limn' mean?

10. In which US state was the prehistoric proglacial Lake Missoula located?

11. Prior to the adoption of the euro, in what country was the punt the unit of currency?

12. In the 2009 film, *Old Dogs*, what do two friends end up caring for?

13. Who was the Muslim prince who defended the Delhi sultanate: Akbar, Babur or Timur?

14. What do the initials in the 'S&P 500 Index' stand for?

15. Which golf term is defined as the 'area of grass surrounding the putting surface'?

16. As of 2013, The Doctor in 'Doctor Who' is supposedly able to regenerate how many times in his lifetime?

The Bumper *PUB* Quiz Book
Quiz 153

1. What type of drug causes an increase in urination?

2. How many columns are there in the Lincoln Memorial in Washington, DC?

3. What is the identification number of the bus in the film *Speed*?

4. What is the main visual feature of the new Wembley stadium?

5. What is a *Bueche de Noel*?

6. What does 'sere' mean?

7. Who holds the Guinness World Record for most plastic surgery?

8. What kind of animal is a 'palomino'?

9. Which of these is not a type of a relief sculpture: high, low, mid or sunken?

10. La Grande Arche is a monument to what in Paris?

11. On what island nation do they speak Patwa or Quashie Talk?

12. What is the capital of the North African country of Chad?

13. The 1928 book titled *Orlando* was written by whom?

14. How many of Henry VIII's wives did he have put to death?

15. Which element has the chemical symbol Be?

16. How many people died aboard the *Hindenburg* when it exploded?

The Bumper *PUB* Quiz Book
Quiz 154

1. Which marriage proposal tradition is said to have been started by Archduke Maximillian of Austria?

2. Which country's concealed nuclear activities were discovered by the IAEA in 2003?

3. In cooking, what are capers?

4. How did Cleopatra test her poisons?

5. What tea company was bought by Starbucks in 1999?

6. In the film, *Pulp Fiction*, what is Honey Bunny's real name?

7. Who wrote the 1922 book *The Forsyte Saga*?

8. What is a male camel known as?

9. What was the main rebel group operating in Sierra Leone from 1991 to 2002?

10. Which UK supermarket uses the slogan 'Live well for less'?

11. What do you traditionally give for a fortieth anniversary?

12. What radioactive gas is the primary cause of lung cancer in non-smokers?

13. Which Greek city was originally built around the Acropolis?

14. What is the name given to a long piece of fabric wrapped around one's neck?

15. In what year did Pope Nicholas I decree that a ring was the sign of marriage intent?

16. Which team played in the UEFA European Championship for the first time in 2012?

The Bumper *PUB* Quiz Book
Quiz 155

1. In what film is Ray Ferrier the central character?

2. What science is the study of the interrelationship of animals and plants to their environment?

3. What does the adjective 'xanthic' mean?

4. What year was the first wine produced in Brazil: 1551, 1651, 1751 or 1851?

5. The part of Sydney in the 2007 film *Gray Matters* was written specifically for what actress?

6. From which French province does Camembert cheese originate?

7. Which Swedish Prime Minister was assassinated in 1986?

8. Which city hosted the 1992 Summer Olympic Games?

9. In which Australian state is James Cook University?

10. Between which two planets does the asteroid belt lie?

11. Which later Queen was a first cousin, once removed, of Elizabeth I?

12. Who's *Got a New Face* according to a Vampire Weekend song?

13. What does 'asperse' mean?

14. Which nation in Western Africa gained its independence from France on August 3, 1960?

15. What is the camera process whereby highlights and shadows are exposed properly?

16. What country is just north of the border of the United States?

The Bumper *PUB* Quiz Book
Quiz 156

1. In world politics, who is Vicente Fox?

2. What programming language is native to webpages?

3. Who plays the lead villain in *Die Hard*?

4. Which breed of dog, named after a Mexican state, is generally considered to be the smallest?

5. In geology, what is 'orogeny'?

6. Gwen Stefani is part of which group?

7. What capital is situated at the mouth of the largest estuary in South America?

8. Which music mogul was involved in creating RocaWear?

9. What multi-purpose condiment can help revitalize hair: ketchup, mayonnaise or mustard?

10. Who was Zeus' grandfather?

11. Which Hilary Mantel novel won the 2012 Booker Prize?

12. What is the medical term for generally painful, red and warm swelling?

13. In what year was the first modern bicycle built: 1865, 1885, 1905 or 1920?

14. Who earned an Oscar for his role as veteran Chicago cop Jimmy Malone in 1987's *The Untouchables*?

15. Which capital city is on the Han river?

16. How many Formula One grand prix did Damon Hill win?

Quiz 157

1. In 1993, the Maastricht Treaty finally came into place, renaming the European Community what?

2. What is the classic topping for a pastitsio?

3. Whose capture is commemorated every November 5th with bonfires and fireworks?

4. What does the 'B' in the programming language BASIC stand for?

5. In 2003, the US dropped bombs on what Iraqi city, beginning its invasion of Iraq?

6. Which breed did the English call a 'coach dog'?

7. What would you be served in a Japanese restaurant if you ordered 'kappa'?

8. Who was known as 'The Virgin Queen'?

9. Where in Australia was Hollywood actor Errol Flynn born?

10. In which year did Mats Wilander win 3 out of 4 Grand Slam events: 1986, 1987, 1988 or 1989?

11. What were the Stone Temple Pilots 'Trippin' on a hole in'?

12. The cocktail known as a Mohawk is made with what unusual ingredient?

13. Four-time British Grand Prix winner Nigel Mansell was known by what nickname?

14. What is the only colour Friesian horses ever are?

15. Who portrayed Bruce Wayne in the film *Batman Begins*?

16. Which country has Kigali as its capital?

The Bumper *PUB* Quiz Book
Quiz 158

1. In 2007 Sun Microsystems changed their stock ticker symbol from SUNW to what?

2. Which fruit is Slivovitz made from?

3. What is a 'yogini'?

4. What is another name for an inverted French braid?

5. An alkene reacting with water produces which of the following: an alcohol, an aldehyde, an ester or an ether?

6. At what age did Jack Nicklaus win his first national golf title?

7. What was the Egyptian form of early paper called?

8. Who played keyboards on the majority of The Beatles' later recordings?

9. Which English King ascended the throne in April 1509?

10. The assassination of which heir to the Austro-Hungarian throne precipitated World War 1?

11. What was a 'Cutie' in World War 2?

12. What is 'poltroonery'?

13. Whose house blew down in *Winnie the Pooh and the Blustery Day*?

14. Sao Tome is a nation in what region of the world?

15. Which season does the part of Earth tilted towards the sun experience?

16. What are the symptoms of an asthma attack?

Quiz 159

① Which wine-growing region in France borders Germany?

② What is the dictionary definition of 'exigency'?

③ Which country has San Jose as its capital city?

④ Who was Mandela praising when he said, 'a source of inspiration to all freedom-loving people'?

⑤ What became the world's tallest man-made structure in 1889?

⑥ Who ascended the English throne after the death of Elizabeth I?

⑦ The colour of light is determined by what?

⑧ Who co-wrote the 1972 film *The Discreet Charm of the Bourgeoisie* along with Luis Bunuel?

⑨ What is the main ingredient of Splenda?

⑩ A painting of an apple, a book and flowers would be called what?

⑪ In what year did the Qing dynasty of China end?

⑫ How many compulsory pit stops are there in a German Touring Car race?

⑬ What is the fastest land animal?

⑭ Who was the first ruler from the House of Windsor?

⑮ What is the name of the UAE state-owned company that manages seaports?

⑯ What is the 'Arabic' number for the Roman numeral XC?

Quiz 160

1. In the fraction 3/4, which number is the denominator?

2. What is the square root of 625?

3. What company originally produced the 'Walkman'?

4. What type of phenomenon are microwaves?

5. On which body of water is the city of Berbera, Somalia, situated?

6. What colour flame does mercury burn with?

7. Who invented the steam locomotive?

8. In *Swordfish*, John Travolta starred along with which actress?

9. What country borders the United States along the US's southern border?

10. What is the Greek alphabet equivalent of the letter 'd'?

11. Who was Hymen, in Greek mythology?

12. What footballer played his entire professional career for Manchester United?

13. Who was one of the architects of St. Peter's Cathedral in Rome: Rodin, da Vinci or Michelangelo?

14. Which African country's highest elevation point is Mount Afadjato?

15. In Greek mythology, who is the god of wine?

16. Who was Hampton Court Palace built for?

The Bumper *PUB* Quiz Book
Quiz 161

① Which Mediterranean island country is south of Sicily?

② Mustafa Kemal was the first President of which country?

③ In what year was the first *Harry Potter* book published?

④ What do meteorologists use to track local storms in real-time?

⑤ What did most Irish immigrants come to America to escape?

⑥ Which dinosaur is named after the Greek for 'three-horn face'?

⑦ What is the capital of Gabon, on the west coast of Africa?

⑧ What is *Sim City*?

⑨ What claims to be the first self-balancing electric transportation device?

⑩ In what city and year did the 2007 musical film *Hairspray* take place?

⑪ Which country does ciabatta come from?

⑫ How long does it take for lobster roe to mature to a full grown lobster?

⑬ In colour theory, what is the name given to a colour which is neither warm nor cool?

⑭ Which American golfer was victorious at the 2012 Masters?

⑮ What sort of animal is an 'alce'?

⑯ What is the name of Google's web browser?

The Bumper *PUB* Quiz Book
Quiz 162

1. How many aircraft carriers did Japan lose during World War 2?

2. Members of what moon-visiting spacecraft received a congratulatory message from Queen Elizabeth II?

3. Who wrote *The Golden Notebook*?

4. In *Guardians of the Galaxy*, which actor voices Groot?

5. Who created US television show *Seinfeld*?

6. How many gold medals did Jesse Owens win at the 1936 Olympics?

7. In what British city is the Roman Temple of Sulis Minerva located?

8. What is an ailurophobic person fearful of?

9. Freetown is the capital of what country?

10. Who sang *The Millennium Prayer*?

11. What does 'infract' mean?

12. What company was originally named Blue Ribbon Sports?

13. Who is the Patron Saint of Wales?

14. What does 'mit hefe' on a beer label mean?

15. Cynophobia is the fear of what?

16. What year did the USSR become a formal entity?

The Bumper *PUB* Quiz Book
Quiz 163

1. What does the acronym 'MPEG' stand for?

2. Which country's name is Magyarország in its native language?

3. Boxer Barry McGuigan's 1985 bout with Eusebio Pedroza led to what title besides WBA Championship?

4. What is a person who poses for a painter called?

5. Which galaxy might eventually collide with the Milky Way?

6. In what year did Edward I become King of England?

7. Who was the recipient of the Cecil B. DeMille Award at the 2013 Golden Globes?

8. Where does most evaporation of water occur?

9. How many calendars did the Ancient Chinese use?

10. Who plays Professor Plum in the 1985 film, *Clue*?

11. Which element has the chemical symbol F?

12. What is the name of the flatbread eaten with most Indian cuisine?

13. What is the capital city of the country once known as Abyssinia?

14. What type of armous was an 'armet'?

15. Which London theatre burnt to the ground during a performance of Henry VIII in 1613?

16. Who played the Hulk on the big screen in 2003?

The Bumper *PUB* Quiz Book
Quiz 164

1. What 1988 film starring Bob Hoskins matched animation with live action?

2. Panama City is the capital of what country?

3. Which bodily system includes the brain and spinal cord?

4. What was the last territory to join Canada?

5. Which French artist retired from his position as a Customs Official at the age of forty to take up painting full time?

6. Before they were scientifically identified, manatees were occasionally confused with what mythical creatures?

7. What major battle directly preceded Napoleon's occupation of Moscow?

8. What does Alvin from *The Chipmunks* want for Christmas?

9. A rainbow lorikeet is what type of animal?

10. What special feature does Harry Potter's wand share with Voldemort's?

11. What castle in Ireland was the fortified seat of British rule in Ireland until 1922?

12. What nation has the lek as its currency?

13. In what country did the Mau Mau Uprising take place?

14. Eminem and Royce Da 5-9 make up what group?

15. *Heart of a Champion* was about the life of which fighter?

16. Who invented the hole in the doughnut?

The Bumper *PUB* Quiz Book
Quiz 165

1. In which year did the Coca-Cola Company release 'New Coke'?

2. The book *Silent Spring* was written by what environmental pioneer?

3. What is next in this sequence: era, period, ___?

4. What is the sun mostly made up of?

5. What was unique about Mohenjo-Daro in Ancient India?

6. In what decade was the original *Bambi* film first released?

7. What does the logic gate operation 'NOR' mean?

8. In what year did the US host the World Cup?

9. Who did Leonid Brezhnev replace as Soviet Premier in 1964?

10. Who was the inventor of Coca-Cola?

11. What is the name of the award bestowed on the top scorer in the World Cup?

12. Which jazz drummer has Four Tet made albums with?

13. What country is famous for ceviche?

14. Which European country occupied Libya until 1951?

15. What is the capital of Albania?

16. What do you call another person's name used by an author?

The Bumper *PUB* Quiz Book
Quiz 166

1. What US airline did TWA merge with?

2. Which country was renamed the Democratic Republic of Congo in 1997?

3. Brazil shares its most southerly border with which country?

4. How many goals did the USA score in the 2006 World Cup?

5. A Black Russian is made with vodka and what?

6. In Myanmar, what is a 'kyat'?

7. What character did Kathy Bates play in the 1997 film, *Titanic*?

8. A mantel is a shelf that goes on top of what?

9. A googol is a one followed by how many zeroes?

10. Before she married Justinian, what was Theodora's profession?

11. What computing device did incoming US President Barack Obama fight to keep in 2009?

12. On the first of November, Spain celebrates *Todos los Santos*, which means what?

13. The poisonous fish that can swallow water in order to double its size is known as what?

14. What molecule are all sugars converted to prior to absorption into the bloodstream?

15. Which earthquake energy waves travel the fastest: C, L, P or S?

16. PJ Harvey changed from a band into a solo artist in what year?

The Bumper *PUB* Quiz Book
Quiz 167

① What animal codename did Macintosh version Mac OS X 10.5 have?

② In what year did Mario Andretti win the Formula One Championship?

③ What television series gave Charlie Hunnam his first lead role?

④ In which capital city is Tower Bridge?

⑤ Where and in what year did an audience first pay to see a cinema show?

⑥ Where in Northern Europe would you come across the Storbaelt bridge?

⑦ What product is Kleenex most famous for?

⑧ What country is split into 443 named islands and also holds the territory of Greenland?

⑨ Which author wrote *The Scarlet Letter*?

⑩ In archaic English, what is a 'carl'?

⑪ Who invented Dutch process chocolate?

⑫ Which artist's canine subjects are named Fay Wray and Man Ray?

⑬ About how many domestic cats are there in the world?

⑭ The Maltese Language is what type of language?

⑮ What was Fred Casely's profession in the film *Chicago*?

⑯ What are male crabs known as?

The Bumper *PUB* Quiz Book
Quiz 168

① Which is the approximate angle at which the Earth inclines?

② Which English physician first documented that the heart works like a pump?

③ What is the capital of Azerbaijan?

④ What is another name for abnormal cells?

⑤ Which country's national anthem is based on the 18th-century British tune 'The Anacreontic Song'?

⑥ What did Nintendo originally make, when first founded?

⑦ What is featured on the cover of OneRepublic's debut album?

⑧ What is the name of the young boy that works in the bathhouse in the 2001 Anime film *Spirited Away*?

⑨ Which of these is not a Rococo artist: Boucher, Canaletto or Veronese?

⑩ Who is the Greek goddess of the hearth?

⑪ What sort of animal is a 'borzoi'?

⑫ Which German wine region serves wine in glasses called 'Schoppen'?

⑬ What type of animal is a 'colobus'?

⑭ What is the second largest French-speaking city in the world?

⑮ The Saffir-Simpson scale measures the strength of what natural phenomenon?

⑯ Which female shooter won BBC Young Sports Personality of the Year in 2013?

The Bumper *PUB* Quiz Book
Quiz 169

1. On the Richter Scale, how many times more powerful is magnitude 6 than magnitude 5?

2. In September 2013 a UN report stated that the chemical agent Sarin had been used near which Syrian city?

3. When Shabnam Masood returned to *EastEnders* in 2014, which actress took over the role?

4. What vegetable is masa made from?

5. Who was the creator of Melba toast?

6. To the nearest mph, what is the average speed of a housefly?

7. The Yeoman Warders who guard the Tower of London are commonly called what?

8. Which playwright did Marilyn Monroe marry in 1956?

9. In what year was *The Godfather: Part II* released?

10. Guatemala is located on which continent?

11. How many letters are there in the Maltese alphabet?

12. The Lloya Jirga plays a key role in the political process of which country?

13. What is a 'rhetorician'?

14. In which year was George IV crowned King of the United Kingdom?

15. What was the last Formula One race in 2014?

16. What film introduced the lightsabre?

The Bumper PUB Quiz Book
Quiz 170

1. What is the Japanese name for the original Nintendo Entertainment System?

2. True champagne can only come from grapes grown in the Champagne region of what country?

3. What country in Europe with Tirana as its capital uses the lek as its currency?

4. What is a 'peri'?

5. What does a 'sibyl' do?

6. How might a 'green' wine taste?

7. What happens at the end of Edgar Allan Poe's *The Tell-Tale Heart*?

8. The U2 song *Pride (in The Name of Love)* is from which album?

9. What's the name of the system used to describe climate?

10. Which royal dynasty preceded the Stuarts?

11. The wolverine is the largest of which family of mammals?

12. In *The Godfather*, where was Sonny Corleone ambushed and gunned down?

13. Reunion Island, part of the Mascarene Islands in the Indian Ocean, has which capital city?

14. What French Fauvist painter and sculptor lived from 1869-1954?

15. Who did Senegal beat in 2002 to qualify for the first time for the World Cup?

16. Who was the first Stuart monarch to hold the English throne?

The Bumper *PUB* Quiz Book
Quiz 171

1. Which fruit is grown on a vine and harvested by flooding its field?

2. In Shakespeare's 'A Midsummer Night's Dream', what changes the lovers' minds about each other?

3. In display technology, what is the method used to best-preserve detail at a lower resolution?

4. What would you be served in a Japanese restaurant if you ordered 'anago'?

5. At what age did girls typically marry in ancient Athens?

6. San Marino is the capital of which country?

7. In what year did the first World Cup mascot debut?

8. Who was the voice of Yoda in *The Empire Strikes Back*?

9. What did Snickers bars used to be called?

10. Who was US President immediately prior to Gerald Ford?

11. Which African island nation has Moroni as its capital city?

12. What colour of hair is 'Titian'?

13. What is the name given to a fossil that best defines a rock layer's age?

14. Jordan is virtually landlocked except for which major port in the south?

15. Which famous composer did Ludwig van Beethoven study with when he arrived in Vienna in 1792?

16. Which convention in 1929 established the rules for the treatment of prisoners of war?

The Bumper *PUB* Quiz Book
Quiz 172

1. Which animal includes as part of its name a word that means 'lives on the blood of other species'?

2. What number comes next in the sequence: 12, 24, 36?

3. What event afflicted the US Great Plains in the 1930s?

4. Which Canadian Prime Minister introduced conscription during World War 1?

5. Who is the designer of the L.A.M.B. clothing line?

6. Who did Martin Luther directly challenge with his *95 Theses*?

7. In Peru, what colours of potato are grown, in addition to white?

8. What is the capital of Madagascar, the fourth-largest island in the world?

9. Which military action led to a US boycott of the 1980 Olympics?

10. What 1953 event helped ease tensions between the USSR and the USA?

11. With what surname was Cilla Black actually born?

12. Who played Doctor Frasier Crane in *Cheers* and then spin-off series *Frasier*?

13. What type of creature is an 'ayu'?

14. Which city is the capital of Tunisia?

15. In which city was the film *The Elephant Man* set?

16. Which country is Timbuktu in?

Quiz 173

1. The Aswan Dam, completed in 1970, forever changed the physical landscape in which nation?

2. In heraldry, what do you call a shield divided into several vertical stripes?

3. Chile borders which of these countries: Argentina, Jamaica, Malta or Spain?

4. How old was Pele when he played in the 1958 World Cup?

5. Who painted 'The Kiss'?

6. Which ingredient is not commonly found in classic Caesar salad: anchovies, bacon or croutons?

7. Which agricultural by-product is most useful as a construction material for energy efficient homes?

8. Who was the first female President in Latin America, elected in 1990 in Nicaragua?

9. What Italian poet wrote *The Divine Comedy*?

10. What kind of microscope is a SEM?

11. Which was the first Christian country in Africa?

12. What was the name of Captain Cook's ship?

13. What do you call champagne mixed with orange juice?

14. 'The World's Online Marketplace' has been used as an ad slogan by which company?

15. Which natural element is represented by pentacles on a tarot card?

16. For how many weeks did *Borat* remain in first place at the US box office?

The Bumper *PUB* Quiz Book
Quiz 174

1. True or false: adult grey whales reach a length of 15m (50ft)?

2. Cerro Aconcagua, the highest point in Argentina, is also the highest mountain in which larger region?

3. Who is Stanley's best friend in the film *Holes*?

4. What colour were the roses during the 'War of the Roses'?

5. What drink do you get by mixing Champagne and Creme de Cassis?

6. Who succeeded Gamal Abdel Nasser as Egyptian leader?

7. What is Apple's video effects software called?

8. The Alex Fraser Bridge, opened in 1986, is located in which country?

9. What is the title of a 2006 Sugababes singles collection?

10. Who played Fred Flintstone in the live-action 1994 film, *The Flintstones*?

11. Which city is the most-visited tourist destination in Scotland?

12. In what year did the Hindenburg disaster occur?

13. Who wrote *The Adventures of Huckleberry Finn*?

14. In the UK, who is 'Mr Plod'?

15. What country's wine regulatory system is called the Denominazione di Origine Controllata (DOC)?

16. Who won the World Snooker Championship in 2011?

The Bumper **PUB** Quiz Book
Quiz 175

① What is 68 degrees Fahrenheit in degrees Celsius?

② How many appearances did Diego Maradona make as a player at Barcelona?

③ What is 9 squared equal to?

④ What was Gustav during World War 2?

⑤ What are the four bases of DNA?

⑥ What do you include with the chicken to make Chicken Cordon Bleu?

⑦ What song did Eminem perform at the Grammys with Elton John?

⑧ Which film won the Best Motion Picture award in 2012?

⑨ What was the former name of Kiribati?

⑩ Who wrote the 1927 classic *To the Lighthouse*?

⑪ The explorer Marco Polo was alive in which year: 1075, 1275, 1375 or 1475?

⑫ Which is an antitussive drug?

⑬ What country was Aristotle from?

⑭ What note of the major scale is 'doh'?

⑮ What enzyme does the small intestine not make enough of if you are lactose intolerant?

⑯ Household dust is mainly comprised of what substance?

The Bumper *PUB* Quiz Book
Quiz 176

① What nation is the only Asian OPEC member?

② What circle of latitude is located at 23.5 degrees south?

③ What became the world's tallest man-made structure in 1967?

④ What Acorn machine immediately preceded the BBC Micro?

⑤ In *Lord Of The Rings*, who was the father of Legolas?

⑥ *Amaretti* are crunchy biscuits with the flavour of which nut?

⑦ What are 'dicta'?

⑧ An M1911A1 is more commonly referred to as what type of weapon?

⑨ What was Barry McGuigan's first championship boxing title?

⑩ What is the capital city of Wales?

⑪ The tube leading from the kidney to the bladder is called?

⑫ Who wrote *Charlotte's Web*?

⑬ In what year was the Cuban Missile Crisis?

⑭ After physics, what study did Isaac Newton take up until he published *Principia Mathematica*?

⑮ In what year did Picasso paint his 'Lovers and Women'?

⑯ To the nearest hour, how long did the fastest ascent of Mount Everest take?

The Bumper *PUB* Quiz Book
Quiz 177

① What is the minimum depth of the hole in professional golf?

② The General Electric Building, completed in 1933 at a height of 200m (640ft), is located where?

③ The Mozambique Channel separates which island nation from the mainland?

④ Which mammal always bears four identical young of the same sex: armadillo, badger, fox or opossum?

⑤ What was the first ship sunk by submarine warfare during World War 1?

⑥ Wassily Kandinsky loved music because both of his parents were what?

⑦ How many joints can a triarticulate muscle move?

⑧ Dry ice is the solid form of which gas?

⑨ Who played Django in *Django Unchained*?

⑩ For which film was Mickey Rourke nominated for an Academy Award?

⑪ What does 'isochromatic' mean?

⑫ What are the 'Big Dipper' and 'Orion' examples of in the night sky?

⑬ How many countries eventually joined the League of Nations?

⑭ After which King was the first English-language Protestant bible named?

⑮ Who wrote *The Grapes of Wrath*?

⑯ The band Muse is from which English county?

The Bumper *PUB* Quiz Book

Quiz 178

1. Which term means 'relating to dogs'?

2. What indirectly caused the founding of Rome: the death of Admetus or the marriage of Peleus and Thetis?

3. Greek history covers what three ages?

4. From 1962 through 1990, who held the crown as maker of the world's fastest computers?

5. What does the Scots dialect word 'yex' mean?

6. Who wrote the book *Tuesdays with Morrie*?

7. In what year was the Act of Union, joining Scotland to the Kingdom of Great Britain?

8. How many times has Jack Nicklaus finished in the top 5 at Augusta?

9. Michael Moore created what controversial political documentary in 2004?

10. Anorexia causes what medical effect?

11. Which soft drink was invented in 1886 in Atlanta?

12. Which country do millions travel to every year for the annual pilgrimage known as 'Al-Hajj'?

13. Which German city and capital of Bavaria was the home of the original Oktoberfest?

14. How many pockets are there on a pool table?

15. Which disability is the most common in Dalmatians?

16. Who played Chris in the original 1989 West End production of *Miss Saigon*?

The Bumper *PUB* Quiz Book
Quiz 179

1. What became the world's tallest man-made structure in 1975?

2. In the *Harry Potter* books, what is the name of Dumbledore's brother?

3. Who won his first Formula One in a French car at the 1981 French Grand Prix?

4. What is the Christian holy book of scriptures called?

5. What cheese is traditionally used on a Reuben sandwich?

6. Which character in the film *Finding Nemo* is a clownfish?

7. Life-size terracotta warriors of the Qin Dynasty were discovered in what country?

8. What was the name of the USA's first artificial Earth satellite?

9. Which Dubai building is 883 feet tall: 21st Century Tower, Emirates Tower Two or Wells Fargo Plaza?

10. Paul Cezanne painted many pictures of people doing what by rivers?

11. Which monarch visited Nelson Mandela on a state visit to South Africa in 1995?

12. The airport code LHR designates which European airport?

13. *To Sir With Love* was both a film and a hit song sung by whom?

14. What type of vegetable provides the body with vitamin K?

15. On a clear day, you can see which high volcano from Mexico City?

16. Which aeronautical term is a combination of the function of the rudder and elevators in one?

The Bumper *PUB* Quiz Book
Quiz 180

1. If something is 'tintinnabulating', what is it doing?

2. What British scientist and lecturer discovered electromagnetic induction?

3. Who wrote *Lolita*?

4. Yaounde is the capital, and Douala is the largest city of which country?

5. What is the perception of frequency called?

6. For which holiday were evergreen trees originally used as decoration?

7. The Streets' third album talked about 'the hardest way to' what?

8. For what film did writing team Matt Damon and Ben Affleck win an Oscar?

9. What illness did the first Prime Minister of Canada suffer from: alcoholism or malaria?

10. Who developed the reset key combination Ctrl + Alt + Delete?

11. How many American hostages were seized by Iranian militants in 1979?

12. In Formula One racing, the 10-second time penalty is also known by what name?

13. Which element has the chemical symbol C?

14. German wine-growing is primarily based along which river?

15. In what year was the emperor Caligula stabbed by his own guards?

16. What is Adobe's audio-editing software called?

The Bumper *PUB* Quiz Book
Quiz 181

(1) What is the capital of Yukon, Canada?

(2) Dennis who was a major developer on the UNIX computer operating system?

(3) Which number appears opposite '1' on a dartboard?

(4) Who wrote the book *Touching the Void*, later turned into a BAFTA-winning British film?

(5) What country was once called Mesopotamia?

(6) What natural biological defence system protects the body from disease and fights off germs?

(7) What was the name of James Bond creator Ian Fleming's island retreat?

(8) What is the name of the medieval ruin near Salisbury in Wiltshire which was a royal residence once used as a hunting lodge?

(9) Which capital city was designed by Pierre L'Enfant?

(10) On the Sam Sparro song *Sick*, he sings 'I'll be your' what?

(11) How many quarks are there in an electron?

(12) What Mexican spirit is most often used in a margarita?

(13) What type of creature is an 'eft'?

(14) What word for a style of beer means 'goat': bock, lambic, porter or stout?

(15) What is Ron's new owl called in *Harry Potter and the Goblet of Fire*?

(16) What is a 'kapok'?

The Bumper *PUB* Quiz Book
Quiz 182

1. How long was an Ancient Egyptian year?

2. What did the Romans call the city now known as London?

3. In what year was Charles Dickens' *A Christmas Carol* first published?

4. What is the most popular exported New Zealand beer?

5. What is the gestation period of the African elephant?

6. Which team won the hockey gold medal at the 1972 Sapporo Olympics?

7. Which ancient poet wrote *Theogony*?

8. What opera is the musical *Miss Saigon* based on?

9. In *Star Wars Episode IV: A New Hope*, who raised Luke Skywalker?

10. Which of these airplanes has three engines: Boeing 707, Boeing 727 or Boeing 737?

11. Jewish refugees often fled to what neutral European country to escape the Nazis in World War 2?

12. What is the largest bird that cannot fly, but runs very quickly?

13. Which gem is considered the modern birthstone for December?

14. In the 'Forgotten Realms' of *Dungeons and Dragons*, which Drow has not been a House Weapon master?

15. What athlete was nicknamed 'Fenomeno' (The Phenomenon) by the Italian media?

16. Who sold Broadcast.com to Yahoo for $5.7 billion?

The Bumper *PUB* Quiz Book
Quiz 183

1. Which classic book by Iris Murdoch was published in 1954?

2. Singer Chris Brown was arrested on October 27, 2013 in which US city?

3. Which part of the country do the majority of Mexican wines come from?

4. The Maldives is a group of atolls in what ocean?

5. What do you traditionally give for a twenty-fifth anniversary?

6. How are the title characters in the 1982 film *Fanny And Alexander* related?

7. What two colours are on the Swedish flag?

8. Members of the Maasai tribe of Kenya measure wealth by ownership of which animal?

9. Who makes 'Volum' Express' mascara?

10. Which of the following nations lies within the Sahara Desert: Albania, Congo, Liberia or Morocco?

11. Edward VI ascended the English throne in which year?

12. Who won the 2013 Australian PGA Championship?

13. What is the second largest living animal?

14. What Rob Thomas track took home three Grammys including Song of the Year in 1999?

15. What is a step-by-step method of accomplishing a task: an algorithm or an analysis?

16. In cooking, what is cutting herbs or vegetables into very fine strips called?

The Bumper *PUB* Quiz Book
Quiz 184

1. In what year was sci-fi novel *Hyperion* published?

2. Which House ruled over Britain from 1714-1901?

3. What noteworthy feat did Kelly Holmes achieve during the 2004 Olympic Games?

4. In which country is the city of Auxerre?

5. In what film did Maggie Smith and Whoopi Goldberg first collaborate?

6. 'Liber', the Latin word from which 'liberate' and 'liberty' are derived, means what?

7. In what year did Mikhail Baryshnikov defect from the Soviet Union?

8. Which country did cheesecake originate in?

9. In networking security, an ACL is what type of list: Access control, Acquired control, Actual contact or Allowed client?

10. Which 2011 album by Coldplay became their 5th to debut at number 1 on the US Billboard?

11. What was the name of Stanley's dog in *The Mask*?

12. Where was the World Puzzle Championship held in 2014?

13. In 1996, who became the first person to compete in nine Olympics?

14. Which earthquake energy wave causes the most damage: C, L, P or S?

15. In what decade did the last cable tram operate in Melbourne, Australia: 1920s, 1930s or 1940s?

16. What strange self-defence mechanism do turkey vultures have?

The Bumper *PUB* Quiz Book
Quiz 185

1. How is the woodchuck more commonly known?

2. What is 973 + 1541?

3. What is the name of the famous private school located close to Windsor Castle?

4. In February 2008, Prince Harry returned from military duty in what war zone?

5. Which actresses won Oscars for *The Piano*?

6. McAfee primarily makes what kind of software?

7. In the *James Bond* franchise, what is Q's real name?

8. What is a 'rem'?

9. What company was the first to earn $1 billion dollars in one year?

10. How many snooker World Championships did Steve Davis win?

11. *Phoenix and Dragon* is what food item?

12. What are the three main colours of the African Liberation flag?

13. Eleven per cent of what island country is covered by glaciers?

14. Who was the first woman in space?

15. Who wrote the book *Les Miserables*?

16. Who succeeded Stanley Baldwin as UK Prime Minister?

The Bumper *PUB* Quiz Book
Quiz 186

1. In what year were East and West Germany re-united?

2. Which instrumentalist typically leads an orchestra, second only to the conductor?

3. What clothing company uses a crocodile as its logo?

4. What is the title character in the ballet *Petrushka*?

5. Which city is the capital of Malawi?

6. Which country developed the *Titan* series of rockets?

7. What is the main reason your body needs protein?

8. Are sunspots cooler or hotter than the sun?

9. Who was the author of *Gulliver's Travels*?

10. A vine fungus that attacks the green part of the vine is called: black rot or whitefly fungus?

11. In olden times, what did 'avaunt' mean?

12. The narrowest part of the Taiwan Strait, which separates China from Taiwan is how wide?

13. What country's immigrants founded the wine industry in southern Brazil?

14. What was the name of the female World War 1 spy 'Agent H-21'?

15. Which golfer once lost the Masters by signing an incorrect scorecard?

16. How many Bond films were made in the 1980s?

The Bumper *PUB* Quiz Book
Quiz 187

1. Which Arab country borders the eastern shore of the Dead Sea?

2. The Windows file extension .wav denotes what type of file?

3. In which constellation was the first double star observed?

4. What is the first name of the famous Beat Generation author Kerouac?

5. What colour ball must be potted first in snooker?

6. According to a Jack McManus song title, 'You Can' what?

7. Which aircraft holds the record for fastest in-atmosphere speed?

8. What kind of Greek bread is used in a US gyro sandwich?

9. Which element has the atomic number 4?

10. What was Jack Nicholson's character in *The Witches of Eastwick*?

11. What is the capital of Nicaragua?

12. Which Shakespeare play features Brutus, Cassius and Cicero?

13. What is a 'macle'?

14. Who succeeded James Callaghan as UK Prime Minister?

15. Which predecessor served as Nelson Mandela's deputy when he became President of South Africa?

16. Who created the first photograph on paper of a human figure in 1840?

The Bumper *PUB* Quiz Book
Quiz 188

1. Huaraches are what type of footwear?

2. Which golf event did Paul Casey win in 2007?

3. Whose motorcycle did Butch drive away on in the film *Pulp Fiction*?

4. Which planet is the second closest to the sun?

5. What iconic Brazilian drink is made from cachaca, lime and sugar?

6. For what period of years did the Iran-Iraq war last?

7. If you win six out of twelve times, what percentage of the time do you lose?

8. Which Greek playwright wrote *The Bacchae*?

9. Who was the first US astronaut to go into orbit?

10. What country hosted the 1968 UEFA European Football Championship?

11. Which simple shoe was most often worn by citizens of Ancient Rome?

12. Where does Charlie Weasley, older brother of Ron Weasley, work with dragons in *Harry Potter*?

13. What factor determines the sex of newborn alligators?

14. Which vegetable is the main ingredient in hash browns?

15. What was the first German site bombed by the US in World War 2?

16. How many weeks after Germany attacked France in World War 2 did Paris fall to German troops?

The Bumper *PUB* Quiz Book
Quiz 189

① In world politics, who is José López Portillo?

② What gas product of burning fossil fuels can cause death by preventing oxygen from getting to cells?

③ What do you call a doctor who specializes in treating the heart?

④ Which of these is in the same vegetable family as cabbage and broccoli: carrots, cauliflower or potatoes?

⑤ Which US President succeeded John F. Kennedy?

⑥ How long did the Anglo-Zanzibar War of 1896 last?

⑦ Where is the heart of a shrimp?

⑧ In what year did Belarus become an independent country?

⑨ Which film won the Best Picture Oscar for 2000?

⑩ Mount Fuji is the highest mountain in which Asian country?

⑪ What does 'HDMI' stand for?

⑫ What is 'obloquy'?

⑬ What did more than 40% of adults report to the England National Health Survey released in 2010?

⑭ About how many miles is it from Paris to New York?

⑮ Who was the author of *Don Quixote*?

⑯ What are the names of the two major soccer stadiums in Barcelona?

The Bumper *PUB* Quiz Book
Quiz 190

1. In the late 1960s to early 1970s, the United States military fought a war in which Asian country?

2. Which country has Nuuk (Godthåb) as its capital?

3. In the 1997 film *Titanic*, what is the name of Rose's granddaughter?

4. What artist painted 'Les Demoiselles d'Avignon'?

5. On a piano, what does the right-hand pedal do?

6. Deimos is one of Mars's moons – which is the other?

7. Dr. Jonas Salk developed a vaccine for which virus in 1954?

8. What was the name of the first Russian law code, issued by Yaroslav the Wise?

9. What did the US army find near Merkers, Germany, towards the end of World War 2?

10. Who composed the theme music for the Australian TV series *Skippy the Bush Kangaroo*?

11. Who played the Engineer in the original 1989 West End cast of *Miss Saigon*?

12. What disorder causes respiration to cease for several seconds during sleep?

13. The infamous 'Zidane Headbutt' happened in which World Cup?

14. Which word refers to an aeroplane that has three similar-sized pairs of wings?

15. What is the name of the part of the grape vine that is left from year to year?

16. Which Stuart monarch married George, son of Frederick III of Denmark?

The Bumper *PUB* Quiz Book
Quiz 191

① What's the telephone country code for Australia?

② In what country did the bloodhound originate?

③ What was Rihanna's first released single?

④ Nairobi National Park in Kenya is home to what long-necked animals?

⑤ 'Papier mâché' means 'mashed' what in French?

⑥ The average life expectancy of beluga whales is approximately how many years?

⑦ Where do Nemo and Marlin live in the film *Finding Nemo*?

⑧ Which food is high in cholesterol: apples, broccoli, egg yolks or oatmeal?

⑨ In what year did Jack Johnson become world heavyweight boxing champion?

⑩ Which Australian man won the Australian Open in 1976?

⑪ In mobile phones, what generation is EDGE technology?

⑫ What does 'glyptic' mean?

⑬ Who wrote *The Name of the Rose*?

⑭ From which part of the plant is horseradish made?

⑮ What is 'shiatsu'?

⑯ Which city was the first capital of Japan?

The Bumper *PUB* Quiz Book
Quiz 192

1. How many internal right angles does a square have?

2. Who plays the Gotham Mayor in *The Dark Knight*?

3. What was La Casa Pacifica?

4. What currency does the Republic of Belarus use?

5. Which is the strongest type of covalent bond

6. Emily Brontë was born in which decade?

7. What is the name for a collection of small dishes or appetizers in Spain?

8. Which scale is used to describe a mineral's hardness?

9. Which animal is the only one with four true knees?

10. What is the male counterpart to 'yin'?

11. What event prompted Martin Luther to become a monk?

12. In what city did Dolce and Gabbana meet?

13. Which sport involves the balance beam, uneven bars and rings?

14. Which country is the number one producer of mangos?

15. Which herbal medicine is most often used to treat stomach disorders?

16. April 23rd is the feast of which English patron saint?

The Bumper *PUB* Quiz Book
Quiz 193

1. What is calligraphy?

2. What does a chequered flag indicate in Formula One racing?

3. What is the perimeter of a circle called?

4. What are large male gorillas often called because of the colouration of their hair?

5. Which European city combines two former cities, joined by bridges across the Danube?

6. Who was The Ugly in *The Good, The Bad, The Ugly*?

7. If you cube the number three, what is the result?

8. In heraldry, what do you call an animal that is asleep?

9. Nelson Mandela tried to negotiate an end to the First Congo War in what country?

10. In what century was Harold I crowned King of England?

11. Which mythical creature was supposedly born from the egg of a rooster?

12. Who was runner-up to Will Young in *Pop Idol*?

13. Pablo Picasso painted a famous picture depicting which bombed city?

14. Which continent is Samoa considered to be on?

15. In addition to coffee, what ingredients are in a coffee nudge?

16. How many years are there in a sunspot cycle?

The Bumper *PUB* Quiz Book
Quiz 194

1. To which family does the caracal belong?

2. What two versions of the BBC Micro were originally released?

3. What are the small bones that make up a backbone called?

4. What film was released about a year after a horror film with a mutant killer snowman of the same name?

5. Who started the Prada label?

6. In which year did Elizabeth II ascend the British throne?

7. What term is used in geography for arrows which are drawn on a map to show movement?

8. How tall are the letters in the famous Hollywood sign in California?

9. In which musical form does a solo instrument contrast with an ensemble or an entire orchestra?

10. What did European explorers originally call the Murray River in Australia?

11. Which is the third-largest city in the UK, by population?

12. In what year did Xerox introduce their photocopying machine: 1821, 1959, 1962 or 1981?

13. Who was Cassius Clay's first pro opponent?

14. What was the declaration in which British and Irish Prime Ministers worked for peace in 1993?

15. Which beer is typically both the darkest and the strongest?

16. What is the chemical symbol for mercury?

The Bumper *PUB* Quiz Book
Quiz 195

1. Who is the only man to raise the World Cup trophy as both a captain and a manager?

2. Which London tube station was used for filming the underground scenes in *Skyfall*?

3. 'The Bridges of Madison County' was written by whom?

4. The airport code LAX designates which international airport?

5. Which south-east Asian country's highest elevation point is Doi Inthanon?

6. Which planet takes 84 Earth years to orbit the sun?

7. Which Asian country admitted to developing nuclear arms in October of 2002?

8. Which member of the Black Eyed Peas joined the group in 2003 with a tryout for 'Shut Up'?

9. What was the title of cricketer Bobby Simpson's book, published in 1977?

10. What character is resurrected in *X-Men: The Last Stand*?

11. What is the name for the process by which yeast causes bread to rise?

12. What country is called 'Land of Fire and Ice'?

13. What type of creature generally lives on land but starts life in the water?

14. How many 'geese-a-laying' are there in *The 12 Days of Christmas*?

15. Who was the physicist responsible for 'A Method of Reaching Extreme Altitudes'?

16. What fruit is used in flavouring 'Kriek' Belgian beer?

1. What is the capital city of Malta called?

2. In what year was Coca-Cola first sold in New Zealand: 1918, 1922, 1939 or 1943?

3. The Renaissance Tower, completed in 1975 at a height of 270m (886ft), is located where?

4. Besides shrimp, what are the other two primary ingredients in the Greek dish 'garides saganaki'?

5. UEFA Euro 2012 took place in which two countries?

6. Which Whoopi Goldberg film had this famous line: 'Dogs barking. Can't fly without umbrella'?

7. About a third of the average rubbish tip consists of which recyclable items?

8. Who was the first Liberal UK Prime Minister?

9. Which former Wimbledon finalist was convicted of killing his wife?

10. What scientist first showed that a changing electric field produces a magnetic field?

11. What celebrity underwent a double mastectomy because she carries a specific gene in 2013?

12. Which European capital city is actually two separate cities?

13. Which word processing program keyboard shortcut in Windows allows you to undo?

14. The eye of what creature is used in the witches' brew from *Macbeth*?

15. What sort of plant is 'liana'?

16. Which Swiss mathematician was the author of *Mechanica*?

The Bumper *PUB* Quiz Book
Quiz 197

① Roseau is the capital of which country?

② Noumea is the capital of which French collectivity?

③ What does 'friar' mean in Latin?

④ Ogden Nash is known for what type of writing?

⑤ Which mobile phone brand claims 'We're better connected'?

⑥ Tomatoes grow on which type of plant?

⑦ Which film did Ewan McGregor star in with Catherine Zeta-Jones?

⑧ Who founded the study of genetics?

⑨ Which country developed the *Atlas* series of rockets?

⑩ Which North American country's highest elevation point is Volcan Pico de Orizaba?

⑪ According to Formula One racing rules, what must appear on the nose of each car?

⑫ What projectile weapon dominated the Battle of Agincourt?

⑬ What is the scientific term for cells responsible for root growth: apexical stemmer or apical meristem?

⑭ Who wrote the 1984 book *The Sicilian*?

⑮ What was the first web browser available to the public?

⑯ What Spanish word, also a type of drink, can mean either 'queue', 'tail' or 'glue'?

The Bumper *PUB* Quiz Book

Quiz 198

① Which Nordic country has a capital which is located on an island?

② How was *Harry Potter and The Philosopher's Stone* retitled in its US edition?

③ What country borders Namibia, Botswana, Zimbabwe, Mozambique, Swaziland, and Lesotho?

④ What is the characteristic ingredient in 'spaghetti vongole'?

⑤ Which of the following factors does not affect the resistance of a conductor: area, capacitance, length or temperature?

⑥ What are you being called if someone calls you a 'WASP'?

⑦ In what year did Edward II ascend the throne to become King of England?

⑧ Which African empire invaded southern Morocco in the 16th century?

⑨ If you were mining 'galena', what would your end product be?

⑩ Who, according to Greek mythology, was the first woman?

⑪ Which sea animal is parasitic and attaches itself to fish to suck their blood: barnacle, lamprey or lantern fish?

⑫ In the film *Doogal*, what is the name of the evil sorcerer?

⑬ How many appearances did Petr Cech make for Chelsea in the 2012-13 season?

⑭ What did Napoleon call the British?

⑮ What is a soft-shell crab?

⑯ What is the total voltage of a series circuit using three D cells?

1. What is Warner's full name in the film and musical *Legally Blonde*?

2. A provision of the Peace of Augsburg was that a German ruler could choose what for his state?

3. Where does the female marine catfish lay her eggs?

4. What does 'mornay' denote in the name of a dish?

5. What is a female turkey less than one year old called?

6. Which British monarch has reigned the longest, as of 2014?

7. In which English county is Stonehenge?

8. Which country is Chisinau the capital of?

9. What type of food is a 'tartufo'?

10. What ocean does the Orinoco discharge into?

11. In what three years did Frank Lampard win the Chelsea Player of the Year award?

12. Which Irish singer recorded the hit single *Only Time* in 2001?

13. Which quick, easily mass-produced art form did Joan Miro create?

14. What former Prime Minister was the first native-born Prime Minister of Israel?

15. What is the English word for the French seafood called 'anguille'?

16. In Greek mythology, how many Muses were there?

The Bumper *PUB* Quiz Book
Quiz 200

1. Which explorer gave Spain claim to Florida by establishing a base in St. Augustine?

2. Vatican City is the capital of what country?

3. What were the subtitles of the two 'new' Game Boy Colour *Zelda* games?

4. What is a hellbender?

5. The words 'Allah u Akbar' on the Iraqi flag mean what in English?

6. From which Spanish city does tennis pro David Ferrer originate?

7. What is the average number of hairs on the human head: 1,000, 20,000, 50,000 or 100,000?

8. What is the capital of Angola?

9. Who was the author of *Nineteen Eighty-Four*?

10. Which influential female singer had a hit with *Running Up That Hill*?

11. What does the medical term 'prenatal' mean?

12. What group of mammals lays eggs?

13. Who was Catherine the Great's husband?

14. Bouillabaisse is a form of seafood... what?

15. Who played James Bond in *On Her Majesty's Secret Service*?

16. Where in Sweden is the capital Stockholm situated?

The Bumper *PUB* Quiz Book
Quiz 201

1. What emblem did many soldiers wear during the First Crusade?

2. In what year did Margaret Atwood win the Booker Prize with *The Blind Assassin*?

3. Which country has Bissau as its capital?

4. Which of these bones are human babies born without: kneecap, mandible, metacarpal or sternum?

5. Record-holder Antonio Carbajal has played in how many World Cups?

6. Who succeeded Galba as Roman Emperor in the Year of the Four Emperors?

7. Musically, what is a 'gue'?

8. Which wine region is located in the Mexican states of Coahuila and Durango: Baja, Laguna or Zacatecas?

9. What country uses the kyat as its currency?

10. What is the name of the drug which was referred to numerous times in the film *Max Payne*?

11. Which two organs of the body continue to grow even for a while after death?

12. What is the English translation for the Spanish *no hay problema*?

13. What kind of bread is usually used to make a Reuben sandwich?

14. Which South American country's highest elevation point is Bellevue de l'Inini?

15. A buck, or male deer, is also called a what?

16. Who won the World Snooker Championship in 2012?

The Bumper *PUB* Quiz Book

Quiz 202

1. How many days are there in three weeks?

2. Which Irish political party did Bertie Ahern become leader of in 1997?

3. What 2013 film is about the mid-orbit destruction of a space shuttle and the attempts to return home?

4. What sort of medical specialist is a cardiologist?

5. What part of the brain primarily controls appetite?

6. What originally provided the inspiration for Chinese take-away boxes?

7. Which river in Africa carries the most water?

8. Who wrote the book *The Forever War*?

9. What is the distance around a shape called?

10. Who won the 2014 Ryder Cup?

11. The average life expectancy of sperm whales is approximately how many years?

12. What was the 'Anzio Express' in World War 2?

13. Which city has been proposed as the capital of the European Union?

14. What device consists of one or more cells that produce direct current?

15. In East Asia, who is an 'amah'?

16. Which part of the microprocessor is responsible for all mathematical computations?

Quiz 203

① What Christian feast falls on the US Groundhog Day?

② In the song *Grace Kelly*, Mika sings 'So I tried a little' what?

③ Where would you find a Russian 'cosmonaut' at work?

④ How much plastic is used per year to make bottles for bottled water?

⑤ Which model created and hosted the reality show *America's Next Top Model*?

⑥ Which disgraced rider was known for wearing out the most bike chains during a Tour de France?

⑦ What year did the Second Boer War begin in South Africa?

⑧ Who wrote *The War of the Worlds*?

⑨ An 'okonomiyaki' is what?

⑩ In what year was *2001: A Space Odyssey* released?

⑪ How wide is the Island of Malta?

⑫ Which female reptile may produce eggs as long as four years after mating?

⑬ Which country is the island of Zanzibar now part of?

⑭ Botticelli's 'Nascita di Venere' is better known as what?

⑮ Oman, in the south-east corner of the Arabian Peninsular, holds which capital city?

⑯ Which do you call a sweet wine that has been fortified with grape spirits?

The Bumper *PUB* Quiz Book
Quiz 204

1. Who was elected Israeli Prime Minister in 2001?

2. At what age are female walruses sexually mature?

3. In Maltese, what does the word 'bonswa' mean?

4. What famous 1831 bridge was moved from London to Arizona in 1967?

5. Which Pop Artist lived from 1928-1987?

6. Which member of the cat family cannot retract its claws: cheetah, jaguar or leopard?

7. Who is considered the father of the modern Italian language?

8. What inspired the lead singer of No Doubt to write the song *Don't Speak*?

9. What country did Saladin rule?

10. What is Dominic Greene's goal in *Quantum of Solace*?

11. What is the name of the former home of the Duke and Duchess of Gloucester located by the village of Barnwell?

12. What salad item is called 'arugula' in the US?

13. What was the first cooking show on television, hosted by James Beard in 1946, called?

14. Who succeeded Macquarie as New South Wales governor in 1821?

15. Which V8 Supercar race is known as 'The Great Race'?

16. When was the Mosaic web browser version 1.0 released?

The Bumper *PUB* Quiz Book
Quiz 205

1. What is Garam Masala?

2. In what year did Sweden host the World Cup?

3. Who produced the first computer to be sold with bundled software packages?

4. What were the only two African nations to be colonies of Portugal?

5. How long did Dickens take to write *A Christmas Carol*?

6. In heraldry, what do you call a shield divided into two vertical stripes?

7. What is the piece of metal on a bridle that goes into the horse's mouth?

8. For which film did Marilyn Monroe win a Golden Globe in 1960?

9. Who was Grandma Moses?

10. What Swedish pop singer discovered Robyn's talent when she was 13?

11. What oil or salt preserved fish are *filletti di acciughe* made from?

12. Which country was the first European nation to reach Japan?

13. Who is the Greek King of the Gods?

14. What number in the *Scream* series of films premiered in 2011?

15. Why did more than 100,000 people line the streets of Sydney on October 16, 1959?

16. What colour is the fuel cap on a dual-fuel vehicle?

The Bumper *PUB* Quiz Book

Quiz 206

1. What was the first successful English colony in the current-day USA?

2. The condition where someone can easily see things far away but not up close is called what?

3. Where were Anck-Su-Namun's vital organs placed in the film *The Mummy*?

4. The Canadian Grand Prix takes place in what city?

5. Which of the following bands does not contain a set of brothers: Hanson, Oasis or Silverchair?

6. In which organ is Vitamin A primarily stored?

7. What group of animals is warm-blooded and has fur or hair?

8. What word describes a young and instantly drinkable wine?

9. For how many years did the Ming dynasty rule China?

10. Which gem is considered the modern birthstone for February?

11. What is an arete?

12. Where did the earliest-known manufactured glass come from?

13. What is the name of the large coral reef off Australia's Eastern shore?

14. Which monarch founded King's College, Cambridge?

15. What is a giant crack in a rock called?

16. What is the monetary unit of Georgia?

Quiz 207

1. What do antioxidants neutralize in cells?

2. The term 'Second World' described what type of countries?

3. Neil Simon is known for being what kind of artist?

4. Italy beat West Germany to win its third World Cup title in what year?

5. Which country replaced the Indian rupee with the riyal in 1966?

6. Where did Kofi Annan receive his Master's Degree in 1972?

7. What year was Mozilla Firefox 1.0 released?

8. In what year did Nixon visit China?

9. As of January 2012, how many eponymous albums has Weezer released?

10. What note of the major scale is 'fa'?

11. What chef's first book was titled *I'm Just Here for the Food*?

12. What type of bed has a high scrolled headboard and footboard?

13. *Quantum of Solace* is the direct sequel to which Bond film?

14. Who had a huge Christmas hit with *Merry Xmas Everybody*?

15. Which is the largest dwarf planet orbiting the Sun?

16. How many eyes does a bee have?

The Bumper *PUB* Quiz Book
Quiz 208

1. How many years did Nelson Mandela spend in prison before being freed in 1990?

2. Lithuania, on the shores of the Baltic Sea, has what capital city?

3. Which family member did Cleopatra marry?

4. Which brand of gin is named after the guards at the Tower of London?

5. What British artist burned his art school to the ground because he was smoking in bed?

6. The film, *In the Mouth of Madness*, was directed by whom?

7. By what nickname is the mathematician William Gosset known?

8. Which one of Geoffrey Chaucer's *Canterbury Tales* comes first?

9. What is the name of the diamond-shaped muscle in the back that is worked when rowing?

10. What is a 'Bouncing Betty'?

11. What is the only bone in the human body not connected to another bone?

12. Which European capital was built on the Seven Hills?

13. Prior to 2006, who was the last player to score a hat trick in a World Cup match?

14. What is the currency of Turkey?

15. What song did *Pop Idol* winner Will Young release in 2002?

16. What name are your third molars better known by?

The Bumper *PUB* Quiz Book
Quiz 209

1. How many legs does an ant have?

2. How many countries eventually made up the Allied forces of World War 1?

3. What was the name of the first personal computer?

4. Which Taiwan building was tallest in the world from 2004 to 2010?

5. What is another name for the vitamin B6?

6. What type of element is argon?

7. Who directed *Django Unchained*?

8. How many people were inducted into the World Golf Hall of Fame in 2013?

9. Which Arctic country's highest point is Gunnbjorn?

10. What is the female counterpart to 'yang'?

11. The Greenpeace ship *Rainbow Warrior* was sunk by the French in a harbour of which country?

12. A toga would have been worn by a man from which part of the world?

13. What is a wine-like drink that is made with fermented honey?

14. For what award-winning television series is Bryan Cranston best known?

15. What 19th century opera singer was known as the 'Swedish Nightingale'?

16. Which famous author lived from 1882-1941?

Quiz 210

1. Which animal waste product is a significant greenhouse gas?

2. Which vegetable grows on long cobs?

3. What light-sensitive cells in the eye detect colours?

4. What does 'stegosaurus' literally mean?

5. Which English King was born in June 1491?

6. What does it mean if a French wine is described as 'alcooleux'?

7. What do you call a golf club especially designed for putting?

8. In what year were the first women seated in the House of Lords?

9. Where would you find the Atlas Mountains?

10. What is the capital of the Falkland Islands?

11. In which film did Angela Bassett make her film debut?

12. What is a 'loquat'?

13. Comoros is an island nation included in what continent?

14. Which brick-building toy includes *Technic* and *Mindstorms* series?

15. What country did boxer Adrian Diaconu represent in the 2000 Summer Olympics?

16. Which Roman emperor succeeded Claudius in 54AD?

The Bumper *PUB* Quiz Book
Quiz 211

1. Renamed in 2012, what is the new name of the famous clock tower located at the Palace of Westminister in London?

2. When texting, if you type 'BFN' what are you telling someone?

3. Who voiced Ted in the 2006 film *Curious George*?

4. The 1938 book, *Scoop*, was written by whom?

5. Which German soldiers had the highest casualty rate during World War 2?

6. How would a violinist play 'pizzicato'?

7. What was the focus of the Geometric period of Ancient Greek art?

8. In World War 2, who was known as 'The Good Man of Nanking'?

9. What does the prefix 'neo-' mean?

10. Which Australian bird has a rose-pink body, pale grey wings and a white head?

11. Which country is Rangoon the capital of?

12. To brew Egyptian or Sumerian beer, what type of bread is made?

13. When something foreign is placed inside the body, how would you refer to it?

14. What are compounds that contain carbon called?

15. From which professional tour was golfer Vijay Singh suspended in 1985?

16. In a triple bond between two atoms, how many pi and sigma bonds are there?

The Bumper *PUB* Quiz Book
Quiz 212

1. How is the Prime Meridian best defined?

2. Sunburn is caused by overexposure to what kind of light?

3. Who was the first African-born rider to win the Tour de France?

4. What country was soccer's Diego Maradona born in?

5. Which nation was not an original member of NATO in 1949: Belgium, Canada, Iceland or Spain?

6. What are canapes?

7. What do you call a group of geese flying together?

8. Which British actor played Sergeant Robert 'Popeye' Wynn in *Band of Brothers*?

9. What is the name of the place where Greek gods lived?

10. The capital city of China's Guangdong Province is Guangzhou, formerly known by what name?

11. Which musical group did White Stripes' Jack White form with Brendan Benson in 2005?

12. Which actress played Poison Ivy in *Batman and Robin*?

13. What is the Apgar score?

14. The airport code HKG designates which international airport?

15. After 30 years of construction, when was the Arc de Triumphe completed?

16. Oil is to frying as water is to what?

The Bumper *PUB* Quiz Book
Quiz 213

① In photography, what is an F-stop?

② What European island has St. Peter Port as its capital?

③ Which band does Hadouken! remix on their *Not Here to Please You* E.P.?

④ Who scored the so-called 'Hand of God' goal in the World Cup of 1986?

⑤ Which is the largest lake in terms of area in Norway?

⑥ What type of cnidarian makes up an underwater reef?

⑦ In what year did the Pancho Villa raids into New Mexico occur?

⑧ In *RV*, who is the 15-year-old daughter in the family?

⑨ Tequila, grenadine and orange juice make up what drink?

⑩ The 7th Secretary-General of the United Nations, Kofi Annan, was born in what African country?

⑪ Which insurance brand has a dog as its mascot?

⑫ With which city do you associate a Wiener schnitzel?

⑬ What, in Spain, is Port Aventura?

⑭ Who played Captain James T Kirk in the original *Star Trek*?

⑮ In 1957, James Agee wrote which classic?

⑯ How old was boxer Marco Antonio Barrera when he turned pro?

The Bumper *PUB* Quiz Book
Quiz 214

1. A belletrist is a writer of what?

2. Which ocean surrounds Africa on the east side?

3. Who was the British observer during the atom bomb drop on Nagasaki in World War 2?

4. What insect jumps 200 times its own body length and is a pest on cats and dogs?

5. Where did yoga originate?

6. In the film, *Top Gun*, what is Goose's real first name?

7. What was the name of the group of early twentieth century French artists, which, in English, means wild beasts?

8. The airport code CDG designates which European airport?

9. In which sea is Jamaica located?

10. The Dutch team pioneered 'Total Football' during which World Cup?

11. Former French President Nicolas Sarkozy previously served in what other political capacity?

12. In Greek mythology, which princess of Troy was cursed with visions that nobody believed?

13. Which monarch was defeated and executed following the English Civil War?

14. Which of the following terms refers to a learning disorder: dyslexia, dynasty or dystopia?

15. Mandela's 1988 70th birthday tribute involved how many artists?

16. What spice needs 75,000 blossoms to make one pound (0.45kg) of spice?

The Bumper *PUB* Quiz Book
Quiz 215

1. What are the boulders that glaciers carry with them to far places called?

2. What is the Russian word for 'caviar'?

3. Colombia shares its shortest border with which country?

4. Which hero of the Trojan war had a weak heel?

5. Which boxer was nicknamed 'The Cincinnati Cobra'?

6. Who did George Clooney marry in September 2014?

7. In what year did 800,000 die in a Tokyo earthquake?

8. To the nearest hundred, how many generals served Germany during World War 2?

9. In what English county is the River Len?

10. What is the name of Khaled Hosseini's second novel, published in 2007?

11. Which research team is credited with pioneering the scientific study of human sexuality?

12. Which Grand Prix track boasts the infamous 'Nordschleife'?

13. The border between Victoria and New South Wales in Australia is along which river?

14. In which Japanese climate zone does most wine grape growing occur?

15. Hitler started writing *Mein Kampf* in what year?

16. How many title defences was Rocky said to have had in *Rocky III*?

The Bumper *PUB* Quiz Book
Quiz 216

1. What do you call a small, wooden house in the woods?

2. What does the 'FM' in FM radio station stand for?

3. Which historical leader said 'jaw-jaw is better than war-war'?

4. What is Austin Powers' middle name?

5. What kind of star system is Algol?

6. Who crowned Charlemagne 'Emperor of Romans'?

7. What name was given to nomadic warriors from the Central Asian plains?

8. What is the fastest moving spider in the world?

9. The Pulitzer-Prize-winning book *A Confederacy of Dunces* was written by whom?

10. What UN agency monitors international public health?

11. Jose Luis Castillo had a bout with Diego Corrales for which WBC-WBO title?

12. Where did jambalaya originate?

13. What do Adobe call their desktop publishing software?

14. What is the main ingredient in lipstick?

15. In June 2001, Mis-Teeq released a hit single called *All I Want* or *All You Need*?

16. Who did the British replace as the major European presence in India?

The Bumper *PUB* Quiz Book
Quiz 217

1. What hit Mika single shares its name with a classic film star?

2. Who won the 2014 PGA Championship?

3. Hong Kong is a Special Administrative Region of what large Asian nation?

4. What is a 'thaumaturge'?

5. How long is an ostrich's intestinal tract?

6. In the 2007 Mexican film *Bad Habits*, what did Matilde believe she had to do to save the world?

7. What is the name of the fossil resin that is often used in jewellery making?

8. In what country is Korvatunturi?

9. What spice creates the yellow colour in paella?

10. Which city-state was called the 'Impregnable Fortress' by the British?

11. Who was Time's Person of the Year in 2012?

12. The lower Himalayas located in India are also known by what name?

13. How many of Henry VIII's wives outlived him?

14. Which is the southernmost capital in Asia?

15. What Scandinavian pop group came to prominence after winning the 1974 Eurovision Song Contest?

16. What was the original name of the Harvey Wallbanger cocktail?

The Bumper *PUB* Quiz Book
Quiz 218

1. Animals from South America of the genus *Pseudalopex* have what common name?

2. Who won golf's Mercedes Championship in January 2006?

3. Which planets in the solar system do not have moons?

4. Which of these European capitals is not located on the Danube River: Belgrade, Bratislava, Budapest or Prague?

5. Who won an Oscar in the 1990s for playing the character Frank Slade?

6. In what year did Roald Amundsen's Antarctic expedition reach the South Pole?

7. Basement Jaxx remixed what Pet Shop Boys song in 1997?

8. With its origins from the Ming Dynasty, what is the most famous Beijing dish?

9. Where is the Parthenon, built around 450 BC?

10. El Al is the flag-carrier airline of which country?

11. What is a crotchet called in US music terminology?

12. Who wrote *Eugene Onegin*?

13. Which Chechen leader was assassinated in Grozny in 1996 by a Russian air attack?

14. Which mushroom is not poisonous to humans: fly agaric mushroom or Jew's ear mushroom?

15. Nassau is the capital city of which country?

16. Which continent is New Zealand considered to be part of?

The Bumper *PUB* Quiz Book
Quiz 219

1. The 'Good Friday Agreement' helped establish peace in which part of the UK?

2. How much do an £80 pair of jeans cost if 30% is deducted from the price?

3. What is the orca also known as?

4. Which brand claims to be 'The World's Local Bank'?

5. Where did 'bubble tea' originate?

6. What is the capital city of Austria?

7. Which succinctly-titled track by the Foo Fighters was nominated for Best Rock Song at the 2012 Grammy Awards?

8. What is the product of an object's velocity and mass called?

9. Which pro-democracy leader was suppressed by Myanmar's government beginning in the 1980s?

10. In 1624, in which country was the first submarine tested?

11. What did Bill Gates buy for $30 million at a 1994 Christie's auction?

12. Where in the world can you find a town called Rumford Compact?

13. In the Ian Fleming novels, what was the name of James Bond's wife?

14. What country was once the centre of the Ottoman Empire?

15. How many goals did Chile score in the 1962 'Battle of Santiago'?

16. What French author wrote the novel *Les Miserables*?

The Bumper *PUB* Quiz Book
Quiz 220

1. What is the top layer of skin called?

2. In ancient Athens, what was the systematic study of oratory called?

3. Pierre Charles L'Enfant, a French architect, designed what major American city?

4. As of 2014, how many UK no.1 albums have Blur had?

5. What was British hair removal brand Veet originally called?

6. What do you call permanently frozen ground?

7. Nepal is located on which continent?

8. Which film won the Best Picture Oscar for 2008?

9. Which player won the inaugural Grand Slam Cup in 1990?

10. Eating apricots can help keep what kind of pressure down?

11. What type of creature are 'olms'?

12. The Great Barrier Reef is located off the north-east coast of what country?

13. Who were the 'immunes' in the Roman Legion?

14. How old was Victoria when she became Queen of England?

15. Who wrote the sci-fi book 'Time Enough For Love'?

16. If you form a stack of alternating layers of zinc, blotting paper soaked in salt water, and silver, what do you create?

The Bumper *PUB* Quiz Book
Quiz 221

① The former French colony of Ubangi-Shari is now known by what name?

② How many symbols were there in the Phoenician alphabet?

③ Which metal has the highest boiling point?

④ At what temperature does water freeze?

⑤ What is *Vitis vinifera*?

⑥ In what year did Ho Chi Minh create the Viet Minh party?

⑦ Which country with a total area of 500,000 square miles (800,000 square kilometres) has Maputo as its capital city?

⑧ Which UK bank is 'Always giving you extra?'

⑨ Which of these players won the most tennis Grand Slams: Billie Jean King or Martina Navratilova?

⑩ What is the national flower of Spain?

⑪ What connected the various worlds of Norse mythology?

⑫ Which famous actor's wife wrote the screenplay for *E.T.*?

⑬ Which Arab country lost the Golan Heights region in the 1967 Arab/Israeli war?

⑭ In the 1960s it was rumoured that which Beatle was dead and had been replaced by a look-alike?

⑮ Which acting Russian President was formally chosen for the post on March 25th, 2000?

⑯ What is the official Internet domain for 10 Downing Street?

The Bumper *PUB* Quiz Book

Quiz 222

① What is the thinnest form of straight pasta commonly available?

② The land speed record of 763.035mph (1227.986km/h) is slightly faster than the speed of what?

③ Who was the last bare-knuckled heavyweight boxing champion?

④ In US slang, what is a 'gofer'?

⑤ Which American golfer won the 2010 Masters?

⑥ How many people died from scurvy on Captain Cook's first voyage?

⑦ Before pie was a dessert, when did people eat pie?

⑧ The sting of what creature is used in the witches' brew from *Macbeth*?

⑨ As of 2014, how many Grammy Awards has Leona Lewis won?

⑩ What lake lies between the Godavari and Krishna river deltas near Eluru in India?

⑪ Which US state, although widely known for seafood, only has eight miles of Atlantic Ocean coastline?

⑫ Who starred in the original 1960s *Pink Panther* films?

⑬ Which South American country has Cerro Aconcagua as its highest elevation point?

⑭ How many years did Rip Van Winkle sleep?

⑮ Which mountain range is the only one in India to have snow-capped peaks?

⑯ What drink replaced beer in the Royal Navy in 1655?

The Bumper *PUB* Quiz Book
Quiz 223

1. Which of Jupiter's moons is covered by active volcanoes?

2. Which literary character used to stay at 221B Baker Street in London?

3. What title does the political leader of Canada hold?

4. How many degrees are there in a full circle?

5. In a medical context, something that is pertaining to the skin is known as what?

6. Which Queen song has Katy Perry said influenced her to follow a career in music?

7. Where is the Labrador Sea?

8. The Gulf economy relies largely on exports in what industry?

9. Which country banned instrumental and choral music during the Reformation?

10. What was the code name for *Windows 95* in its early stages of development?

11. What cocktail is made from coffee liqueur, vodka and cream?

12. In what film did Ed Harris play the svengali, Christof?

13. What did Balboa originally name the Pacific Ocean?

14. The Gulf of Mexico lies in which direction from Cuba: east or west?

15. On a shield, what is the 'umbo'?

16. FIA regulations state that drivers must be able to exit a Formula One car in how many seconds?

The Bumper *PUB* Quiz Book
Quiz 224

1. What did Kublai Khan name his dynasty after declaring himself emperor of China?

2. In Stephen King's *The Stand*, who did Trashcan Man meet on his trip to Las Vegas?

3. For the fashion label 'DKNY', the initials stand for what?

4. Julius Caesar was assassinated on the Ides of March in which year?

5. Who was the male lead in the 2006 remake of *The Shaggy Dog*?

6. Hannibal of Carthage defeated the Romans in which battle during the Second Punic War?

7. Which artist created the famous painting 'The Starry Night'?

8. What type of plant is 'lantana'?

9. What was Portugal's best-ever finish at the football World Cup?

10. What do you call a rotation about an axis aligned with the direction in which an aircraft is flying?

11. What is a 'usurer'?

12. In what year was the whaling settlement of Hobart begun on Australia's Derwent River: 1798, 1804, 1812 or 1819?

13. Who published the groundbreaking book *Principles of Geology* in 1830?

14. What are unstable molecules that attack the body's cells called?

15. What sort of government does Italy have, formally?

16. What kind of food is 'satay'?

The Bumper *PUB* Quiz Book
Quiz 225

1. Who founded the Church of Jesus Christ of Latter Day Saints in 1830?

2. Electrical circuits that have only one path for electricity to flow are called what?

3. In music, what does 'accelerando' mean?

4. Which element has the chemical symbol H?

5. What country with capital Baku uses the manat as its currency?

6. What is the ninth-most-massive body directly orbiting the Sun?

7. Which golf term refers to the clubhouse bar?

8. Which New Wave group of the 1980s sang about ripping her rival to shreds?

9. Brazil was originally colonized by which European country?

10. How tall is Ricky Gervais' writing partner, Stephen Merchant?

11. Which fruit is traditionally 'bobbed for'?

12. What is the largest lake in New Zealand?

13. Aunt Marge, the sister of Harry Potter's uncle, has what hobby?

14. Who was elected President of the Czech Republic in 1993?

15. Which film superstar was model Angie Everhart engaged to in 1995?

16. What was the first major feature film release with a digital soundtrack?

The Bumper *PUB* Quiz Book
Quiz 226

1. Which film starred Demi Moore as a woman in Navy SEALS training?

2. Which African country's highest elevation point is Pico Basile?

3. As of 2014, who holds the record as the longest-ruling non-royal national leader?

4. When was the last time that Great Britain won tennis's Davis Cup?

5. What 1960 event led to the creation of the armed wing of the ANC co-founded by Mandela?

6. What colour flame does calcium burn with?

7. What is the term for a wine expert that works in a fine restaurant?

8. What jelly-like substance supports the nucleus and all other parts of the cell?

9. Which of these is a cape located in Cuba: Clooney Cape, Cruz Cape, Depp Cape or Pitt Cape?

10. In ballet, what is a barre?

11. When did Russian President Boris Yeltsin resign?

12. Where did Daniel Bedingfield famously write his first track *Gotta Get Through This*?

13. What Australian organization is abbreviated as 'AFL'?

14. How many medals did the US win in gymnastics in 2000 in Sydney?

15. How many parts were there to HBO mini-series *Band of Brothers*?

16. How many dominos are there in a standard set?

The Bumper *PUB* Quiz Book
Quiz 227

1. Charlotte Amalie is the capital of which country?

2. In what year did wrestler Ken Patera compete in the Olympic games?

3. The MesseTurm building, completed in 1990, is located where?

4. In World War 1, what were the French *Voisin 3* planes nicknamed?

5. Traditionally, what do Japanese women wear during a tea ceremony?

6. In Norse mythology, what female spirits carried dead heroes from the battlefield?

7. What is xeriscaping?

8. Who played Miss Moneypenny in most of the early James Bond films?

9. Where is Paramount Canada's *Wonderland* located?

10. What is The Cure's first live album called?

11. What does 'subrogate' mean?

12. Who did the Emancipation Edict, issued by Czar Alexander II, free?

13. In medieval times, what was a 'surcoat'?

14. What do you call the process of boiling liquid down to concentrate flavour?

15. The Ancient Egyptian calendar was divided into how many months?

16. Fluids with a high viscosity resist what?

The Bumper *PUB* Quiz Book
Quiz 228

1. In a computer, adding more RAM increases the system's what?

2. What event during the 1919 Tour de France immortalised rider Paul Duboc?

3. Which film won the Best Picture Oscar for 2001?

4. What is a garbanzo?

5. Which famous German artist became King's Painter to Henry VIII in 1535?

6. Which English monarch was the son of Ethelred II and Emma of Normandy?

7. The Amazon, partly located in Brazil, is second in size behind which other world river?

8. Where did OneRepublic film the music video for *Say (All I Need)*?

9. What sort of fabric is 'chenille'?

10. Which of these is formed after a supernova explodes and shrinks: neutron star, red dwarf or white dwarf?

11. In what country would you find Mt. Egmont?

12. Which metal is commonly used in catalytic converters due to its properties as a reducing agent?

13. In which Dickens novel does the Artful Dodger appear?

14. What was the second all-metal building to be constructed in the world, after the Eiffel Tower?

15. Where was artist Roy de Maistre born?

16. To the nearest thousand, how many different kinds of spiders are there?

The Bumper *PUB* Quiz Book
Quiz 229

1. In what year did Oliver Cromwell become Lord Protector, with the same authority as a King of England?

2. What colour is the head-skin of an Egyptian vulture?

3. What does Baloo sneak into to visit Mowgli at the beginning of *The Jungle Book 2*?

4. Games company SEGA was originally founded as an importer of what electronic devices?

5. Dominican Republic is considered to be part of which continent?

6. How many gallons of fuel does a Boeing 747 hold: 26,123, 57,285 or 78,435?

7. In 2009, Sirs Ian McKellen and Patrick Stewart performed which Samuel Beckett play?

8. What song by The Kooks was released on the Internet on March 31, 2008?

9. What is the name of the traditional Spanish rice dish cooked in a large pan?

10. Which Australian novelist wrote the humorous novel, *Here's Luck*, in 1930?

11. How many of Rafael Nadal's first 25 matches of 2006 did he win?

12. Who did King James VI of Scotland become upon the death of Elizabeth I?

13. Who is the founder and CEO of Real Networks?

14. ISO 1007 is another name for what film format?

15. Which tiny country has Hamilton as its capital city?

16. During what month does the *Geminids* meteor shower take place?

The Bumper PUB Quiz Book
Quiz 230

1. In the fourth 'Harry Potter' book, what muggle does Voldemort kill?

2. What was the original name of The Bank of America?

3. In medicine, what is a 'haematoma'?

4. Which musical term means 'two rapidly and repeatedly alternating notes'?

5. What would you be served in a Japanese restaurant if you ordered 'Buri'?

6. What film did Morgan Freeman win an Academy Award for?

7. Who was The Beatles' drummer before Ringo Starr?

8. Who was the money-laundering title character in a 2005 French film directed by Jerome Salle?

9. In Australia, what is a 'bora'?

10. Former Australian PM Paul Keating likened himself to which opera singer?

11. What is an alpha particle made up of?

12. Name either of the two leaders of Chile's Independence movement from 1810 until 1818?

13. What do we call a machine inserted to control the heart muscle's regularity?

14. How many points is a yellow ball worth in snooker?

15. Which country became the 190th member of the United Nations on September 10, 2002?

16. What animal is also known in US slang as a woods-pussy?

The Bumper PUB Quiz Book
Quiz 231

1. What is the capital and largest city of Wales?

2. For what purpose was the programming language 'C' originally invented?

3. What type of government prevailed in Cuba from 1970 into the 21st century?

4. What was Ivan Boesky found guilty of in the 1980s?

5. In what year was Halley's Comet last pass by Earth?

6. The 'September Massacres' refers to the slaughter of political prisoners in what country?

7. Prince George, son of Prince William and Catherine the Duchess of Cambridge was baptised in which year?

8. Which Canadian company is best known as the developer of the BlackBerry smartphone?

9. What flowering plants produce seeds inside fruits that form from flowers: angiosperms or monosperms?

10. Which artist has won the most Grammy Awards, as of 2014?

11. For which film did George Clooney win an Academy Award as an actor?

12. What is the natural process by which rocks break down into smaller chunks?

13. Which city hosted the 1998 Winter Olympic Games?

14. In what year did Seth MacFarlane's *Family Guy* first air in the US?

15. In what country did 'okonomiyaki' originate?

16. Who voiced Rocky the Rooster in the movie *Chicken Run*?

The Bumper *PUB* Quiz Book
Quiz 232

1. Which Chris Brown song says, 'You know this ain't been no walk in the park for us'?

2. In what US state is the Kennedy Space Center?

3. Which film won the 2002 Academy Award for Best Picture?

4. What is a Holter Monitor?

5. What currency did Slovenia use until 2006?

6. Who is the Patron Saint of accountants?

7. What did Edward Andrade invent in World War 2?

8. Which Italian town claims to make the world's best balsamic vinegar?

9. What do minnows have in their throat?

10. If you 'prang' your car, what have you done?

11. What magnate is known as the 'Oracle of Omaha'?

12. Who was Jack Nicklaus' teacher?

13. In Greek mythology, who created the labyrinth in which the Minotaur hid?

14. HIPC is an initiative providing what to poor countries?

15. Which farm animals appeared in a Gustav Klimt garden painting?

16. LAN Airlines is the flag-carrier airline of which country?

The Bumper *PUB* Quiz Book
Quiz 233

1. What does the 'CAT' in CAT scan stand for?

2. What is the name of the female vocalist in Portishead?

3. Which country won the most gold medals at the 2012 Olympics?

4. How many above-ground storeys does The Pentagon have?

5. 'A tropical cyclone with a maximum sustained windspeed of 38 mph' describes what?

6. Which star, other than the sun, is closer to Earth than either *Alpha Centauri* star?

7. In what decade did Wasserman develop the syphilis test?

8. Where does the 2007 film *The Nanny Diaries* take place?

9. What, in medicine, is a 'pica'?

10. Who was the first Roman emperor?

11. What describes gauge pressure plus atmospheric pressure: Absolute Pressure or Binary Pressure?

12. What royal castle is located in the English county of Berkshire?

13. The 1940 book, *The Heart Is a Lonely Hunter*, was written by?

14. What is the southernmost county in Wales?

15. What bean and pork stew is known as Brazil's national dish?

16. Margaret Thatcher was Chancellor of which US university from 1993 to 2000?

The Bumper *PUB* Quiz Book
Quiz 234

1. What was the name of the political alliance formed by Julius Caesar, Pompey and Crassus?

2. Where is the Great Rift Valley located?

3. Which of the following prefixes indicates the smallest amount: Pico, femto, atto or zepto?

4. What is 'lassitude'?

5. How many beats per measure are in Dave Brubeck's 'Unsquare Dance'?

6. Low blood potassium level is known as what?

7. Who won Taiwan's first democratic public elections in 1996?

8. Victoria is the capital of which country?

9. What sweet, red pepper is often used to stuff olives?

10. In *Promise Me* by Harlan Coben, who replaces Jessica Culver as Myron Bolitar's new girlfriend?

11. Jim Courier was coached by whom as a junior?

12. In what band did Robert Plant sing *Sea of Love*?

13. What is flat land that is adjacent to a river called?

14. What was one of Napoleon's drinking cups made of?

15. In what year did *Casablanca* win the Academy Award for Best Picture?

16. In science, a 'revolution' is best defined as what?

The Bumper *PUB* Quiz Book
Quiz 235

1. What number is 10% of 660?

2. What note of the major scale is 'ti'?

3. Which island country has the capital Avarua?

4. What unit of measurement is one-thousandth of a gram?

5. What is the largest planet in the solar system?

6. Who was Hayden Christensen's co-star in *Star Wars: Episode II*?

7. Tamales are a food item of what type of cuisine?

8. What is the name of the Swiss dish that involves melted cheese or chocolate?

9. In what category of art is Rene Magritte's work classified?

10. Where did Yasser Arafat escape to after leaving Lebanon?

11. What was a major hit from the Muse album *The Origin of Symmetry*: *Classical Music*, *Hyper Music* or *Sad Music*?

12. Which country has Mogadishu as its capital city?

13. Which monarch succeeded William III as sovereign?

14. Peter George's book *Red Alert* became a film called *Dr. Strangelove or: How I Learned to...* what?

15. Who was the first US President to use the email address president@whitehouse.gov?

16. Which city hosted the 2000 Olympic Games?

The Bumper *PUB* Quiz Book
Quiz 236

1. What is the first rule of *Fight Club*?

2. A 'fisheye' lens is what type of camera lens?

3. What does 'plenary' mean?

4. The Bekka Valley is located in the eastern part of which Arab country?

5. What year did North Korea invade South Korea?

6. Which Graham Greene classic features Henry Scobie?

7. How did Eric Williams escape from a German POW camp in World War 2?

8. In what city was designer Kate Spade's collection founded?

9. At which awards show did Britney Spears and Madonna kiss on stage?

10. The 'Baker Rifle' was developed and used during which military action?

11. From what does a GPS device receive its information?

12. At the age of 18, Kelly Holmes left athletics to pursue a career in what?

13. What is *Cougnou*?

14. Which Roman emperor was given the nickname 'little boots'?

15. What currency is used in South Africa?

16. At how many degrees south is the Tropic of Capricorn located?

The Bumper *PUB* Quiz Book
Quiz 237

① The scale of points awarded in F1 racing gives points to how many top finishers?

② What is the most south-western county in England?

③ Which element has the atomic number 7?

④ Where was the term 'Iron Curtain' first used?

⑤ At what time of day do ducks usually lay their eggs?

⑥ What is an adult female turkey called?

⑦ What is Tyler Durden's occupation in the film *Fight Club*?

⑧ While the Nile is the longest, which world river is the widest?

⑨ In which capital city would you find Shisha Houhai Lake?

⑩ In heraldry, what do you call an animal in a rearing position?

⑪ Which Russian author wrote *Anna Karenina*?

⑫ What is the process of blending ingredients to make a mayonnaise creamy called?

⑬ Which Persian ruler was the son of Darius?

⑭ What is 'jaggery', used in Indian cooking?

⑮ Reggae originated from which country?

⑯ In India, what was a 'nawab'?

The Bumper *PUB* Quiz Book
Quiz 238

1. What Middle Eastern country uses the riyal as its currency?

2. From which country does Carlsberg beer originate?

3. Which British Prime Minister presided over the Falklands War?

4. What year did Nicophore Niopce take the first permanent photograph, an image of a boy leading a horse?

5. What hereditary disease allows large amounts of mucus to build up in the lungs?

6. In what film did Courtney Vance play George Grandey?

7. What is 'thanatophobia'?

8. What is the name of the Palestinian uprising that began inside Gaza and the West Bank in 1987?

9. 'Come on over, and do the twist', is in what Nirvana song?

10. What is the first name of boxing's Tyson?

11. Which river in the Greek Underworld was known as the 'River of Fire'?

12. Who was the first aboriginal to be knighted by Australia's head of state?

13. What standards body defines the 802.11g wireless standard?

14. What meat is traditionally used in spaghetti carbonara?

15. In what year was South African golfer Retief Goosen born?

16. Why did Queen Elizabeth I imprison Sir Walter Raleigh in the Tower of London?

The Bumper *PUB* Quiz Book
Quiz 239

1. What was the name of Jamie Oliver's first live cookery road show?

2. Early in his presidency, Nelson Mandela said that 'courageous people do not fear' what?

3. What kind of dog does Dave Douglas turn into in the film *The Shaggy Dog*?

4. Which city was formerly known as Constantinople?

5. Which volcano has showered ash on Sicily?

6. How many points is a green ball worth in snooker?

7. Which of these Canadian lakes has a higher salt content than normal: Albert Lake, Lake Erie, Lake Michigan or Lake Superior?

8. What is *tachycardia*?

9. If a DVD or Bluray disc has 'DTS', what does this mean?

10. Who won the Nobel Peace Prize in 1990 for his efforts to lessen Cold War tensions?

11. Which of the following is NOT a computer language: BASIC, CMOS, C# or Pascal?

12. Which desert was referred to as the 'Red Land' in Ancient Egypt?

13. The St. Lawrence Seaway opened in 1959 allowing ocean-going ships to reach which Minnesota city?

14. How did the Romans handle prisoners during the Siege of Jerusalem?

15. Luxair is the flag-carrier airline of which country?

16. What field of physics focuses on the behaviour and properties of light?

Quiz 240

1. Which is the principle ingredient of beer?

2. What spirit is used to make a Screwdriver cocktail?

3. What is the longest length of human fingernail ever recorded?

4. What is hyperopia as it relates to vision?

5. What new high-intensity fitness trend originates from Oslo: corebar, pilates, spinning or zumba?

6. Pufferfish and boxfish are deadly to humans because of the presence of what poison in their skin and organs?

7. What small, terrestrial mammal is an extremely close relative of the elephant: hyrax, mole-rat, vole or weasel?

8. What actress played Edna Spalding in the film *Places in the Heart*?

9. Feta cheese, basil, grape leaves, olives, and figs, are traditional food used in what type of cooking?

10. *Percale* is a lightweight sturdy cotton fabric often used for what?

11. In what year was the People's Republic of China proclaimed?

12. Which Greek philosopher was a boyhood tutor to Alexander the Great?

13. Which organization did the Czech Republic, Poland and Hungary join in 1999?

14. What country in the world is known for XXXX beer?

15. The British Grand Prix is held on what circuit?

16. The word 'danke' means 'thanks' in what country's language?

Quiz 241

1. The obscuring from sight of one celestial body by another is known by what scientific term?

2. On which date was Princess Diana born?

3. What two colours are on the flag of Poland?

4. Which dinosaur film was a box office smash in 1993?

5. What alcoholic ingredient is essential to the US dish 'Lobster Newburg'?

6. What was the original name of Burkina Faso?

7. After Japan captured China's capital during World War 2, what became the wartime capital?

8. When did Napoleon Bonaparte institute the Legion d'Honneur?

9. What is the name of the Irish town south of Belfast where St. Patrick was reputedly buried?

10. What is a stag with twelve-point antlers known as?

11. What nickname is boxer Ricky Hatton known by?

12. What fast-food brand uses the slogan 'Have it your way'?

13. Which of the following was originally a Czech peasant dance: mambo, polka or foxtrot?

14. Edmund Spenser was the first poet to hold what honorary post?

15. The platform shoe was a staple of what dance-themed fashion era?

16. Who was Prime Minister of Canada during World War 2?

The Bumper *PUB* Quiz Book
Quiz 242

1. How many zeros are there in an octillion?

2. What is the process by which wine is exposed to air to 'relax' the drink?

3. An outbreak of what animal disease afflicted the UK in 1967, 2001 and 2007?

4. Which is the most popular Internet search engine portal in Europe?

5. Which mammal has the longest fur?

6. Which role did Bill Murray play in the film *Ghostbusters*?

7. Which country has Phnom Penh as its capital city?

8. Who is the lead singer for the band The Kooks?

9. Who was given the task of rebuilding St Paul's Cathedral after the Great Fire of London?

10. How many total World Cup championships has Brazil as of 2014?

11. What opera is the musical *Rent* based on?

12. Who was the first Secretary of the USSR Communist Party?

13. The commercial port of Sidon is located in which Arab country?

14. Which drink brand calls itself 'The King of Beers'?

15. How is the constellation *Leo* known in English?

16. On which US exchange would you buy crude oil futures?

Quiz 243

① Aerobic exercise increases what rate?

② How many bits per pixel do you need for a 256 colour image?

③ Which vegetable was used in the title '___ Patch Kids', a brand of dolls?

④ What is the name of Jack's love interest in *The Nightmare Before Christmas*?

⑤ What odourless and colourless gas is known as 'marsh gas'?

⑥ What became the world's tallest man-made structure in 1930?

⑦ Crocodiles, but not alligators, make which of these countries their home: Australia, Poland or the USA?

⑧ In 1934, Henry Roth wrote which classic?

⑨ In what year did *War and Peace* author Leo Tolstoy die?

⑩ Situated on the Western coast of Africa, what is the capital of the Republic of Guinea?

⑪ What is a 'kakuro' puzzle?

⑫ Who was the architect of the Pantheon in Rome?

⑬ What cut of meat is traditionally used for the dish 'osso buco'?

⑭ In 1977, which Israeli Prime Minister resigned due to a scandal?

⑮ Who was expelled from the 2014 World Cup for biting another player?

⑯ Which unit is used to measure loudness?

The Bumper **PUB** Quiz Book
Quiz 244

1. Which term is used for the four main compass directions?

2. Who wrote the sentence 'Rose is a rose is a rose is a rose'?

3. The Amazon rainforest extends over how many South American countries?

4. In cosmetics, what is a 'neroli'?

5. In which 2006 Israeli film did young Israeli Noam date Palestinian soldier Ashraf?

6. Where do dogs sweat from?

7. King Louis XIV influenced the creation of which French palace?

8. Socotra is an island belonging to what country?

9. How many mechanics are usually involved in changing each wheel at Formula One pit stops?

10. By means of what snake did Cleopatra supposedly kill herself?

11. If you're hungry in northern Germany and order 'eintopf', you're getting a bowl of what?

12. How many wire pairs does CAT5 twisted pair cable contain?

13. What year was the first Teddy Bear sold?

14. Generically, what are the structures found in the cytoplasm of living cells called?

15. In the Enrique Iglesias song *Addicted* how many mistakes did he make?

16. Which was the first German army to surrender to US troops during World War 2?

The Bumper *PUB* Quiz Book
Quiz 245

1. Where in the human body would you find your corrugator?

2. On the coast of which country were the battles of El Alamein fought during World War 2?

3. In which Spielberg film did Jude Law play the character Gigolo Joe?

4. How old was Mother Teresa when she died in 1997?

5. What is the international airport code for London Heathrow?

6. In J. R. R. Tolkien's *The Lord of the Rings*, what is the capital of Rohan?

7. What natural response would a human have to being cold?

8. Which herb is saltimbocca generally flavoured with?

9. During what month does the *Leonids* meteor shower take place?

10. Which nation won the UEFA European Football Championship for the third time in 2012?

11. How many days does it take Mercury to revolve around the sun?

12. What does the archaic word 'devoir' refer to?

13. Square dance is a modern term to describe which type of dance?

14. What was the Backstreet Boys' first single?

15. What is the traditional name of the soy bean soup which is a staple of the Japanese?

16. During the 20th century, how many French victories were there in the Tour de France?

The Bumper *PUB* Quiz Book
Quiz 246

1. On a die, what number is on the opposite side to 2?

2. On a bottle of French wine, what do the letters 'AOC' stand for?

3. What car company ran an ad in Britain seemingly showing a man attempting suicide in his car?

4. In what year did Nelson Mandela marry Graça Machel?

5. If someone is 'agued', what are they?

6. Who won the World Snooker Championship in 2010?

7. In the Second Punic War, how many battles did Hannibal lose on Roman soil?

8. What island is mentioned in the Enrique Iglesias song *Rhythm Divine*?

9. How old was Vincent Van Gogh when he passed away?

10. Which of these Stephen King stories is set in Castle Rock: *Carrie*, *Misery* or *The Body*?

11. What term is used for the bone shield formed by the fused bases of an African buffalo's horns?

12. What is the name of Google's mobile operating system?

13. What is the boiling point of water on the Celsius scale?

14. What film featured Madonna and Rupert Everett?

15. Which French Caribbean island group has an area of 629 square miles (1628 square km)?

16. On which continent is Turkmenistan located?

The Bumper *PUB* Quiz Book
Quiz 247

1. What is the 'Arabic' number for the Roman numeral IV?

2. Who was the first male figure skater to land a triple loop in competition?

3. What is Shoe Fly Pie made from?

4. Who wrote the best-selling novel *Carrie*?

5. In what county is the port of Dover?

6. Which country unified its East and West sides in 1990?

7. What word means a widespread loss of electrical power?

8. Which painting by Barnett Newman first exhibited the 'zip'?

9. What do Google call their own-brand phones and tablets?

10. The highest elevation point of which Middle Eastern country is Qurnat as Sawda'?

11. Which African capital is closest to the equator?

12. What colour are deathstalker scorpions?

13. In the UK, what holiday is celebrated on the day after Christmas?

14. What food does Alex learn to eat at the end of the film *Madagascar*?

15. Who sponsored Christopher Columbus' trip to reach land by sailing west?

16. In what casino game do both the dealer and player draw a card, and the highest card wins?

The Bumper *PUB* Quiz Book
Quiz 248

1. How many sides of the same length does a rhombus have?

2. In 2012 the world population hit a milestone of how many billion?

3. Which *Malcolm in the Middle* actor was the voice of the abandoned zebra in *Racing Stripes*?

4. What product is designed to clean hair and nourish the scalp?

5. Where did Bhangra dance originate?

6. Hair grows on average how many inches a day?

7. A popular food in Brazil is *manioc* which is most similar to which foods?

8. What does 'olfact' mean?

9. What right-handed curve follows Priory and Brookfield curves at Silverstone?

10. Indira Gandhi was Prime Minister of which country?

11. What was the first broom Harry Potter owned?

12. For how long did original episodes of the serial *When a Girl Marries* run on Australian radio: 19 years, 23 years, 26 years or 30 years?

13. What is a Schipperke?

14. What insect is 'emmet' a dialectal word for?

15. Which original member of the *Glee* cast died in 2013?

16. The Supreme Council of the United Arab Emirates consists of how many individual rulers?

The Bumper *PUB* Quiz Book
Quiz 249

1. Which European country's highest elevation point is Zugspitze?

2. What year did Alicia Keys release her album *The Diary of Alicia Keys*?

3. Where did the common pet gerbil originate?

4. Which company unveiled the disastrous 'PC jr.' in the 1980s?

5. In what year did the Korean War end?

6. Which star portrayed Charles in the film *Diary of a Mad Black Woman*?

7. During the Counter-Reformation, what did Pope Paul III bring to Rome from Spain?

8. In religion, what is an 'introit'?

9. True or false: the horns of an oryx are on average 76cm (30 inches) long?

10. What is the repeating cycle of precipitation, condensation and evaporation called?

11. What is the capital city of Mexico?

12. In heraldry, what colour is 'vert'?

13. Who was the first emperor of Rome?

14. Who wrote the *Do the Bartman* song for *The Simpsons*?

15. What is the name of the 2000 film starring boxer Barry McGuigan?

16. What does the HP in 'HP Sauce' stand for?

The Bumper **PUB** Quiz Book
Quiz 250

1. What is a 'granny flat'?

2. What is the most famous wine-producing region within Japan?

3. What was the 'Wehrmacht' during World War 2?

4. On which river does Dresden stand?

5. The snow leopard is the national animal of which country?

6. In which James Bond film did Grace Jones star?

7. What 1980s fashion item was originally designed for dancers?

8. What herb is said to help improve your memory: ginkgo biloba, ginkogen or milk thistle?

9. What theory proposes that Earth's landmasses were once connected and drifted apart?

10. In which European city is the Manneken Pis statue?

11. Alex Arthur's title was 'Interim World Champion' after a 2007 match with whom?

12. What happens to Mrs. Norris in the second Harry Potter book?

13. What do OneRepublic say goodbye to in a 2007 song title: apathy, inactivity or mercy?

14. What psychological theory bases much importance on birth order: Adlerian, Existential, Gestalt or Jungian?

15. When was the Great Schism in the Catholic Church?

16. Who played the Eleventh Doctor?

The Bumper *PUB* Quiz Book
Quiz 251

1. About how fast does sound travel in metres per second?

2. Vinegar typically has what percentage of acetic acid?

3. Who sang the theme song to 1997's *Titanic*?

4. Which male model starred as Jack Darius on *Baywatch*?

5. How many full-length Sherlock Holmes novels were originally written?

6. In what year were the first National Assembly of Wales elections?

7. Which two colours are on the flag of Albania?

8. Which of the following is not a Viennese Waltz step, or figure: backwards twirl, left whisk or natural turn?

9. What film shares its name with a widely-used nickname for golfer Colin Montgomerie?

10. What is the name of the city in England known to be the home to William Shakespeare?

11. What spice is used to flavour liquorice sweets?

12. What would you call medicine that attacks bacteria inside your body?

13. What currency is used in Swaziland?

14. Who was the leading American 'Ace' in the Pacific Theatre during World War 2: Major Greg Boyington or Major Thomas McGuire?

15. Which is the only continent without snakes or reptiles?

16. Who did the Roman Emperor Caligula famously appoint to the Senate?

The Bumper *PUB* Quiz Book

Quiz 252

① The FinePix series of digital cameras is made by what company?

② Which Russian czar emancipated the serfs?

③ Which journalist and author was the first to infiltrate the Hell's Angels?

④ What artificial sweetener was invented at Searle Laboratory in the US in 1968?

⑤ In 2001, four men were convicted of the 1998 bombings of US embassies in which two countries?

⑥ What is another common name for farfalle pasta?

⑦ What is 'venustraphobia'?

⑧ In which country was golfer Annika Sorenstam born?

⑨ Who directed the original *Nightmare on Elm Street*?

⑩ Which Danzig album featured the songs *Left Hand Black* and *Sistinas*?

⑪ The Mosquito Coast rests largely in what country?

⑫ In what country would you celebrate *carnival*?

⑬ How many wives did Henry VIII have?

⑭ Which planet is not only the morning star but also can be the evening star?

⑮ The Pereto Merino, located in Argentina, is what type of natural phenomenon?

⑯ In music, what speed is 'allegro'?

The Bumper *PUB* Quiz Book
Quiz 253

1. Which computer company ran an infamous commercial during the 1984 US Super Bowl?

2. What fruit forms the main ingredient of a Bloody Mary cocktail?

3. Which of the following cats was originated in 1985 by Carol Anne Brewer: Pixie-bob, Siamese or Turkish van?

4. What country's cuisine includes dishes such as kielbasa and pierogi?

5. In what year did Lech Walesa become President of Poland?

6. What sight problem does Mark Zuckerberg suffer from?

7. 'IBM' is an acronym for what?

8. What smash hit song from Adele's *21* reached number 1 in 11 countries?

9. Why was Australian comedian Joff Ellen called Joff?

10. Which element has the chemical symbol Ne?

11. What Asian country has Pyongyang as its capital?

12. How many legs does a butterfly have?

13. Who did Yasser Arafat replace as Palestine Liberation Organization leader in 1969?

14. Who was originally cast to play Christian Grey in *Fifty Shades of Grey*?

15. What is the name of the main character in Stephen King's *Gerald's Game*?

16. Tim Henman won his only Masters Series title at which tournament?

The Bumper **PUB** Quiz Book
Quiz 254

1. Which medical term means 'situated on or outside the spinal cord'?

2. Which company originally used the MMCD video format?

3. What is a family group of warthogs called?

4. Who played Mr Darcy in the original BBC production of *Pride and Prejudice*?

5. Who was the first Olympic gold medalist?

6. What colours are used on the Facebook app icon on the iPhone?

7. What alcohol-related event occurred on April 7th, 1933?

8. Who won Iran's Presidential election in 2005 with 62% of the vote?

9. What are the deepest canyons in the ocean called?

10. The Solomon Islands, whose natives were once head-hunters, has what capital city?

11. In *RV*, what Californian city do the Munros come from?

12. What was the 'Big Switch' in the Korean War?

13. Who preceded Hadrian as Roman Emperor?

14. Situated on the Western coast of Africa, what is the capital of the Republic of Guinea-Bissau?

15. What destroyed the Bolshoi Theatre in 1805?

16. Which Stephen Crane short story starts, 'None of them knew the colour of the sky'?

The Bumper *PUB* Quiz Book
Quiz 255

① In what year did Haiti end Italy's record 19-game World Cup streak?

② Upsilon is the Greek alphabet equivalent of which English letter?

③ Which breed of dog cannot bark?

④ Which former Beatles member was once married to Heather Mills?

⑤ The film *Lonely Hearts* is set in what decade?

⑥ What country did Jawaharlal Nehru lead?

⑦ Which is the second largest country in Iberia?

⑧ Which of the following happens when air cools: it becomes denser or it becomes lighter?

⑨ The Japanese art of paper-folding is called what?

⑩ What sort of dinosaur is the Flintstones' pet Dino?

⑪ What is the capital of Equatorial Guinea?

⑫ Which is a spice that might be added to mulled wine: cinnamon, rosemary or thyme?

⑬ On average, how many calories does a male adult need every day?

⑭ What is the English name for the man French kids call 'Papa Noel'?

⑮ Which sportsman did Marilyn Monroe marry in 1954?

⑯ The IEEE is the professional society for what branch of engineering?

The Bumper *PUB* Quiz Book
Quiz 256

1. What do you call an instrument that measures atmospheric pressure?

2. What country's team does ex-FC Barcelona manager Gerardo Martino now manage, as of 2014?

3. Paganini was famous as a virtuoso on what instrument?

4. What is the last stop on the westbound Jubilee line on the London underground?

5. What is the name of Ron Howard's production company?

6. Corel Corporation bought what ubiquitous PC file compression utility in 2006?

7. Who preceded Harold Wilson as UK Prime Minister?

8. Where is the Zwingler Museum?

9. How is the American Longhair cat better known?

10. What is the medical term for high blood potassium?

11. Deforestation in the Peten Forest is a concern in what nation?

12. In which century was Isaac Newton's *Principia Mathematica* published?

13. Who directly preceded James II as English monarch?

14. Approximately how many glasses of wine can be made from one cluster of grapes?

15. What royal residence in England was best known as the official home of Diana, Princess of Wales?

16. What does the adjective 'vernal' refer to?

The Bumper *PUB* Quiz Book
Quiz 257

1. Gabriela Isler won the 2014 *Miss Universe*; what country is she from?

2. How many goals were scored in the 2008 UEFA European Football Championship? 33, 55 or 77?

3. How many official languages does the nation of South Africa have?

4. How many zeros are there in a billion?

5. What type of meat would you typically use for Irish stew?

6. Geologically, what is an 'esker'?

7. Which Roman general defeated the Carthaginians at the Battle of Zama?

8. What group of animals has hollow bodies and stinging cells?

9. In 1492, where did Christopher Columbus make his first landing in the New World?

10. How many generals are there in the game *Junta*?

11. Whose face can you change by switching his stick-on facial features?

12. What is an adult male turkey called?

13. What was Velvet Underground's first studio album?

14. What music star plays Otis in the 2005 film *Because of Winn-Dixie*?

15. Which cylindrical New York museum was designed by Frank Lloyd Wright?

16. Which board game has a car, top hat and dog as players' game pieces?

The Bumper *PUB* Quiz Book
Quiz 258

1. What is the remainder when 2638 is divided by 24?

2. In years, what does BC stand for?

3. Which country is part of the Lesser Antilles: Andorra, Barbados or Chile?

4. In music, what does 'a tempo' mean?

5. What is the capital city of New Brunswick, Canada?

6. What percentage fat should a healthy male's body have?

7. Who is the Greek god of the underworld?

8. The tagline *The Heat Is On* comes from which 1984 film?

9. Prior to Theo Walcott, who was the youngest player ever to play for the England football team?

10. In what year did Nat Turner lead a slave revolt in Southampton County, Virginia?

11. In 2005, which Liberian became the first female elected head of state in African history?

12. What was the name of the first artificial satellite launched into space?

13. What kind of drink is 'julep'?

14. Many of Paul Cezanne's paintings were of which type?

15. What is the speed of sound called?

16. Which of the following is not a type of cheese: bocheron, cabrales, panache or tetilla?

The Bumper *PUB* Quiz Book
Quiz 259

1. The corpse of which pope was dug up and put on trial in 897?

2. What birthday party does Bella celebrate in *The Twilight Saga: New Moon*?

3. Trotsky was assassinated on the orders of Stalin in which city?

4. Which actress played Willow Rosenberg in *Buffy the Vampire Slayer*?

5. What is the name of Jordan's capital city?

6. How old was Dr Seuss when he wrote about the Grinch?

7. What is the tenth-most-massive body directly orbiting the Sun?

8. Which sport uses the smallest ball?

9. What colour flame does arsenic burn with?

10. Stone Age man hunted which mammal to extinction: goat, bison, mammoth or ox?

11. Which meat is the most commonly consumed at Easter in Italy?

12. ECOWAS was founded in 1975 as an organization consisting of nations in what region?

13. Carl Kempe won an Olympic silver medal in which year?

14. Which two countries have had a long-running dispute over Kashmir?

15. What was Lamborghini first known for?

16. What does the Sanskrit word 'yoga' literally mean?

The Bumper *PUB* Quiz Book
Quiz 260

1. What is the repetition of speech by a child learning to talk called?

2. Who was the creator of the Mongol empire?

3. What is the capital of Sri Lanka?

4. What type of gem is the *Star of Africa* or the *Cullinar II*?

5. Who is the Amy Macdonald song *Poison Prince* about?

6. Which ex-British Prime Minister died prior to the beginning of World War 2: David Lloyd George or Herbert Asquith?

7. If a wine is not clear, what is it?

8. Which amphibian is boiled first in the witches' brew from *Macbeth*?

9. What quadrilateral is a parallelogram with all sides of equal length?

10. What superpower does Dashiell have in the film *The Incredibles*?

11. In Australia, if you 'barrack', what do you do?

12. What musical time signature is referred to as 'common time'?

13. In which American city was tennis pro Jennifer Capriati born?

14. As which Russian leader was Vladimir Ulyanov better known?

15. In what year did Steve Wozniak and Steve Jobs build the first Apple personal computer?

16. From which language does the word 'collage' originate?

The Bumper *PUB* Quiz Book
Quiz 261

1. What is the name of the London area the zero degrees longitude Prime Meridian is centred on?

2. How many points is the letter 'J' worth in the game of *Scrabble*?

3. How many knockout victories did Mohammed Ali have in his career?

4. Kokanee Lager is native to which country?

5. Who directed the film *Wag The Dog*?

6. What was Microsoft's defunct personal finance management program called?

7. What is Fred Flintstone's best friend called?

8. Juniper berries are often used to flavour which alcoholic beverage?

9. Who were Rolls and Royce?

10. What does the Greek word 'philosopher' mean?

11. Which word means that an object contains no iron?

12. Relating to chemistry, what is a catalyst?

13. In what year was Heathrow Terminal 3, then called the Oceanic Terminal, first opened?

14. What were Akkadian weapons made from?

15. Which city in Europe receives the most tourists, as of 2013?

16. What was the period immediately preceding the English Restoration called?

The Bumper *PUB* Quiz Book
Quiz 262

1. Gothic fashion features clothing that is primarily what colour?

2. Who ascended the English throne after the death of James I?

3. What is the remainder when you divide 30 by 4?

4. What kind of electromagnetic radiation arises from nuclear explosions?

5. Reconstructive surgery first emerged after which war?

6. Which was the subtitle of the first Game Boy *Zelda* game?

7. What is the meal that combines breakfast and lunch called?

8. Which European capital city contains the Prado boulevard?

9. What is the capital of the eastern Mexican state of Quintana Roo?

10. What English weapon destroyed the French at Agincourt in 1415?

11. Anna Kournikova comes from which country?

12. What is a 'tisane'?

13. Which famous Hollywood actor was in the Annie Lennox music video, *Walking On Broken Glass*?

14. In Russia, what was a 'ukase'?

15. John C. McGinley plays which doctor in *Scrubs*?

16. The 1980 book titled *Kane and Abel* was written by whom?

The Bumper *PUB* Quiz Book
Quiz 263

1. The island of Mauritius was once the home of what extinct species of flightless bird?

2. Which measure of time is equal to one hundred years?

3. The BOCOM Financial Towers, completed in 1999, are located where?

4. What was the occupation of most Babylonians?

5. What is the name of the leader who ruled Cuba for 49 years until 2008?

6. Which element has the atomic number 10?

7. In what year did *Sputnik 1* launch?

8. Which cuisine does *Moo goo gai pan* belong to?

9. Which capital city is situated furthest east of London: Ankara, Beirut, Cairo or Moscow?

10. Which US state's flower is the forget-me-not?

11. What is 'ennui'?

12. In what year was *The Moon is a Harsh Mistress* published?

13. What are the main ingredients of a ganache?

14. In English football, who is Sheila Parker?

15. What deceased icon rapped on Michael Jackson's *Unbreakable*?

16. Which character did John Travolta play in *Pulp Fiction*?

The Bumper *PUB* Quiz Book
Quiz 264

1. Who assassinated Archduke Ferdinand and his wife on June 28, 1914, to precipitate World War 1?

2. What islands lay off the south-eastern coast of Argentina?

3. How many stomachs does a cow have?

4. What Formula One racer moved to Ferrari in 2007, replacing Michael Schumacher?

5. How is Beth Gibbons dressed in the music video for the song *Glory Box*?

6. Who did Montezuma believe Hernan Cortes was?

7. What is the currency of Laos?

8. How many people own a sole proprietorship business?

9. Which scientist discovered insulin?

10. Which sport is the 2007 film *Blades of Glory* about?

11. A New York City theatre with fewer than 500 seats is known as what?

12. What 1985 novel by Margaret Atwood is a dystopian, speculative fiction?

13. Which country has Cayenne as its capital?

14. How are pockets of air in soil made?

15. What retransmits radio signals in a new direction?

16. In which year did Neil Armstrong walk on the moon?

The Bumper *PUB* Quiz Book
Quiz 265

1. When was Women's Soccer first included in the Olympics as a full-medal event?

2. On what film did Johnny Depp and Tim Burton first collaborate?

3. Which artist most famously employed the technique known as pointillism?

4. In which US state is Niagara Falls?

5. Who played the character Sarah in the film *Regarding Henry*?

6. Who did the Romans defeat during the Battle of Narbonne in 436 AD?

7. What cheese's name literally means 'recooked' in Italian?

8. The northern & southern regions of what Gulf Arab country were re-united in 1990?

9. Which Shakespeare play features Ferdinand and the Princess of France?

10. Bolivia lies directly north of which country beginning with 'A'?

11. What is seitan?

12. If you throw a ball in the air, what type of curve does it trace out?

13. The wedding gown worn by Al Gore's daughter was designed by whom?

14. Where was the world's first human heart transplant performed in 1967?

15. Where was porcelain first invented?

16. What is a person called who specializes in the physical structure and process of the Earth?

The Bumper **PUB** Quiz Book
Quiz 266

1. What type of food is 'ajiaco'?

2. What is a sub-basement?

3. Who wrote the Australian novel that begins 'My name is Herbert Badgery'?

4. Which of the following stories did Edgar Allan Poe not write: *King Pest*, *Metzengerstein* or *The Monkey's Paw*?

5. What was the 'Daisy Cutter' in World War 2?

6. In electronic devices, what is a 'tuner'?

7. What objects did the Ancient Sumerians use to write?

8. The first line of Sean Kingston's *Take You There* mentions what sort of drink?

9. Which sub-species of tiger is the largest?

10. What is the value of a resistor that has the following colour bands: red, red, red?

11. Who was the famous Polish female scientist who won a Nobel Prize?

12. Who plays Mrs Lovett in the 2007 film *Sweeney Todd*?

13. What country in South America, with Santiago as its capital, uses the peso as its currency?

14. In what year did the Soviet Union disband?

15. Which country hosted the FIFA World Cup in 1994?

16. Which 1985 film is about an Amish boy who is the sole witness to a murder?

Quiz 267

① In computing, what does 'www' stand for?

② What nation was the first to be sanctioned for the sale of blood diamonds?

③ Who wrote *The Lord of the Rings*?

④ How many goals did Ronaldo score in the 1998, 2002 and 2006 World Cups combined?

⑤ What is the name of the school in *The Breakfast Club*?

⑥ Edinburgh, Glasgow and Dundee are cities in what country?

⑦ Which of these is a classic personality type: Ambivalent, Aristocrat, Humanoid or Vivarium?

⑧ As of 2014, how tall is the world's shortest living man?

⑨ What is a jalapeno?

⑩ What does 'Magna Carta' mean?

⑪ Henri Matisse is known for being what?

⑫ Who was known for his famous 'oil-drop' experiments to determine the charge of the electron?

⑬ Which bird is also known as a 'windhover'?

⑭ Who originally sang *When A Child Is Born*?

⑮ What substance were Alexander the Great's remains preserved in?

⑯ To the nearest number of hours, what is Pemba Dorje's record for the fastest ascent of Mount Everest?

The Bumper *PUB* Quiz Book
Quiz 268

1. By what name was the Sioux chief 'Tashunka Witco' more commonly known?

2. What term defines a network computer which acts as a service or resource provider?

3. The medical term 'transdermal' is best defined as?

4. Which country is not a member of the League of Arab Nations: Bahrain, Iran, Mauritania or Syria?

5. Where is Wolfgang Amadeus Mozart buried?

6. Which Space Shuttle was built to replace *Challenger*?

7. Who was China's first Olympic medallist in figure skating?

8. Which is the longest river in Britain?

9. Medically, what is 'oedema'?

10. In what year did *Gandhi* win the Academy Award for Best Picture?

11. What country calls Father Christmas 'Der Weihnachtsmann'?

12. Who was the author of *The Adventures of Huckleberry Finn*?

13. Which animal's cocoon is harvested to make silk thread?

14. What are 'love handles'?

15. In cooking what would you use a 'dredger' for?

16. Which African country's highest elevation point is Ras Dejen?

The Bumper *PUB* Quiz Book
Quiz 269

① Mount Everest straddles which two countries?

② How many stages are there in the life of a mosquito?

③ As part of the Dada movement, who put a moustache on the 'Mona Lisa'?

④ Which dish is a combination of sliced pork and soft noodles: pork chow mein or pork lo mein?

⑤ Who directed the 2001 French film *Amelie*?

⑥ Whose vacant number 16 shirt did Michael Carrick take over for Manchester United?

⑦ What is another name for the vitamin B3?

⑧ What is the capital city of the Republic of The Congo, home of the Bantu tribes?

⑨ In wine-making, what is 'argol'?

⑩ How many series of US show *Seinfeld* were made?

⑪ Which Canadian city means 'place of meeting' in its original native American language?

⑫ What was the main ingredient in the UK Ministry of Food's 'mock apricot flan' recipe?

⑬ What is the name of the royal residence located in Kensington Gardens?

⑭ What gas is the primary component of natural gas?

⑮ What does 'footslog' mean?

⑯ Who wrote the cult novel *Fight Club*?

Quiz 270

1. How many UK singles were released from the 11 tracks on Michael Jackson's *Bad* album?

2. What is Apple's portable music player called?

3. Whose claim to the English throne, made following the death of Edward VI, led to her execution a year later?

4. What are plants that grow, reproduce and die all in one season called?

5. What class was the most numerous in Egyptian society?

6. Brazil is bordered by how many countries?

7. In Ancient Rome, who allied with Octavian and Lepidus to form the Second Triumvirate?

8. Which country is considered one of the most underdeveloped in the world: Chad, China or Cuba?

9. Which of the following is a Pepsi product: Fanta, Hires, Slice or Sprite?

10. In heraldry, what colour is 'purpure'?

11. How many buttons were there on the original Pudsey Bear design?

12. Burgundy is famous for what two grape varietals?

13. What is a thick-walled resting cell that forms inside a bacteria cell called?

14. How many teams competed in the Bank Asya 1 football league in Turkey in 2011?

15. Who wrote *Cider with Rosie*?

16. In *Sense and Sensibility*, who took the three sisters to London?

The Bumper *PUB* Quiz Book
Quiz 271

1. Who was voted Italian Footballer of the Year in 2000-1, 2003-4 and 2007?

2. Which element is the primary component of steel?

3. What does the word 'zeitgeist' mean?

4. What download technology superseded GPRS?

5. Which is the highest mountain in Switzerland?

6. What electronic component decreases current flow?

7. What is the name of the major UK theme park located in Staffordshire?

8. Where did the enduring Britpop band Oasis get their name?

9. Who is the main character in the animated film *An American Tail*?

10. Who invented a system of raised dots, allowing blind people to read?

11. Which leader was known for his 'Cultural Revolution'?

12. What is an 'alerce'?

13. How much of a person's body weight is water?

14. What part of the carrot is eaten as a vegetable?

15. What kind of food is 'pho'?

16. Name a significant disease that an endocrinologist might generally study?

The Bumper **PUB** Quiz Book
Quiz 272

1. What TV cookery competition did chef Gordon Ramsay initially host in both the UK and US versions?

2. Which Greek goddess was depicted in a colossal bronze statue near the Acropolis?

3. Who has been named European Tour Player of the Year in four different years?

4. Which actor recorded the voiceover at the end of Michael Jackson's *Thriller*?

5. How many points is a blue ball worth in snooker?

6. What happens to water when it gets close to freezing?

7. What herbal medicine was Beatrix Potter's Peter Rabbit given to calm his stomach?

8. In what year did the McDonald's Corporation go public?

9. What type of insect is a 'dor'?

10. Part of the Leeward Islands in the Caribbean, Saint Kitts and Nevis boasts what scenic capital city?

11. Who famously said 'They kill good trees to put out bad newspapers'?

12. Who became the first Labour Party Prime Minister to win three successive terms?

13. Which film won the Best Picture Oscar for 2011?

14. Which Dean Koontz book features a dog who communicates using a computer?

15. What Caribbean country has Kingstown as its capital and uses the dollar as its currency?

16. What are the printed reports of the debates and procedures of the British parliament called?

The Bumper *PUB* Quiz Book
Quiz 273

1. In *Much Ado About Nothing*, who says 'Lady, as you are mine, I am yours'?

2. How many countries are in NAFTA?

3. In which country can you find Ayers Rock?

4. In what country was boxer Urbano Antillon born?

5. What poet did the students learn about in *Dangerous Minds*?

6. A calorie is a unit of measurement used to measure what?

7. What are the male sperm cells formed in flowering plants called?

8. In clothing terminology, what is a *shrug*?

9. What is the name for an area of land surrounded by water on three sides?

10. A 1634 Spanish decree called what city 'Key to the New World and Rampart of the West Indies'?

11. Which cosmetics brand uses the tagline 'Maybe she's born with it'?

12. Roughly how many tons of ore are typically mined to produce one carat of rough diamond?

13. Who was the first Tudor monarch?

14. Which was the subtitle of the second original GameCube *Zelda* game?

15. What Southern-Italian style of cooking is also the name of a type of ice cream?

16. What famous ship sank to the bottom of the Atlantic Ocean in 1912?

The Bumper *PUB* Quiz Book
Quiz 274

1. What year was the first canned tuna packaged: 1789, 1846, 1850 or 1907?

2. Which Agatha Christie novel was first published in 54 parts in the *London Evening News*?

3. What do the French call Father Christmas?

4. In what year did a ballerina first wear a tutu on stage: 1659, 1783, 1832 or 1920?

5. What word means 'pertaining to medical care'?

6. What colour is Masaharu Morimoto's costume on the show *Iron Chef*?

7. Which 2005 hit film, now a West End musical, starred Johnny Depp as a quirky candy maker?

8. 'Neuf', 'nueve' and 'neun' are all ways of saying which number?

9. What song by The Kooks did OneRepublic cover for a Radio 1 'Big Weekend'?

10. Brussels is the capital of which country?

11. Mysophobia is the fear of what?

12. In Spain, what is a 'pueblo'?

13. Which team knocked the hosts, Italy, out of the 1990 World Cup?

14. Who succeeded Gordon Brown as UK Prime Minister?

15. What is the scientific name of the great white shark?

16. Michael Jackson has how many Brit Awards to his name?

The Bumper *PUB* Quiz Book
Quiz 275

① Which sport is often associated with tendonitis of the elbow?

② Parts of the film *Lara Croft: Tomb Raider* were shot in what African country?

③ What type of dessert with a slip of paper inside is served at the end of a Chinese meal?

④ As of 2014, how old is Jonathan, the world's oldest tortoise?

⑤ Which pop singer was responsible for *Wrecking Ball*?

⑥ Which genus of snakes are considered the most venomous land snakes?

⑦ Which US President gave Soviet Premier Leonid Brezhnev a kiss?

⑧ In what country is the NATO headquarters located?

⑨ What is the medical name for 'a tube for withdrawing or introducing fluids'?

⑩ The 1924-28 book *Parade's End* was written by whom?

⑪ What 2002 film are the characters John Klein and Alexander Leek from?

⑫ What would you be served in a Japanese restaurant if you ordered 'shako'?

⑬ What species of whale is known for singing long, complex songs?

⑭ What is 'hexakosioihexekontahexaphobia'?

⑮ Which was the winning team in the 2013 Solheim Cup for women golfers?

⑯ What is the name of the plant tissue that gives rise to the xylem and phloem?

The Bumper PUB Quiz Book
Quiz 276

1. In what state in the USA will you find a town named Christmas?

2. What member of English royalty worked as a Spartan reconnaissance vehicle commander?

3. What was the nickname of the first plane to break the sound barrier?

4. What is another name for continental glaciers?

5. In *Harry Potter*, what is Harry's godfather's name?

6. Which season begins with the vernal equinox?

7. Which of these farm animals comes from the Andes mountains: camel, deer, llama or turkey?

8. Winston Churchill ordered the restocking of which animal at Gibraltar in 1942?

9. What kind of animal is Samson in the 2006 film *The Wild*?

10. Benin borders which of the following countries: Angola, Burkina Faso or Cote D'Ivoire?

11. What 2007 NME Award did Lily Allen win?

12. What did Spain call the divisions of its conquered land in the Americas?

13. What river flows through Cambridge, UK?

14. What do Microsoft call their slide creation software?

15. Which Dutch artist was so unrecognized in his lifetime that almost nothing is known about him today?

16. What nationality is Arsenal coach, Arsene Wenger?

The Bumper *PUB* Quiz Book
Quiz 277

1. Who directed the 2014 film *The Equalizer*?

2. What company produced the first hand-held calculators?

3. What vegetable, other than a pumpkin, is sometimes carved into a jack-o-lantern?

4. In what year did American bombing of North Vietnam begin?

5. On a piano, what does the left-hand pedal do?

6. How long is the periodical cicada life span from egg to adult?

7. What type of animal is an arctic tern?

8. In *Fushigi Yugi*, which two members of the Suzaku 7 are never killed?

9. Elizabeth I ascended the English throne in which year?

10. What lake was formed when the Akosombo Dam was built in Ghana?

11. Early Grand Prix cars used a combination of benzene, alcohol and: aviation fuel, diesel or methanol?

12. Which Nobel-Prize-winning author wrote *Disgrace*?

13. In which country would one find the largest concentration of impact craters due to meteoroids?

14. What is the capital of the British Virgin Islands?

15. Which drink brand uses the slogan 'What's the worst that could happen?'

16. What was Usain Bolt's world-record-breaking 100m time on 16th August 2009?

The Bumper PUB Quiz Book
Quiz 278

1. According to Ohm's Law, what would the resistance be in a circuit of 40 volts and 8 amps?

2. What 3D image is made by splitting a laser light into two beams through a silver mirror?

3. Baklava is a traditional food of which country?

4. In a helicopter, what does the 'collective' control?

5. Which of these countries was not a member of the Quadruple Alliance established in 1815: Britain, France, Prussia or Russia?

6. Complete this U2 song title, *Hold Me, Thrill Me, Kiss Me*?

7. Which 19th century painter was Pablo Picasso's artistic idol?

8. Which film won the Best Picture Oscar for 1976?

9. Which city of Germany is famous for its world-class marzipan?

10. What medal did Lucian Bute receive at the 2001 Francophonie Games?

11. On which date was Richard III killed in battle?

12. Gujarat, Manipur, Assam and Punjab are states in what country?

13. Who wrote the 1953 book *Go Tell It on the Mountain*?

14. The film *Rocky III* was directed by whom?

15. What does Plato's work *The Republic* describe?

16. Under British rule, Myanmar was once a part of what nation?

The Bumper *PUB* Quiz Book
Quiz 279

1. Which device is fitted to the exhaust system of a motor vehicle in order to reduce toxic emissions from the engine?

2. Which organization acts as the bank of last resort to countries in financial trouble?

3. Who directed and starred in the 2003 western *Open Range*?

4. Which scientists received the Nobel Prize for discovering the structure of DNA?

5. What term is used to describe the split in the Christian church in 1054?

6. What are the major ingredients in beer?

7. What kind of 'buttons' are named in a 2005 Broadcast album title?

8. Which female player joined the English Football Hall of Fame in 2014?

9. What is the capital city of Fiji?

10. Whom did President John F. Kennedy appoint COMSAT President in 1963?

11. Charles I ascended the English throne in which year?

12. What did Sir Arthur Conan Doyle think was his best Sherlock Holmes story?

13. What name does the 'B' stand for in the name of US President Rutherford B. Hayes?

14. 'Starry Night' was painted in 1889 by which famous artist?

15. Which mythical hero of the Trojan war founded the Roman people?

16. In which country does the word 'strand' mean beach?

The Bumper *PUB* Quiz Book

Quiz 280

1. For what is Indra Devi best known?

2. Which film won the Best Picture Oscar for 2005?

3. What club did Real Madrid beat in their first match of 2014?

4. What was the name of Joey and Chandler's pet chicken on *Friends*?

5. At the end of 'Smells Like Teen Spirit', how many times does Kurt Cobain yell 'A denial'?

6. Pizza margherita is considered to be a part of which cuisine?

7. Where in Asia can you find the two adjacent islands of Coloane and Taipa?

8. What is Adobe's video-effects software called?

9. Which fashion designer's family name means 'king' in Chinese?

10. What type of disease does the adenovirus cause?

11. Where was Anne Frank born?

12. What is the name of the pub located at one end of *Coronation Street*?

13. Which capital city lies 8,727 feet above sea level in the mountains of Colombia?

14. In anatomy, what does 'buccal' mean?

15. In what year are the earliest swords known to have been made: 1300 BC, 1400 BC or 1500 BC?

16. Which underwater animal is reputed to live the longest?

The Bumper *PUB* Quiz Book
Quiz 281

① What number of the alphabet in alphabetical order is the letter 'W'?

② Which two European countries share Mont Blanc as their highest point?

③ Which are the four largest Balearic islands?

④ Where can you find 'pulp' in the body?

⑤ Which band features Robert Smith as the lead singer?

⑥ Which studio made the film *Chicken Little*?

⑦ What is the more common name for the Helvetian Mountains?

⑧ Which ingredient can change a dry martini into a wet martini?

⑨ Where was golf's Vijay Singh born?

⑩ When the acronym was first chosen, what did 'ARM' originally stand for in the CPU name?

⑪ What is used on roofs to reduce storm-water run-off and to keep the roof cool: asphalt, grass or tar?

⑫ What is the currency of Morocco called?

⑬ Which company produces the concealer make-up called 'CX'?

⑭ What party was Tony Blair the leader of when he became Prime Minister?

⑮ What kind of bird is an 'ani'?

⑯ What is the trapping of the sun's solar energy and radiation called?

The Bumper PUB Quiz Book
Quiz 282

1. Emmental cheese is best known for what?

2. Who was the first screen actor to play Dracula in a tux and cape?

3. Han Myeong Sook became the first female Prime Minister of which country in 2006?

4. In *Thunderball*, where was James Bond originally assigned to go?

5. Which of these is a record label founded by Dizzee Rascal: Boyo, Dirtee Stank or Vexed?

6. Actor Nicholas Hoult made his film breakthrough in which movie?

7. What is the name commonly used to refer to the University of Paris?

8. Who is the Roman goddess of chastity?

9. Which spiritual system was founded by Li Hongzhi in 1992 in China?

10. What was the name of the Spanish fleet sent to invade England in 1588?

11. What colour flame does potassium burn with?

12. What are indigenous bards and performers called in West Africa?

13. How is the island of Bahrain connected to Saudi Arabia?

14. In what year was Alan Shearer named captain of the England national team?

15. What does a king cobra use to immobilize and kill its prey?

16. How many tablespoons of butter are there in one pound of butter?

The Bumper *PUB* Quiz Book
Quiz 283

1. Who became notorious for trying to blow up the English Houses of Parliament?

2. What percentage of table salt is sodium by weight?

3. Which European country has Vietnamese as an officially recognized minority language?

4. What field of mathematics are John Tukey and David Blackwell interested in?

5. The educational system of medieval England resembled that of which ancient city: Athens, Cairo or Rome?

6. Which drink brand uses the slogan 'Live young'?

7. According to the International Flat Earth Society, where is the hub of the world?

8. Which song by the band Sevendust repeats the word 'save' throughout the song?

9. In 2005, soccer great Ronaldo became co-owner of what international racing team?

10. What do you call an Arctic plain with permanently frozen subsoil?

11. What is Alyson Hannigan's annoying catchphrase in the film *American Pie*?

12. What does 'importune' mean?

13. What's the term for the weight of air pushing down on the Earth's surface?

14. Which actor played d'Artagnan in the 2011 *Three Musketeers* film?

15. What did family females do to their faces when a man died in Ancient Egypt?

16. What country did fruit cake originate in: America, Ancient Egypt, Ancient Greece or Japan?

The Bumper *PUB* Quiz Book
Quiz 284

1. What is the Sun's age estimated at?

2. What nationality is former World Boxing Champion Alex Arthur?

3. Who wrote *Alice's Adventures in Wonderland*

4. Which is the oldest independent country in Africa?

5. Somers Island is the former name of what island nation?

6. Which one of the following best describes the Norwegian government: Colony Of Sweden, Constitutional Monarchy or Sovereign Republic?

7. Which country was the only new member to join the EC in the 1981 enlargement?

8. What is an 'erf', in South Africa?

9. Which of these best describes how light travels: in capsules, in circles, in leaps or in waves?

10. In 1997, Nelson Mandela organized a National Day of Solidarity with which people?

11. What is the Italian word for 'dessert'?

12. Why did Austin Powers punch Expedition's mother?

13. Which airport can be reached directly using the westbound Piccadilly line on the London underground?

14. Mark Ronson worked with Domino on what 2007 song?

15. Of these Asian countries, which one does not have access to the sea: Cambodia, Nepal, Pakistan or Syria?

16. Who painted *Nighthawks*, a view of 'Phillies Diner' at night?

The Bumper *PUB* Quiz Book
Quiz 285

1. Which golfer won the European Tour Order of Merit every year from 1993 to 1999?

2. The 2011 comedy *Take Me Home Tonight* was written by former writers for which TV show?

3. What type of light radiation from the sun can damage the skin?

4. In what English county is Stonehenge located?

5. What is the medical term for a reshaping of the ear?

6. Where do the 'fish swim' in Sam Sparro's *Black and Gold*?

7. What fashion designer was shot dead in the streets of South Beach in Miami?

8. Which Canadian province has the most breweries?

9. Aspirin went on sale as the first pharmaceutical drug in which year?

10. Which are the Benelux countries?

11. The Spanish brought billiards to America. When and where did this occur?

12. What does 'pelagic' mean?

13. In which Sydney suburb was the block of apartments that was home to the characters of *Number 96*?

14. Other than a drink, what is a 'nog'?

15. A district in which Dutch city was mistakenly bombed by the RAF in March 1945?

16. What do you call a fractional number whose decimal representation never terminates?

The Bumper *PUB* Quiz Book
Quiz 286

1 How many *Rings of Power* were there in *The Lord Of The Rings*?

2 How much do the cremated ashes of the average person weigh?

3 What is the normal body temperature for a sheep?

4 What young people's movement was chosen to lead Mao's Cultural Revolution?

5 In 1956, Mandela was one of how many charged with treason for supporting the Freedom Charter?

6 A pea is which part of the plant?

7 The airport code PAR designates which European airport?

8 In what year did Stephen first become King of England?

9 In which language did the word 'acrobat' originate?

10 What is the driest continent on Earth?

11 What 2007 Amy Macdonald song shares its name with an American city?

12 How many pairs of ribs are in a typical human body?

13 What causes the Earth's varying seasons?

14 What sport returned, as an event, to the 1984 Summer Olympics?

15 What are the two colours of Bahrain's flag?

16 Eric the Red, the Viking, was born during which century?

The Bumper *PUB* Quiz Book
Quiz 287

① Which country uses the dong as its currency?

② What is Alcatraz?

③ Which family of mammals does the quokka belong to?

④ What is a Benedictine monk allowed to own?

⑤ Who is the character that smokes a pipe in *Alice in Wonderland*?

⑥ In a duck confit, the duck meat is preserved in what ingredient?

⑦ What is an 'ague'?

⑧ Which Spanish town is situated on the coast called 'Finisterre' in the British shipping forecast?

⑨ What year was the sci-fi book *A Clockwork Orange* first published?

⑩ Who plays Mr Popper in the film *Mr Popper's Penguins*?

⑪ In what gymnastic event did Kim Zmeskal win her only Olympic medal?

⑫ What does AOL stand for?

⑬ Which is the largest wine-growing region in Germany by area?

⑭ Who postulated that the process of stimulated emission in atoms must exist?

⑮ The Huguenots in France had their rights taken away by the revocation of what document?

⑯ What is the Eagle bone whistle?

The Bumper *PUB* Quiz Book
Quiz 288

① What do you call the image pick-up chip device on a camera?

② In which country would you find the spectacular Millau Viaduct?

③ The United States bought the Louisiana Purchase from what country in 1803?

④ Which Britpop duo released *West End Girls* in 1986?

⑤ In Japan, what is an 'eta'?

⑥ What is the largest living bird in the world?

⑦ Which Hindu goddess is depicted with money and seated on a lotus leaf?

⑧ In Sir Arthur Conan Doyle's *The Adventure of the Dancing Men*, what are the 'dancing men'?

⑨ What was the first event of the 2013-14 PGA Tour Season?

⑩ Who led the Palestine Liberation Organization (PLO) from 1994-2004?

⑪ Which shark is considered the most dangerous?

⑫ Which South-East Asian country's highest elevation point is Bukit Pagon?

⑬ In what European country is the 2006 film *The Lives of Others* set?

⑭ What kind of food is 'filleted finney'?

⑮ Which 20th-century female novelist and short story writer wrote *Ethan Frome*?

⑯ What is any permanent change to a gene called?

The Bumper *PUB* Quiz Book
Quiz 289

1. How many 'bits' are there in a 'byte'?

2. In what year did the French Revolution begin?

3. What discredited science studied skull shape and bumps to predict personality traits?

4. What is the main Jewish holy scripture called?

5. What mountain range is traversed by the highest railway in the world?

6. In the animated feature *Mulan*, who does Mulan substitute for in the fight against the Huns?

7. What year did Germany win the World Cup held in Switzerland?

8. What light-absorption phenomenon creates the sugar in grapes?

9. Which Roman emperor succeeded Tiberius in 37AD?

10. In 1066, King Harold fought battles at Hastings and at which lesser-known location?

11. Which fashion designer's daughter starred on MTV's *Rich Girls*?

12. What work was the poodle originally bred for?

13. What term is used to name the main character in a story?

14. What Mediterranean country has the capital Nicosia?

15. What does the Latin expression *caveat emptor* mean?

16. What type of transmission medium is used for TV?

The Bumper *PUB* Quiz Book
Quiz 290

1. In which country would you say 'Auf Wiedersehen' to say 'goodbye'?

2. Which country does the chorizo sausage come from?

3. What is the name of the city famous for the white cliffs that can be seen gleaming from afar?

4. Who was the original drummer for The Beatles?

5. What is another name for the vitamin B1?

6. Which 2010 British movie opened in 2014 as a West End stage show in London?

7. A young male horse is called a what?

8. Which boxer defeated Ricky Hatton's brother, Matthew, in a 2011 fight?

9. How tall is Mount Kilimanjaro?

10. What is the waxy covering on plant leaves?

11. Which of these is a drug that kills bacteria and other germs: antimicrobial, epidural or anaesthetic?

12. Which New York hotel has been home to writers William S. Burroughs, Tennessee Williams, and Allen Ginsberg?

13. Which US President did Nelson Mandela support during his impeachment hearings?

14. Which *In Bruges* character says 'I hated history, didn't you?'?

15. Who was US President immediately prior to Barack Obama?

16. What do we call the amount of space a solid figure takes up?

The Bumper *PUB* Quiz Book
Quiz 291

① How many gifts are there in total in *The Twelve Days of Christmas*?

② What name was given to seven French poets who applied Greek and Roman forms to create new poetry?

③ Raphael's 'School of Athens' features all but which famous figure?

④ On which continent is Israel located?

⑤ What duo rose to fame with their 2014 hit *#SELFIE*?

⑥ Is Indira Gandhi related to Mohandas Gandhi?

⑦ What planet does Europa orbit?

⑧ Prior to 1984, how many Summer Olympics had made a profit?

⑨ How is the constellation *Scorpius* known in English?

⑩ Who wrote *Tom Jones*?

⑪ Which Oceania country's highest elevation point is Mount Wilhelm?

⑫ Which English monarch was born in November 1600?

⑬ What country's calendar includes the Years of the Rat, Monkey, and Sheep?

⑭ In what year was Diet Coke first introduced?

⑮ What is a 'sea breeze'

⑯ Who distributed the 2008 film *Twilight*?

The Bumper *PUB* Quiz Book
Quiz 292

1. Which former Soviet Republic was known as the 'Bread Basket of the Empire'?

2. Who is this series named after: 1, 1, 2, 3, 5, 8?

3. Which country is Great Barrier Island part of?

4. Who won the Men's Singles at the 2013 US Open tennis tournament?

5. What spread the Black Death through Medieval Europe?

6. In which James Bond film does Bond not drive a car?

7. What was the number 1 UK single from the Sugababes' album *Three*?

8. What is a wine bottle that holds 1.5 litres (51 fl oz) of wine known as?

9. What medical term means 'within the body'?

10. What is the literal meaning of the cocktail 'caipirinha'?

11. According to the US government, how much of an adult's calorie intake should come from fat?

12. What animal is a large, flightless, nocturnal, solitary parrot from New Zealand?

13. Mandela was awarded his Bachelor's degree in what year: 1932, 1942, 1960 or 1986?

14. Who is the main culprit in the book *The Da Vinci Code*?

15. Which UK supermarket uses the slogan 'Saving you money everyday'?

16. Which body part does a butterfly use for tasting?

The Bumper *PUB* Quiz Book
Quiz 293

1. Which is the busiest British railway station outside London?

2. On *Friends*, what was the favourite film of Ross, Joey and Chandler?

3. Which of these did Thomas Gainsborough paint: Blue Boy, Green Boy or Yellow Boy?

4. The Netherlands finished second in which three World Cups?

5. In what year did King George V die?

6. Who is the Greek god of war?

7. The toe of what creature is used in the witches' brew from *Macbeth*?

8. What is the main ingredient in falafel?

9. What breed of dog is known for the playful way it uses its front feet: boxer, Maltese or sausage-dog?

10. Who was Henry VIII's last wife?

11. Matters related to what sense are referred to as olfactory?

12. Who was US President immediately prior to Jimmy Carter?

13. What is the pH of a .1 M solution of HCl?

14. What country is bordered by Somalia, Ethiopia, Tanzania and Uganda?

15. In medicine, what does 'enteric' mean?

16. What is the English translation of the Japanese plane built specifically for World War 2 kamikaze attacks?

The Bumper *PUB* Quiz Book
Quiz 294

1. What was Linford Christie's gold-winning 100m time in the 1992 Olympics?

2. Which herb of the parsley family has feathery leaves and smells like liquorice?

3. Who was the first foreigner to rule in China?

4. What is the busiest railway station in the world?

5. What did Henri Nestlé originally manufacture?

6. If you are working your obliques, what part of the body are you working?

7. What is the largest animal that lives at the North Pole?

8. Who finished 2nd at the 2012 Masters after a 2-hole, sudden-death playoff?

9. What is the name of the bar in *The Pina Colada Song*?

10. Which country uses the taka as its currency?

11. The ending theme for *Frasier* mentions 'tossed salads and...' what?

12. What art form was invented by the Phoenicians: glass-blowing or painting?

13. In mathematics, what is a 'point'?

14. Which was not a fortress of Sauron in *Lord Of The Rings*: Barad Dur, Dol Guldur or Minas Anor?

15. Which Trojan prince was made cup-bearer of the gods?

16. What percentage of the earth's water is drinkable?

Quiz 295

1. What is an electrical tracing of the heartbeat or heart rhythm called?

2. If a person has been defenestrated, what has happened to them?

3. In what year was the dwarf planet Eris discovered?

4. Who wrote the sci-fi book *Solaris*?

5. How were Mustafa Rizi, Kemal Ataturk and Mustafa Kemal connected?

6. Which was the subtitle of the first Nintendo 64 *Zelda* game?

7. A grown-up female pig is called a what?

8. Tippett, Britten, Elgar, and Stanford are all composers from what country?

9. How many different types of vitamins are there?

10. Which of these is not a name for the former Russian capital on the Baltic Sea: Leningrad, Petrograd, St. Petersburg or Stalingrad?

11. The US Open Cup annual soccer tournament was originally called what?

12. What is the term for the Earth's crust where it underlies oceans?

13. According to a 1649 decree, what type of clothing could Japanese peasants wear?

14. Who challenges Andie to a step battle in the film *Step Up 2: The Streets*?

15. How long did Saturnalia last?

16. With which country does Chile share the world's third-longest border?

The Bumper *PUB* Quiz Book
Quiz 296

1. What number must be multiplied by 8 to get 152?

2. What type of particle is a beta particle?

3. Which creature squirts blood from its eyes at its attackers?

4. Who won the 1966 World Cup?

5. What is the largest country in Africa?

6. Which South African Prime Minister was considered the architect of apartheid?

7. What do Samoan tattoo artists use to apply their designs?

8. Who played Chief Miles O'Brien on *Star Trek: Deep Space Nine*?

9. Which two regions of France are famous for their Grand Cru vineyards?

10. What is the body's main source of energy?

11. In which continent can you find the Amazon River?

12. What is the portion of wine that evaporates during the ageing process called?

13. The Huguenots of France can attribute their religion to which reformer of the Catholic Church?

14. When did the US sign the Oregon Treaty with the British?

15. Which famous biker did *CSI* actor George Eads portray in a 2004 movie?

16. What microorganism causes the development of Lyme's disease?

The Bumper *PUB* Quiz Book
Quiz 297

① Which country has the oldest democratic parliament still in use?

② What is the national flower of Bangladesh?

③ What is 'humus'?

④ Victor Hugo's 'The Hunchback of Notre Dame' is set in which city?

⑤ How much did each of the RMS *Titanic*'s anchors weigh?

⑥ In which Australian wine region is the winery 'Poet's Corner' located?

⑦ In Scotland, what was a 'cottar'?

⑧ What is unusual about Colombia's Magdalena River?

⑨ Which was the subtitle of the first original Game Boy Advance *Zelda* game?

⑩ Which team knocked Sweden out of the 2012 IIHF World Championship?

⑪ Over what people did Montezuma reign as emperor?

⑫ Which film won the 2011 Academy Award for Best Picture?

⑬ What is the Czech word for beer?

⑭ What are organisms that make their own food in a food chain called?

⑮ In 2011, which band began recording their first studio album since 2007's *Era Vulgaris*?

⑯ In architecture, what does 'CAD' stand for?

The Bumper PUB Quiz Book
Quiz 298

(1) What was the name of the world's first communications satellite?

(2) Which Arab country's flag has a green cedar tree in its centre?

(3) Of the four kinds of fire extinguishers, which one would you use on a Class B fire (liquid)?

(4) Revlon produce what kind of products?

(5) In 1973, Rita Mae Brown wrote which novel?

(6) If I 'peregrinate', what am I doing

(7) You can find Great Salt Lake in which US state?

(8) Carnitas are a food item of what type of cuisine?

(9) What name was given to a celebration in honour of a victorious Roman military leader?

(10) How would you describe a disease of unknown cause in medical terms?

(11) In 2013, who became the first snooker player to defend his World Championship title since 1996?

(12) What were 'Mulberries' in World War 2?

(13) Which of these countries has the highest population density: China, India, Japan or Monaco?

(14) What 2013 film starred Robert De Niro, Amanda Seyfried and Diane Keaton?

(15) In what year did the first McDonald's restaurant in the UK open?

(16) Where in New Zealand is Cathedral Cove?

The Bumper *PUB* Quiz Book
Quiz 299

① Which country has Beijing as its capital city?

② What year does The Louvre Palace in Paris date back to?

③ Which nation in south-eastern Asia gained its independence from France in September 1945?

④ Which iPhone model superseded the iPhone 4?

⑤ Who wrote *Salem's Lot*?

⑥ Who became Germany's leader upon the death of Adolf Hitler?

⑦ Now it is no longer a 'planet', what is Pluto?

⑧ What electronic component, critical to modern computers, was first demonstrated in 1947?

⑨ Who does Oscar winner Javier Bardem play in the film *Skyfall*?

⑩ What is *Oplatek*?

⑪ Which Flemish painter was famous for painting buxom women?

⑫ What is the tendency of Earth's rotation to deflect objects right or left called?

⑬ Brandy, Creme de Cacao and cream make what drink: brandy Alexander or brandy spritzer?

⑭ Who was the first female Pharaoh of Egypt?

⑮ Paul Westerberg was the front man for which band, originally named The Impediments?

⑯ How many cars started the 2005 Formula One United States Grand Prix?

The Bumper *PUB* Quiz Book
Quiz 300

1. What element has an atomic number of 14?

2. A 'sparkling' wine is generally characterized by what?

3. Which British island's highest elevation point is Snaefell?

4. Who wrote *Oscar and Lucinda*?

5. To any astronaut, what is an EVA?

6. In *A Charlie Brown Christmas*, who plays the innkeeper?

7. In what year did the *Melbourne Herald* cease publication as a separate newspaper after 150 years: 1970, 1980, 1990 or 2000?

8. What does *ne plus ultra* mean, when used in English?

9. What food additive is an artificial form of the Japanese 'umami'?

10. Where was the first permanent American colony established by English settlers?

11. Which film won the 2010 Academy Award for Best Picture?

12. Titicaca, in Bolivia and Peru, is South America's largest example of which type of body of water?

13. How many original members were there in the Backstreet Boys?

14. Who scored the only own goal of UEFA Euro 2012?

15. Which American art gallery has Constable's sketch of 'The Lock'?

16. Who was the Russian czar assassinated in 1881?

The Bumper *PUB* Quiz Book
Quiz 301

① In 1997, Hong Kong returned to what country's rule?

② What disease swept through London, closing down all playhouses from 1592 to 1594?

③ What was the first species to be removed from the US Endangered Species list?

④ Fendi is a fashion line from which country?

⑤ What is the typical alligator's natural lifespan?

⑥ Which golf term is defined as 'the position of the ball after it comes to rest'?

⑦ What continent is Egypt located on?

⑧ What is the Greek alphabet equivalent of the letter 'i'?

⑨ For how long did the Byzantines resist the Turkish siege in 1453?

⑩ What cooking herb comes in lemon, woolly and silver varieties?

⑪ What type of website is Monster.com?

⑫ In *Apocalypse Now*, what is Colonel Kilgore's first name?

⑬ Amy Macdonald wrote the song *This Is the Life* after seeing what band?

⑭ What religion was outlawed by the Tokugawa shogunate to help Japan remain isolated?

⑮ Who wrote the book *The Head of the House of Coombe*?

⑯ What is the only navigable river located in Iran?

The Bumper *PUB* Quiz Book
Quiz 302

1. Who is the historical figure Temujin better known as?

2. At whose 'Annual Hootenanny' did the Kooks play in 2006?

3. Which stimulant do chocolate and coffee have in common?

4. If you are wearing Speedos what sport are you likely participating in?

5. To blanch a vegetable, you immerse it briefly in what?

6. The Sino-Japanese war was fought between Japan and which country?

7. What is the Lebanese currency called?

8. Which Middle Eastern country's highest elevation point is Jabal Ram?

9. Who turned down the captain's role in 1981's *Das Boot* so he could appear in the film *Blade Runner*?

10. Who wrote *Dinner at the Homesick Restaurant*?

11. In which fluid-filled cavity do organs develop in organisms such as earthworms?

12. What is Jean Valjean's prisoner number in *Les Miserables*?

13. Who founded the first formal laboratory of Psychology at the University of Leipzig in 1879?

14. What did Frida Kahlo say was in both her life and all of her work?

15. How many cats are eaten in Asia each year?

16. Which Asian country has a total area of 11.39 square miles (29.5 square kilometres)?

The Bumper *PUB* Quiz Book
Quiz 303

① What is the capital city of Mali?

② Jack and Rose are the main characters from which film?

③ West Germany played Holland in the World Cup final in which year?

④ Under which category of architecture does Beaux Arts fall?

⑤ *Middle Of The Road* was a catchy, hard-rock hit by which female-led Brit band?

⑥ In wine, what does the adjective 'sec' mean?

⑦ In what city is the National Assembly of Wales debating chamber?

⑧ What breed of cat is known for swimming?

⑨ Where did 'jerk' seasoning originate?

⑩ What are the two primary crops grown on the Indo-Gangetic plain in India?

⑪ The world's first formula for beer was recorded by which people?

⑫ What airline's 747 was blown up by a terrorist bomb over Lockerbie, Scotland, in 1988?

⑬ What star cluster, known as the 'Seven Sisters', shows evidence of planet formation?

⑭ What spirit is made by fermenting molasses?

⑮ What honorary position did Alfred, Lord Tennyson hold from 1850?

⑯ What type of treatment is 'shiatsu'?

The Bumper PUB Quiz Book
Quiz 304

1. In which country did the Industrial Revolution take place?

2. What was the storage capacity of IBM's first hard disk drive?

3. Which future monarch was born at St James's Palace in April 1662?

4. In Philippine cuisine, what is lechon?

5. In what sport is the term 'redpointing' used?

6. Who wrote *Heart of Darkness*?

7. In what year was the English monarchy restored, following the English Civil wars?

8. In the film *Son In Law*, what is Pauly Shore's character named?

9. What two doctors discovered the tuberculosis vaccine?

10. What currency did the Portuguese people use until 2006?

11. What is the maximum possible break in snooker?

12. Over two-thirds of Bolivia is occupied by what type of geographical terrain?

13. Ceviche, a citrus-marinated seafood salad, originated in what South American country?

14. Which film actor appeared in *Friends* episode *The One With The Rumour*?

15. What is a dispersion of fine particles of a solid or liquid in a gas called: Aerosol, dew, diode or seed?

16. The average beluga whale grows to be about how many feet in length as an adult?

The Bumper *PUB* Quiz Book
Quiz 305

① Tallinn is the capital of which country?

② The bottom 80% of US earners account for what percentage of US wealth?

③ What is the official language of Suriname?

④ Which body part of a human senses light information?

⑤ What is a *sabayon*?

⑥ In *Star Wars: Revenge of the Sith*, where is Padme's funeral?

⑦ Which term describes moulded bands that encircle pottery vessels?

⑧ The fans of the Ferrari Formula One race team are called what?

⑨ How many bytes are in a kilobyte?

⑩ Which Aegean Island's previous volcanic eruption may have produced the Atlantis legend?

⑪ A 'frappé' is a drink that always contains what ingredient?

⑫ Which World Cup's stolen trophy was recovered by a dog named Pickles?

⑬ What cellular organelles produce proteins?

⑭ What is the name of Odysseus' loyal wife?

⑮ Who wrote the book *American Jihad*?

⑯ In which French department can you find Chartres Cathedral?

The Bumper *PUB* Quiz Book
Quiz 306

1. What country is notorious for video game addiction?

2. What is the largest island fully encompassed in the Baltic Sea?

3. What layer of the skin is just below the surface?

4. Which UK band had a US hit with the song 'Glycerine'?

5. In which year was the Suez crisis?

6. What is the most common genetic defect in Cavalier King Charles Spaniels?

7. Russia, the United States and the United Kingdom all share which flag colours?

8. Which is the longest river in Canada?

9. Which famous singer played the Green Fairy in *Moulin Rouge!*?

10. Where is the Parthenon?

11. If something tastes 'astringent', how does it taste?

12. What was George Clooney's character called in *E.R.*?

13. Tennis originated in which country?

14. The 'Mona Lisa' was painted by whom?

15. In the 1950s, Ho Chi Minh led a revolution against which country's occupation?

16. How do you 'season' a new pan before you cook in it?

Quiz 307

1. Which company is associated with the BRAVIA brand of high-definition LCD TVs?

2. What year did 'Butterball' turkeys begin to be used for US Thanksgiving dinners?

3. How old must a person be to serve as an elected local councillor in England?

4. What is the name of the part of government that actually produces money?

5. Which fashion designer directed the film *A Single Man*?

6. The residents of Perth, Australia, saluted astronaut John Glenn in 1962 by doing what?

7. In what year did John become King of England?

8. Which medical condition did both Julius Caesar and Alexander the Great have?

9. Which of these is a colourless, flammable liquid used as a solvent: Acetone, camphor or ether?

10. On a prescription medication, what does the abbreviation b.i.d. mean?

11. Roy Lichtenstein's paintings most resemble what style of illustration?

12. Which capital city lies near the mouth of the Rewa River?

13. Who was Zeus' Roman counterpart?

14. What was the first race of the Formula One 2014 season?

15. Which sports brand uses the slogan 'Just do it'?

16. On what day of the year does Halloween occur?

The Bumper *PUB* Quiz Book
Quiz 308

1. What is 360 rounded to the nearest 100?

2. Which of the following is a chelonian: hedgehog, porcupine or tortoise?

3. Eight of the world's ten highest peaks are found in what nation?

4. Brazil's long coastline is along which of its borders?

5. Which word is used to refer to a female dog?

6. What, on your face, is your 'snoot'?

7. What country's revolution started when troops fired on demonstrators in St. Petersburg?

8. What film is an adaptation of a Henry Fielding novel: *Lawrence Of Arabia* or *Tom Jones*?

9. Which owl is the rarest: barn, screech, snowy or wood?

10. In 1865, what drug did Mariani wine contain?

11. How are a map and a model alike?

12. Who was the third US President?

13. Who won the 2014 FIFA World Cup?

14. What *Wire in the Blood* detective is played by Nicola Walker?

15. What colour is the cross on the Finnish flag?

16. Which Brazilian supermodel, formerly in a long relationship with Leonardo DiCaprio, became the spokesperson for Chanel No. 5 in 2014?

The Bumper *PUB* Quiz Book

Quiz 309

1. What is the political party of French Prime Minister, Manuel Valls?

2. 'Win In Africa With Africa' was the theme of which World Cup?

3. Who starred in *Freddy vs. Jason*?

4. Which country hosted the 1958 World Cup?

5. Who wrote the 1985 book *White Noise*?

6. Which of these is an Afghani mountain range: Hari Kush, Hindu Kush or Kabul Dari?

7. Which metal has the lowest atomic number?

8. Petrified wood is an example of what type of petrification fossil?

9. Which Gnarls Barkley album features his hit song *Crazy*?

10. In 1997, which comet came closer to the Earth than it will until the year 4397?

11. In what year was the UK's National Gallery established?

12. In music, what speed is 'presto'?

13. What group of Caribbean islands has Roadtown as its capital?

14. Qantas is the flag-carrier airline of which country?

15. What is the westernmost capital of Africa?

16. The Ono fish, caught off the coast of Hawaii, is what type of fish?

The Bumper *PUB* Quiz Book
Quiz 310

1. Who was the computer pioneer who popularized the term 'debugging' for fixing software?

2. A 'zwitterion' is a neutral molecule that can enter both positive and negative ionic states – true or false?

3. Which vitamins are water-soluble: B and C, A and D or A and E?

4. Originating in Colombia, the Putumayo is a tributary of which larger river?

5. What strong Hawaiian coffee is named after a town on the island of Hawaii?

6. One of the Queen's duties is to send messages to people celebrating what significant birthday?

7. What note of the major scale is 'sol'?

8. In medical terms, what does the suffix '-lysis' mean?

9. What country suffered a 10-year Soviet occupation: Afghanistan, China, Germany or Israel?

10. A tower named for what animal held a zoo inside the Tower of London?

11. In heraldry, what do you call a shield divided into quarters?

12. Who was responsible for the penalty against France in the Euro 2000 semi-final?

13. What would you be served in a Japanese restaurant if you ordered *takenoko*?

14. Which is a character from the film *Boogie Nights*: Amber Waves, Catherine Tramell or Sophie?

15. What is the biggest artery in the human body?

16. In what year did Richard III ascend the English throne?

The Bumper *PUB* Quiz Book
Quiz 311

1. To what does the title of *The Shell Seekers* by Rosamunde Pilcher refer?

2. What was the name of Henry Rollins' first band?

3. Which designer has a famous private yoga room in Manhattan?

4. What film includes the characters Jack Byrnes and Kevin Rawley?

5. Who was Henry VIII's fourth wife?

6. What is the primary diet of sperm whales?

7. In geology, what is 'schist'?

8. What type of computer document is a 'JPG' file?

9. Which member of royalty was shot at twice in Sydney, Australia, in 1994?

10. People of the Akan ethnic group are most likely to be found in what nation: Cote d'Ivoire, Samoa, Serbia or Zambia?

11. What was John Barnes, Liverpool FC star of the 1980s, nicknamed?

12. As of 2014, how many UK Parliamentary constituencies are there?

13. In what year were the terms 'weblog' and 'weblogger' added to the Oxford English Dictionary?

14. What Mali ruler's wealth astounded Egyptians during his pilgrimage to Mecca in 1324?

15. Which other dog breed does the whippet most resemble?

16. What do you call a Mexican dish made of a tortilla filled with melted cheese and folded in half?

The Bumper *PUB* Quiz Book
Quiz 312

1. How many vertebrae are there in a giraffe's neck?

2. What is the energy released from the sun called?

3. Which was the last barbarian group to come into the central valley of Mexico around 1325: Aztecs, Incas or Mayans?

4. When one suffers from Plantar Fasciitis, what part of the body is hurting?

5. How many blocks of bluestone is it thought originally made up Stonehenge?

6. Who painted the famous picture of Napoleon crossing the Alps?

7. Which English ale is nicknamed 'the dog'?

8. Where did Ancient Greeks believe was the home of the gods?

9. What playing card has the greatest value when playing Blackjack?

10. Which Stuart monarch was the father of two future Queens of England, Mary II and Anne?

11. Where are the Petronas Towers, officially opened in 1999?

12. Who wrote *Tinker, Tailor, Soldier, Spy*?

13. What is the medical term for gas produced in the bowel?

14. What is the name of the popular browser made by Mozilla?

15. K.J. Choi is a native of which country?

16. In which 2001 film did Kurt Russell play the character Michael Zane?

The Bumper *PUB* Quiz Book
Quiz 313

1. Where were Lhasa Apso dogs originally bred?

2. What do you call a computer program that reproduces itself over a network?

3. The ingredients of the Scottish dish Haggis are boiled in what container?

4. Who played Randle McMurphy in the film *One Flew Over the Cuckoo's Nest*?

5. What is the return paid on savings deposits called?

6. Whose claim to the Falkland Islands do the UK and US not recognize?

7. What note of the major scale is 'mi'?

8. Who were Madonna's two major collaborators in her early years?

9. To the nearest million, how many square miles does the Sahara Desert cover?

10. How many pounds are there in 64 ounces?

11. Which country replaced Colombia in hosting the 1986 FIFA World Cup?

12. Who is the Greek god of metalworking and crafts?

13. How would you say 'relating to the skin' using a medical term?

14. In what year was the Eiffel Tower completed in Paris?

15. 78% of the earth's atmosphere is composed of which gas?

16. What type of dentist specializes in root canals?

The Bumper *PUB* Quiz Book
Quiz 314

1. 'Jambon' is the French word for what food?

2. What was tinsel originally used for in France?

3. What is the name of the King in the film *Madagascar*?

4. Situated on the southern slopes of the Pyrenees, Andorra has which capital city?

5. How is the pulmonary artery located compared to the pulmonary vein?

6. This act from Germany released the infectious novelty hit *Da Da Da*. Who were they?

7. What Turkish troops were the Sultans' household troops and bodyguards during the Ottoman Empire?

8. What were the Red House and the Red October Plant in World War 2?

9. Which French artist painted pictures to celebrate Bleriot's first flight across the English Channel in 1909?

10. Who wrote *The Code of the Woosters*?

11. On which continent is Tajikistan located?

12. Geologically, what is a 'pudding stone'?

13. Medically, what is the 'pes'?

14. What is the flavour of the Turkish national drink, Raki?

15. Which African country's highest elevation point is Mont Nimba?

16. Where did Muhammad Ali train from the 1970s through to his retirement?

The Bumper *PUB* Quiz Book

QUIZ 1

1. 2kg (4.4lb); 2. Austria; 3. 1988; 4. Thar; 5. South America;
6. Afghanistan; 7. Butterfly or moth; 8. An audio file; 9. George
Costanza; 10. It contains a harmful chemical; 11. Berlin; 12. North
Korea; 13. 21; 14. A sweet-flavoured syrup drink; 15. Mary Kay Ash;
16. 1959

QUIZ 2

1. Egyptian; 2. A Tibetan gazelle; 3. A saltwater shrimp; 4. Patrick
Swayze; 5. Asia; 6. Shirley Temple; 7. Spain; 8. A voodoo priestess;
9. Nigeria; 10. Northern Ireland; 11. *Kako*; 12. Footlights; 13. Saturn;
14. A nerve cell; 15. Emitter, collector; 16. *The Holiday*

QUIZ 3

1. Djibouti City; 2. Forward; 3. Amphibians; 4. Genlock; 5. Human
slaves; 6. To play smoothly, without pauses between; 7. Eva Mendes;
8. William I; 9. Three; 10. Sake; 11. Sani Abacha; 12. Denver; 13. Nine;
14. China; 15. Doris Lessing; 16. Red blood cell

QUIZ 4

1. Umbria; 2. James I (also known as James VI of Scotland); 3. Four;
4. Uday Hussein; 5. Nile; 6. Harold Faltermayer; 7. Rome; 8. Bras; 9. 10
years; 10. Kraeusening; 11. 12; 12. Looking sullen; 13. Hypha; 14. The
gluteus maximus; 15. Paraguay; 16. One take

QUIZ 5

1. House of Commons or House of Lords; 2. 1616; 3. France; 4. Five
per cent; 5. Sea urchin; 6. John Betjeman; 7. Onions; 8. Chris
Froome; 9. A sugar; 10. Leonardo DiCaprio; 11. She committed
suicide; 12. Apparition; 13. Bird; 14. Glacial ice ridge; 15. 1929;
16. Hydroelectric power

The Bumper *PUB* Quiz Book

QUIZ 6

1. Gielgud Theatre; 2. Dhaka; 3. Fort Wilderness; 4. Emerald;
5. International Article Number; the book's barcode; 6. 70 per cent;
7. *Serendipity*; 8. Robert Walpole, 1st Earl of Oxford; 9. Leslie Cheung;
10. J Michael Straczynski; 11. *Close My Eyes Forever*; 12. Shoes or
boots; 13. Nicosia; 14. Coarse; 15. Alexander Graham Bell; 16. 4

QUIZ 7

1. Electroencephalogram; 2. World War 1; 3. Grenadine; 4. Lycanthropy;
5. Lob; 6. Gertrude; 7. America Ferrera; 8. Auto Union Deutschland
Incorporated; 9. Pa'anga; 10. OneRepublic; 11. Bird; 12. Mexico;
13. Slow; 14. Ivan IV's private army; 15. Africa; 16. Medicine

QUIZ 8

1. Vomiting; 2. 2; 3. 6; 4. Amstel; 5. Lactose intolerance; 6. 1974;
7. Ferdinand and Isabella; 8. Tom Brokaw; 9. A finger callus;
10. *Godzilla*; 11. Libya; 12. Mozambique; 13. Youtube.com; 14. Blogger;
15. Wine from hybrid vines; 16. Earth

QUIZ 9

1. Venice; 2. *Bohemian Rhapsody*; 3. United Kingdom; 4. Browser;
5. Chocolate; 6. Italian; 7. France; 8. Bad breath; 9. Bantu-Hamitic;
10. Rabbits, hares and pikas; 11. Edward Cullen; 12. The medieval
name of Wales; 13. Cayman Islands; 14. AD; 15. Narwhal; 16. Fuseli's
'The Nightmare'

QUIZ 10

1. Gangtok; 2. Waterloo Barracks, in the Jewel House; 3. 1154;
4. Gingivitis; 5. Kublai Khan; 6. *The Ides of March*; 7. Yellow and black;
8. Clavicle; 9. Renee; 10. Analytic and synthetic; 11. 2; 12. Brittany;
13. The Yellow Sea; 14. Cloth; 15. Aaron Sorkin; 16. Beethoven's 9th
Symphony

The Bumper *PUB* Quiz Book

QUIZ 11

1. 1935; 2. Yemen; 3. Kangaroo; 4. The Lost City; 5. Ralph Bunche;
6. Smiling; 7. Carl Diebitsch; 8. Kiran Desai; 9. Monumental gateways
to the acropolis; 10. Empire Stadium; 11. Single-celled freshwater
alga; 12. Daniel Berta; 13. Espresso with whipped cream; 14. CCCP;
15. Philip II; 16. Dragonfly

QUIZ 12

1. *Cuckooland*; 2. Nassau, Bahamas; 3. 32; 4. 1958; 5. Springerle;
6. Lord Howe Island; 7. Up to 36mph (58km/h); 8. Its skin rolls from side
to side; 9. Orange; 10. Chicken; 11. 18; 12. 70 AD; 13. Virginia Woolf;
14. Brussels; 15. Regeneration; 16. Ore

QUIZ 13

1. 40; 2. *Million Dollar Baby*; 3. 36.5-37.5C (97.7-99.5F); 4. Tweezers;
5. Prime Meridian; 6. 12 yards; 7. Senegal; 8. *She Is*; 9. Lizard; 10. Nine
days; 11. June 30, 1940; 12. Tetley's; 13. Lake Burley-Griffin; 14. Arte
Povera; 15. May; 16. Troposphere

QUIZ 14

1. Rafael Nadal; 2. The Philippines; 3. Turkey; 4. Paul Gauguin;
5. Quantum mechanics; 6. Bay of Bengal; 7. Guar/Indian bison; 8. *The
Alienist*; 9. Swollen lymph nodes; 10. 1066; 11. Flambé; 12. *MDNA*;
13. Gentlemen's Quarterly; 14. Svein Heglund; 15. *Contagion*;
16. Napoleon himself

QUIZ 15

1. William S. Burroughs; 2. Corolla; 3. 1995; 4. Isle of Man; 5. Electron;
6. Colombia; 7. Native South African spear; 8. Round 10; 9. *I'm Not
Really a Waitress*; 10. Riverdance; 11. Ibrahim Agha; 12. Melbourne,
Australia; 13. 1992; 14. South Africa; 15. 1942; 16. Black sapote

The Bumper *PUB* Quiz Book

QUIZ 16

1. Cessation; 2. Jamaica; 3. Fulgencio Batista; 4. Archimedes; 5. Asia;
6. Loch Lomond; 7. *The Machinist*; 8. Philip II; 9. A whip; 10. The British
Museum; 11. Iceland; 12. *Warehouse*; 13. Sebastian Zbik; 14. Women;
15. A concentration camp; 16. Gold

QUIZ 17

1. Bosnia & Herzegovina; 2. 4 times; 3. Flushes; 4. Liv Tyler; 5. Clowns;
6. Qatar; 7. France; 8. Uruguay; 9. Lloyds; 10. 18 cm (7 inches); 11. The
Conqueror; 12. 1422; 13. An axe-like tool with a curved blade; 14. ATP;
15. A month; 16. Ken Kesey

QUIZ 18

1. Sand; 2. *In The Rough*; 3. Prague; 4. Swimming; 5. Baldness;
6. Mexican; 7. Seattle; 8. Inclined plane; 9. Denmark; 10. 24; 11. Beirut;
12. 20; 13. North-west India and south-east Pakistan; 14. 6; 15. Casey
Jones; 16. Japan

QUIZ 19

1. Acceleration; 2. Polder Gothic, or Dutch Brick Gothic; 3. Tunisia;
4. Anne; 5. *Cats*; 6. Biplane; 7. Roberto Benigni; 8. Narrative; 9. Bradley,
Voorhees & Day; 10. Tim Cook; 11. Max Immelman; 12. Joey; 13. A
type of thin, unleavened bread; 14. Robert H. Goddard; 15. Kenneth
Kaunda; 16. 1950

QUIZ 20

1. Hopping; 2. Lake Baikal, Siberia; 3. A round, shallow laboratory
dish; 4. Macadamia; 5. Seether; 6. Belisarius; 7. Yevgeny Kafelnikov;
8. Charles I; 9. Successor to the Prophet; 10. One third; 11. Phillips;
12. *The Shield*; 13. Cabret; 14. Silver; 15. Singapore; 16. A type of
reflecting prism

The Bumper *PUB* Quiz Book

QUIZ 21

1. Georges Pompidou; 2. Dolph Lundgren; 3. He was too old; 4. Fear of dirt or contamination; 5. Pepper; 6. North Korea; 7. 1963; 8. San Jose; 9. Sylvester Stallone; 10. Amber Valletta; 11. The Millennium Dome; 12. John Grisham; 13. 2 hours; 14. Green Park; 15. *Out Of Season*; 16. Tuborg

QUIZ 22

1. Church; 2. South Pacific; 3. Spider-Man's best friend's dad; 4. Saliva; 5. Easter Island; 6. Asia; 7. MPEG 1 or MPEG 2 layer 3; 8. 1970; 9. *The Frogs*; 10. Livia Firth; 11. Chimpanzee; 12. Lois McMaster; 13. Nellie Bly; 14. Cottage cheese; 15. 186,000; 16. Serbia

QUIZ 23

1. The Ting Tings; 2. Arthur Agatston; 3. Maserati; 4. Eight; 5. Red poppy; 6. Oil; 7. Sugar; 8. Bridgetown; 9. Anyang; 10. Henri Cartier-Bresson; 11. Ceremonial anointing; 12. Pollination; 13. Saint Lucia; 14. 20-30mph (32-48km/h); 15. Panama; 16. The Sun

QUIZ 24

1. Merkel; 2. Email; 3. Stan Lee; 4. Zambia; 5. Hanoi; 6. Aaliyah; 7. Lesotho; 8. Royksopp; 9. Opossum; 10. January to March; 11. Salmon; 12. Abraham Lincoln; 13. A reference to prior text; 14. A witch's familiar; 15. Boxing; 16. Elba and St. Helena

QUIZ 25

1. The Kodiak Bear; 2. Amaterasu; 3. *A Midsummer Night's Dream*; 4. Brian Jones; 5. Denmark; 6. Streaming; 7. Spain; 8. More speed; 9. May; 10. The mongols; 11. 1066; 12. Play very loudly; 13. *Cursed*; 14. Christopher Le Brun; 15. Iranian rial; 16. Potatoes and onions

The Bumper *PUB* Quiz Book

QUIZ 26

1. Earthquakes; 2. *2Pacalypse Now*; 3. *Hannibal*; 4. Fijian dollar;
5. Sierra Leone; 6. Jupiter; 7. Sauerkraut; 8. A tone-mixing painting technique; 9. Rupee; 10. Shakti; 11. 25cm (10 inches); 12. John Brunner; 13. Middle East; 14. Ian McKellen and Derek Jacobi;
15. Benetton; 16. Cleopatra's Needle

QUIZ 27

1. Stretching exercises; 2. Cetaceans; 3. The United Nations;
4. Daughter's wedding; 5. Flat-bottomed cargo transport; 6. Goddess of compassion; 7. For soliciting; 8. Acidosis; 9. *Acrobat Reader*; 10. It allows the wine to breathe; 11. Mercury; 12. India; 13. Continental shelf;
14. Sean Connery; 15. Rainforest and savanna; 16. Small rabbit relative

QUIZ 28

1. United Kingdom and Argentina; 2. 1984; 3. Tomato; 4. Songs;
5. Sleuth; 6. Switzerland; 7. Mars; 8. Harold Wilson; 9. Four-wheeled horse-drawn carriage; 10. Dinner; 11. 2012; 12. Japan; 13. Asunción;
14. Five; 15. Kyle; 16. 1.85m (72.8 inches)

QUIZ 29

1. 2008; 2. Fluoride (sodium fluoride, for example); 3. Dim sum;
4. Norway; 5. Denmark; 6. Brasilia, Brazil; 7. Albert Ellis; 8. Allies and Axis; 9. Palaeontology; 10. Lamb; 11. Humidity and temperature;
12. Bulgaria; 13. 16K and 48K; 14. Harold Holt; 15. Turnip; 16. New York

QUIZ 30

1. 4096; 2. Bolivia; 3. Harare; 4. True; 5. Amethyst; 6. St George's Chapel, Windsor; 7. Germany; 8. Margaret Thatcher; 9. Orange;
10. *Lysistrata*; 11. *You*; 12. One; 13. Lionel Messi; 14. *Angelina*; 15. A trigonometry function, the reciprocal of a cosine; 16. Malawi

The Bumper *PUB* Quiz Book

QUIZ 31

1. 1968; 2. Bradley Wiggins; 3. Saint Martin; 4. Nuuk; 5. *Curiosity*;
6. Dark comedy; 7. An end to racism; 8. Charlemagne; 9. Pollen;
10. Islam; 11. *Luna 3*; 12. 50 Cent; 13. Saskatoon; 14. Robert de Niro;
15. Supercalifragilisticexpialidocious; 16. Fried Meat

QUIZ 32

1. Forest person; 2. Worcestershire Sauce; 3. Crécy, France;
4. Invertebrates; 5. Anne; 6. Per Fess; 7. A puddle; 8. Hungary; 9. Berlin;
10. Jack Penate; 11. Fort de France; 12. Scafell Pike; 13. Mitosis;
14. Zen; 15. Salvador Dali; 16. Hufflepuff

QUIZ 33

1. Hotwired.com; 2. Margaret Thatcher; 3. Winston Churchill;
4. Pennines; 5. Eighteen; 6. Burkina Faso; 7. Ferrule; 8. Egypt;
9. Gravity; 10. Egypt; 11. Adjusting the space between letters;
12. Patisserie; 13. 1.07m (3ft 6in); 14. Josh Lucas; 15. London;
16. Ultrasonic

QUIZ 34

1. Jersey; 2. *Logic Pro*; 3. 97,000; 4. Gulf of Aden; 5. Bacon, sausages
and potatoes; 6. Spain; 7. The Hanoverians; 8. Madrid; 9. Vince
Vaughn; 10. 14 months; 11. String theory; 12. Thunder, lightning and
war; 13. 1954; 14. Boublil and Schönberg; 15. 1948; 16. A pulpit

QUIZ 35

1. Edwards syndrome; 2. Hydrogen; 3. Reese Witherspoon; 4. The
laari; 5. Murray; 6. Phil Mickelson; 7. John Major; 8. Robin Williams;
9. Guinea pig relative; 10. Halloween Town; 11. Sinker fund; 12. Be
Missing; 13. China; 14. Atoll; 15. One year; 16. Mosquito

The Bumper *PUB* Quiz Book

QUIZ 36

1. Flavoured wine; 2. Geology; 3. Hurricane; 4. Fly solo across the Atlantic; 5. Autobots; 6. A dolphin; 7. Egypt; 8. Jerry Dammers; 9. Goat; 10. Malossol; 11. Opal Fruits; 12. Punchdrunk; 13. Anne; 14. Nectar; 15. Muamer Hukic; 16. South of London

QUIZ 37

1. Canada's; 2. Leather; 3. The dentist; 4. Roman Catholic; 5. Earth; 6. Scott Fahlman; 7. David Tennant; 8. Hamilton, Ontario; 9. Your entire body; 10. Roll Deep Crew; 11. Pressure; 12. A prehistoric stone implement; 13. *The Departed*; 14. Mexico; 15. A cloud of gas and dust in outer space; 16. Jamie Oliver

QUIZ 38

1. Shah; 2. A desert; 3. South Africa; 4. Miniature; 5. *Unchained Melody*; 6. Medusa; 7. Jane Austen; 8. Peter Rubens; 9. Snail; 10. A voodoo god; 11. Biscotti; 12. *Cinderella*; 13. Light red; 14. Tijuana; 15. Ginkgo; 16. 1189

QUIZ 39

1. Venus Williams; 2. Chemistry; 3. Green; 4. Ahmed Qurei; 5. Sir Robert Borden; 6. Alison Krauss; 7. Egypt; 8. Cats; 9. Baghdad Hotel; 10. Microburst; 11. Matthew McConaughey; 12. Bacchus; 13. *The Fisher King*; 14. Travis; 15. Kangaroo; 16. Praiseful

QUIZ 40

1. 34; 2. Geologist; 3. Orange; 4. Atheist; 5. 70; 6. Jakarta; 7. Dr Pepper; 8. Digital Versatile Disc; 9. A biscuit; 10. Bar Mitzvah; 11. The Turks; 12. Ronaldinho; 13. The giant squid; 14. 1969; 15. Mauritania; 16. Molly Jensen

The Bumper *PUB* Quiz Book

QUIZ 41

1. Red; 2. *No Strings*; 3. Balboa; 4. Bedrock; 5. Small Computer Systems Interface; 6. Vladimir Putin; 7. Eggs; 8. Scandinavia; 9. 11; 10. Joaquin Cosio; 11. David Kay; 12. Facebook.com; 13. Stamp collector; 14. Arachne; 15. Mike McCallum; 16. Painting

QUIZ 42

1. Valery Bykovsky; 2. Dead tissue from a lack of blood supply; 3. Dehydration; 4. Something capable of stopping a wound from bleeding; 5. Breathe; 6. Playwright; 7. *You've Got Mail*; 8. 26; 9. Illinois; 10. 1982; 11. Tearing; 12. Mexico; 13. The Scoville Scale; 14. Adamstown; 15. A compressed image; 16. Snowdon

QUIZ 43

1. Port Vila; 2. A composer; 3. Headache; 4. Endymion; 5. Orange; 6. Four; 7. In a carafe; 8. Earth; 9. Roman baths; 10. Jonathon; 11. 88 days; 12. Jade Emperor; 13. A 17th-century poem form; 14. 1904; 15. A bull used in bullfighting; 16. Peter O'Toole

QUIZ 44

1. Canadian; 2. 44; 3. Kremlin; 4. New York City; 5. Mu; 6. *The Outsider*; 7. *The King of Limbs*; 8. *Snow Flower and the Secret Fan*; 9. Queen; 10. Moray eel; 11. Raphael; 12. Paid fines; 13. Claudius; 14. Dairy group; 15. Twelve; 16. Hear you scream

QUIZ 45

1. Christmas Island; 2. The lower part of a wall, if differently decorated; 3. Friedrich Engels; 4. Grumio; 5. Blubber; 6. Scott; 7. Athena; 8. Opossum; 9. Hello; 10. Chord; 11. 1957; 12. Curved; 13. Grapefruit; 14. Celine Dion; 15. Webb Simpson; 16. 2005

The Bumper **PUB** Quiz Book

QUIZ 46

1. Chelsea FC; 2. Germany; 3. Ant; 4. Cornmeal (maize flour); 5. 1978;
6. Whales; 7. The ancient capital at Pegu in the south of Burma;
8. Venice; 9. 2,123,562 square miles (5,500,000 square kilometres);
10. Vasco Nunez De Balboa; 11. J.D. Salinger; 12. *Jade Warrior*;
13. Rainforest; 14. A South American dish of marinaded raw fish; 15. 30
million; 16. Gonzo

QUIZ 47

1. 1970; 2. Pine cones; 3. Covent Garden; 4. Little Boy; 5. Sana'a;
6. Pinhead; 7. Herbs are specifically from leafy plant parts; 8. Dublin,
Ireland; 9. Popular objects; 10. 4; 11. Felipe Calderon; 12. 1939;
13. Front left side; 14. T; 15. Sapphire; 16. Iraq

QUIZ 48

1. Aubergines, olives and onions; 2. Sissy Spacek; 3. South Africa;
4. The Day; 5. Mary II; 6. Swedish; 7. Entered data on punched
cards; 8. Jimmy Connors; 9. Pastel; 10. Dali; 11. Chick; 12. An uncle;
13. Moccasin; 14. Queen Charlotte; 15. High heat; 16. Michael Shaara

QUIZ 49

1. Comic toast; 2. 1988; 3. Yes; 4. The Pauli exclusion principle;
5. Zoroastrianism; 6. Sausage; 7. Astronomy; 8. Pierre Cardin;
9. George R. R. Martin; 10. California; 11. 1920; 12. Red; 13. Greece;
14. Motorcycles; 15. Hugh Laurie; 16. Andorra

QUIZ 50

1. Winston; 2. Raiders of the Lost Ark; 3. Tornado intensity; 4. Milky
Way; 5. British; 6. Tab; 7. Spider/arachnid; 8. Macavity; 9. Very dry;
10. Dwight D. Eisenhower; 11. Stone; 12. Iron; 13. Rayo Vallecano;
14. The Savoy; 15. Brighton; 16. 1776

The Bumper *PUB* Quiz Book

QUIZ 51

1. Rwanda; 2. Brownout; 3. Two; 4. Ireland; 5. Jägermeister; 6. Carolus Linnaeus; 7. Riddick; 8. Linda Evangelista; 9. Fruit cake; 10. A dentist; 11. Rome Fiumicino; 12. Gorilla Sign Language (GSL); 13. Heart; 14. Peru; 15. 57; 16. Ben Macdui

QUIZ 52

1. 7.5 volts; 2. 2; 3. Skopje; 4. Tip; 5. Insects; 6. Hit it; 7. Sotheby's; 8. 1946; 9. Max; 10. David Hyde Pierce; 11. Li Na; 12. Tin; 13. Spanish Town; 14. Eduard Shevardnadze; 15. Mince; 16. Mushrooms

QUIZ 53

1. Vodka, and coffee liqueur such as Kahlua; 2. Away from the kerb; 3. Death of tissue; 4. Atlantic City Country Club, 1898; 5. *Arthur*; 6. A queen; 7. Agriculture; 8. Barbados; 9. A work in relief; 10. African clawless otter; 11. Jamaica; 12. Sari; 13. Anthony Minghella; 14. Boddingtons; 15. Ontario; 16. *HMS Hood*

QUIZ 54

1. Tony McCoy; 2. Washington, DC; 3. Walker Percy; 4. Kingston, Jamaica; 5. Klimt; 6. Dorsal fin; 7. Darwin; 8. Guadalcanal; 9. 332 BC; 10. Dr. Mae Jemison; 11. Japan; 12. Colditz Castle; 13. Bodega; 14. North Korea; 15. Former unit of weight; 16. 8

QUIZ 55

1. Andy Murray; 2. The Beatles' song *Lucy in the Sky with Diamonds*; 3. Fascist; 4. Econet; 5. Brazil; 6. Love Kraft; 7. European Space Agency; 8. Still life; 9. Yellow; 10. Fyodor Dostoyevsky; 11. 1976; 12. USA; 13. Tim Curry; 14. Batman Begins; 15. Orange; 16. Tennis

The Bumper *PUB* Quiz Book

QUIZ 56

1. Seven; 2. England; 3. Rice; 4. *A Link Between Worlds*; 5. Hyperbaric chamber; 6. Diego Rivera; 7. The Green Goblin; 8. Santo Domingo; 9. *Wuthering Heights*; 10. 14th; 11. Anemometer; 12. Japan; 13. Egypt; 14. Mercury; 15. 1781; 16. Liev Schreiber

QUIZ 57

1. Vatican City; 2. 150000; 3. Zucchini; 4. 1980; 5. William V; 6. Osborne House; 7. Red Bull; 8. *The Passion of The Christ*; 9. Viscosity; 10. Curtis Strange; 11. Apple pancake; 12. 1958; 13. Bactrian camel; 14. Thomas; 15. Norway; 16. Extremely short breed of horse

QUIZ 58

1. Ethiopia; 2. 3 Years; 3. 26; 4. State treasury; 5. Antarctica; 6. Argentina; 7. Oxygen; 8. John and Mary; 9. The emperor; 10. Communist; 11. Kevin Smith; 12. Acorn; 13. The Kardashians; 14. Intermittent; 15. 70 feet; 16. Om

QUIZ 59

1. Salt; 2. 65; 3. Sir Arthur Conan Doyle; 4. Panama; 5. Mars; 6. Takes the Knight Bus; 7. Stale bread; 8. Macy's department store; 9. Chimpanzee; 10. Benigno 'Noynoy' Aquino III; 11. *Dummy*; 12. Henry III; 13. To stop a car by puncturing tyres; 14. English; 15. Rembrandt; 16. Williams

QUIZ 60

1. Eight; 2. 1979 and 1984; 3. Edinburgh Castle; 4. 9 cars; 5. No; 6. Christina Crawford; 7. 22; 8. Stanford; 9. 1995; 10. Very dry; 11. 50,346; 12. Mohandas; 13. James II; 14. Saudi Arabia; 15. Gris; 16. China

The Bumper *PUB* Quiz Book

QUIZ 61

1. Deciduous; 2. Divergent; 3. Base of the brain; 4. Monteverdi;
5. Nyx; 6. 1976; 7. Daniel Ortega; 8. Lorient, France; 9. *The Lord of the Rings: The Return of the King*; 10. Brisbane; 11. *The Iceman Cometh*;
12. Stephen Sondheim; 13. Pope Francis; 14. Iceland; 15. Tapestries and engravings; 16. Whipped cream, raspberries, toasted oatmeal, honey and whisky

QUIZ 62

1. Vatican City; 2. A direct current; 3. Migrate; 4. 221b Baker Street;
5. Argentinos Juniors; 6. 1979; 7. The freedom to make it will;
8. Polyjuice potion; 9. 0; 10. *Party*; 11. *Lincoln*; 12. Tomato; 13. Pinot Grigio; 14. Physical strength; 15. In a free-flowing style, without precise timings; 16. 21 years

QUIZ 63

1. Flute; 2. Jet Li; 3. Transnistria; 4. El Niño; 5. 1931; 6. John Surtees;
7. Australia; 8. Close range; 9. 12 to 19 miles (20 to 30km); 10. Empty, or empty-headed; 11. Cuba; 12. Inductive coupling; 13. 330,000 times;
14. Latvia; 15. That Petrol Emotion; 16. Carcinogenic

QUIZ 64

1. Goose feathers; 2. Lentils; 3. In Papua New Guinea; 4. 1968;
5. Martin Amis; 6. A chilled Spanish soup; 7. 1997; 8. Sugar; 9. His bodyguard; 10. Good Luck; 11. *The Congo*; 12. Poland; 13. A facade;
14. Two; 15. A medieval French poetry farce; 16. Earth-centred

QUIZ 65

1. Sixty; 2. Supplying towns with water; 3. April 25th; 4. The Scottish or Irish Gaelic language; 5. 1314; 6. West Germany; 7. Brazil; 8. Castanets;
9. 191; 10. *The Fly II*; 11. S; 12. Snake; 13. Porto-Novo; 14. Rioja;
15. Rihanna; 16. Supernova

The Bumper *PUB* Quiz Book

QUIZ 66

1. Ski holidays; 2. 141m (465ft); 3. France; 4. Giselle; 5. Triangular; 6. Ice cream; 7. Ruth Negga; 8. AB; 9. Rooster; 10. 15; 11. The Mullanes; 12. Omicron; 13. Ojibway; 14. Helium; 15. 1849; 16. *The Tempest*

QUIZ 67

1. Augustus Pugin; 2. Mascarpone; 3. Westerberg High; 4. Ridge on the surface of the cerebral cortex; 5. Ireland; 6. 1980s; 7. Frog; 8. *Holinshed's Chronicles*; 9. Axons; 10. Queen's Gallery; 11. A Hindu saint or sage; 12. The Sun; 13. Clarifying; 14. Bruno; 15. Enrique Pena Nieto; 16. Santiago

QUIZ 68

1. Screwdriver; 2. 48; 3. 5.87 trillion; 4. Denali National Park; 5. Las Vegas; 6. Hieronymus Bosch; 7. *The Cafe Racers*; 8. Algae; 9. A train; 10. 14; 11. Dominoes; 12. Groundnut or peanut oil; 13. 1968; 14. Harold Macmillan; 15. 1981; 16. Colonel Harlan Sanders

QUIZ 69

1. Wimbledon; 2. Numbing a small part of the body; 3. Tuvalu; 4. Adore life; 5. A menorah; 6. A small orchestra or symphony; 7. Potatoes; 8. Worthy Farm, Glastonbury, Somerset, UK; 9. Chile; 10. Canards; 11. Seismologist; 12. Politics; 13. Mosquito; 14. Awry; 15. Two; 16. Getúlio Vargas

QUIZ 70

1. Han; 2. Cream cheese; 3. 1994; 4. 2; 5. Bamboo; 6. Colonel Nasser; 7. *Bend It Like Beckham*; 8. French officials; 9. Doug Bradley; 10. Longest; 11. Plants; 12. Overconfident; 13. 1946; 14. Slowly unfolding; 15. 1910; 16. 8

The Bumper *PUB* Quiz Book

QUIZ 71

1. Gauchos; 2. Chemotherapy; 3. https; 4. Atacama; 5. Yasser Arafat;
6. Afghanistan; 7. Morden; 8. Clement V; 9. 331 weeks; 10. Olive oil;
11. Monterrey; 12. Local bacteria are required; 13. Stephen Sondheim;
14. Trade winds; 15. Blood disorder; 16. Hawk

QUIZ 72

1. Yeast; 2. Amelia and Oliver; 3. Major axis; 4. A narcotic painkiller;
5. Canada; 6. Jeer loudly to express disapproval; 7. The Vatican;
8. 112mph (180km/h); 9. Optical mouse; 10. August and September;
11. *White Chalk*; 12. Jean Francois Millet; 13. Manuel Neuer; 14. Sally
Field; 15. Nicaragua; 16. IBM

QUIZ 73

1. China; 2. The Bible; 3. Mount Fuji; 4. Netherlands; 5. P!nk;
6. Phoenicians; 7. 1928; 8. An annoyed grimace; 9. Nouakchott;
10. Tiresias; 11. George Washington's; 12. Dionysus; 13. Kingfisher;
14. 1937; 15. Pacific; 16. Puss-in-boots

QUIZ 74

1. First Prime Minister Of Israel; 2. Kritios Boy; 3. Uniform Resource
Locator; 4. 50 frames a second; 5. 4000; 6. 16th; 7. A long, sarong-like
garment; 8. North America; 9. Chevy; 10. The Little Dog; 11. Phoenix;
12. The Alps; 13. Joe Don Baker; 14. 11; 15. The Space Shuttle;
16. Skewer

QUIZ 75

1. Zebra; 2. 1821; 3. 9; 4. Gorillas; 5. Play in an agitated style;
6. Athens, Greece; 7. Lisbon, Portugal; 8. *Cat's Cradle*; 9. Botanist;
10. Fly Emirates; 11. Perugia; 12. South Africa; 13. A computer display;
14. President Ashton; 15. Althea Gibson; 16. John G. Kemeny and
Thomas E. Kurtz

QUIZ 76

1. Up; 2. Sodium hypochlorite; 3. Merlot and Cabernet Franc; 4. Scaling walls; 5. Jakarta; 6. Gustave Flaubert; 7. Wendy Makkena; 8. Beijing Capital International Airport; 9. Mary Quant; 10. Apia; 11. Brandy and Benedictine; 12. China; 13. *Super Mario Brothers*; 14. Silver Birch; 15. Louis Renault; 16. Cenozoic Era

QUIZ 77

1. 2001; 2. 8; 3. Afghan hounds; 4. Zaire, now Democratic Republic of the Congo; 5. Baidu.com; 6. Mezcal; 7. Accountant; 8. Napa Valley; 9. To burn everything/to start again; 10. Italy; 11. Benin; 12. Seismograph; 13. Edmondo Fabbri; 14. Kidney stone; 15. Ozone; 16. A martial arts school

QUIZ 78

1. Czech Republic; 2. Ions; 3. Nicolas Cage; 4. Rorschach's; 5. James Joyce; 6. Martin Luther King, Jr.; 7. Port Moresby, Papua New Guinea; 8. Twice; 9. Tsingtao; 10. Red; 11. Africa; 12. Broccoli; 13. Hermes; 14. Kate Moss; 15. Your Mileage May Vary; 16. Juvenal Habyarimana

QUIZ 79

1. Germany; 2. Peach schnapps and orange juice; 3. Myanmar/Burma; 4. Limnology; 5. Ian McEwan; 6. Love and fertility; 7. Haile Selassie; 8. Shoelace end; 9. Scotland; 10. Exoskeleton; 11. Blue; 12. Bomb; 13. Rufus Wainwright; 14. Croatia; 15. Jen hid the meaning of the Wudan; 16. Andy Warhol

QUIZ 80

1. Greece; 2. 1949; 3. Vincent van Gogh; 4. Eyelid surgery; 5. Norman Jewison; 6. Anne; 7. David Mitchell; 8. An Indian emperor of the Maurya Dynasty; 9. *I Think I'm In Love*; 10. Bread; 11. Lion; 12. 1997; 13. Scarab beetle; 14. Achilles; 15. Africa; 16. 30

The Bumper *PUB* Quiz Book

QUIZ 81

1. France; 2. Amherst College and Phillips Exeter; 3. Charles II; 4. 6502; 5. Northern South America; 6. Alto; 7. Tracks; 8. Israel; 9. Rio Grande do Sul; 10. Olga Kurylenko; 11. Arnold Palmer; 12. Iran; 13. Leeward; 14. 'Cheers!'; 15. Mason Betha; 16. 70

QUIZ 82

1. Emoticon; 2. Bull Head Mountain; 3. Milos Zeman; 4. *The Great Escape*; 5. Everest; 6. 1980; 7. Green; 8. Ivan the Great; 9. London Heathrow Airport; 10. Cu; 11. Benicio Del Toro; 12. Tanzania; 13. After the meal; 14. Ted Lowry; 15. Medium; 16. *Don Quixote*

QUIZ 83

1. 365.25 days; 2. Al-Rashid, Baghdad; 3. Four; 4. Edo; 5. The Tube; 6. Smithsonian Institute; 7. 1838; 8. *Umbrella*; 9. Shire; 10. Henry VII; 11. Five; 12. Ascot; 13. Mexican; 14. The Sydney-Hobart Yacht Race; 15. Geisel; 16. Ray Daniels

QUIZ 84

1. Greenhouse; 2. Peter I (the Great); 3. Thermostat; 4. Mountain laurel; 5. Gozo; 6. Jason; 7. 1960s; 8. Bend and straighten the knees; 9. Cut it into thin strips; 10. *The Mambo Kings*; 11. A thorn; 12. Rockwell B-1A; 13. Suharto; 14. Rotorua; 15. Paris; 16. Lucy

QUIZ 85

1. 5; 2. 27; 3. Betty Boothroyd; 4. White; 5. *Kindle*; 6. Bass; 7. 1714; 8. Papyrus; 9. Resin-flavoured Greek wine; 10. Mrs. Whatsit; 11. Three times as far; 12. A poultice; 13. Malaysia; 14. Brandy; 15. Cilantro; 16. Paella

The Bumper *PUB* Quiz Book

QUIZ 86

1. A delta; 2. Demand; 3. Robert Downey Jr.; 4. Humidity; 5. Rusty nail; 6. *Last Christmas* by Wham; 7. 1603; 8. Tang; 9. 161; 10. An aerodynamic flap; 11. Nepal; 12. Acorn Electron; 13. Banjul; 14. Dong; 15. Sherry; 16. Goldenberg

QUIZ 87

1. 1 year; 2. The Sacrifice; 3. Goalkeeper; 4. Austria; 5. 1982; 6. Crusades; 7. One Direction; 8. 1965; 9. They provide a sense of touch; 10. It is a salt lake; 11. 18; 12. *The Wind Waker*; 13. An Eye For An Eye; 14. Sharp spines; 15. Wladziu; 16. American and International

QUIZ 88

1. 40th; 2. Zebra mussel; 3. Abu Dhabi; 4. South Korea and China; 5. Queen Mary; 6. *Tuff Turf*; 7. Vincente Fox Quesada; 8. 1991; 9. United Arab Emirates; 10. 3; 11. Bordeaux; 12. Kwanzaa; 13. London; 14. Sonoma; 15. Stalagmite; 16. Pharaoh

QUIZ 89

1. Switzerland; 2. Mulberry-crimson; 3. Zimbabwe; 4. Monica Potter; 5. Study of tissues; 6. 8 minutes 20 seconds; 7. Iran; 8. 1977; 9. Poetry; 10. Leather shoes; 11. Ontario; 12. La Brigada; 13. The Moon; 14. Sixth; 15. Queen Elizabeth II; 16. Barley

QUIZ 90

1. Plants and plant extracts; 2. Kay Cottee; 3. 9 months; 4. Trojans; 5. Greg LeMond; 6. A 'sack', or 477 litres (105 gallons); 7. 15th century; 8. Lake Victoria; 9. Repeater; 10. Tearful; 11. Tomato, jalapeno pepper and coriander; 12. Potential energy; 13. 122 years and 164 days; 14. Green; 15. *Mayflower*; 16. Dot

The Bumper *PUB* Quiz Book

QUIZ 91

1. Israel; 2. Italy; 3. Australia; 4. Malaria; 5. The Philippines; 6. 1960s;
7. Evey; 8. Ion Iliescu; 9. John Smith; 10. Natural causes; 11. A woman;
12. Climax; 13. Serbia; 14. An upstart person; 15. Lord Voldemort;
16. 1840

QUIZ 92

1. Tom Daley; 2. London Bridge; 3. Adeline Virginia Stephen;
4. Moscow, Russia; 5. Gruyere cheese; 6. *A Bronx Tale*; 7. France;
8. Noble gas; 9. Russia; 10. Kavala; 11. 1910; 12. Lion; 13. Snail;
14. *Like I Love You*; 15. Red Sea; 16. Andorra

QUIZ 93

1. Cologne Cathedral, Germany; 2. 60; 3. Virgil; 4. Barbarossa;
5. Thornton Wilder; 6. Yerevan; 7. Closet; 8. 245; 9. Atlantic; 10. Papua
New Guinea; 11. Olive brine; 12. Crash; 13. The Stuarts; 14. Red;
15. Coldplay; 16. Cote d'Ivoire

QUIZ 94

1. Israel; 2. Murray Edwards college (formerly known as New Hall);
3. Collagen; 4. Portugal; 5. Iron; 6. Florence and The Machine;
7. Pino Pugliese; 8. X-Y Position Indicator; 9. Igneous, sedimentary,
metamorphic; 10. Reebok; 11. Operation Varsity in World War 2;
12. Slieve Donard; 13. Altimeter; 14. Torvill and Dean; 15. Alexandre
Dumas; 16. Decoupage

QUIZ 95

1. Balance; 2. Win the Junior Grand Slam; 3. Don Rickles; 4. Aldous
Huxley; 5. Emerald Isle; 6. Canada; 7. Neville Chamberlain; 8. Suleiman
goat; 9. Hitler and Rommel; 10. The total vocabulary; 11. Large Asian
sheep; 12. *Alvin*; 13. Vitamins; 14. Angola; 15. 1976; 16. e

The Bumper *PUB* Quiz Book

QUIZ 96

1. Horse; 2. F1; 3. Half the diameter; 4. 4; 5. Purple; 6. *Hey Venus!*;
7. The intellect; 8. Lindisfarne; 9. Thomas Hardy; 10. Spanish;
11. *Something's Got to Give*; 12. Barack Obama; 13. 60; 14. Damascus;
15. Afternoon; 16. Failure

QUIZ 97

1. United Kingdom; 2. Red; 3. Galapagos Islands; 4. Laurence
Sterne; 5. *Thor*; 6. Amelia Earhart; 7. Barley; 8. Entertainment Weekly;
9. Slovakia; 10. The Christian gospel; 11. Irish Wolfhound; 12. Jamaica;
13. *The Boxer*; 14. Elizabeth Short; 15. 2009, for *Viva la Vida*; 16. Wild
dog

QUIZ 98

1. 240; 2. Tap dancing; 3. Dolphin; 4. Cherries; 5. Each of a pair of large
muscles of the pelvis and loins; 6. 15; 7. Mozart; 8. Drake Passage;
9. Kidneys; 10. Leg; 11. Nicolaus Copernicus; 12. Excellence in
Audio Books; 13. HMS *Porpoise*; 14. Nuclear war; 15. Julia Roberts;
16. Colombia

QUIZ 99

1. Lauren Taylor; 2. *Austin Powers: Goldmember*; 3. Mount
Lamington, Papua New Guinea; 4. New Taiwan dollar; 5. Pancreas;
6. Communication; 7. The Crab; 8. France; 9. Max; 10. Ice wine;
11. Curtains; 12. Prague; 13. Tangram; 14. 1981; 15. Dominican
Republic; 16. *Hamlet*

QUIZ 100

1. Malaysia; 2. Three years; 3. Venus and Serena Williams;
4. Microclimate; 5. The Koran; 6. The Gambia; 7. Horus, the god of the
sky; 8. Laurence Fishburne; 9. Asia; 10. Tony Kanal; 11. Grasses and
shrubs; 12. Black; 13. Red; 14. Grendel; 15. Fillet steak; 16. 1970

The Bumper *PUB* Quiz Book

QUIZ 101

1. Emperor; 2. Halle Berry; 3. C.J. Cherryh; 4. The scope or bounds of something; 5. USA; 6. Celtic; 7. *Sing*; 8. Length; 9. Jamaica; 10. Financial problems; 11. Indian Ocean; 12. Nerve weakness; 13. 4,350 miles; 14. Accepted custom; 15. Bangkok; 16. Black Death

QUIZ 102

1. Three quarters; 2. Babe; 3. *Round Midnight*; 4. Teen powerlifter; 5. Australia; 6. Nero; 7. Resembling fish; 8. *Dark of the Moon*; 9. Princess Victoria; 10. Demi-tasse; 11. De Havilland Comet; 12. Desmond Tutu; 13. Eritrea; 14. Simple Minds; 15. Nick; 16. Forget-me-not

QUIZ 103

1. 3072; 2. Cristiano Ronaldo; 3. A stringed Indian instrument; 4. Broadband; 5. Bikram; 6. Arwen; 7. Bing Crosby; 8. Rome Ciampino; 9. Edgar Bronfman Sr.; 10. Blast; 11. A code name; 12. Kingston; 13. Parmesan; 14. 10 years; 15. 1968; 16. Anasazi

QUIZ 104

1. Turkey; 2. Chrysler Building, New York; 3. Kingston; 4. Qin dynasty; 5. Funeral home; 6. 1; 7. Art and Design; 8. Puffer fish; 9. *Fahrenheit 451*; 10. Silver; 11. 0; 12. Grilled meats; 13. Desdemona; 14. Brahmaputra; 15. One month; 16. 46C (115F)

QUIZ 105

1. Walrus; 2. Ecuador; 3. Los Angeles; 4. 1845; 5. Mercury; 6. Kim Dae Jung; 7. In Centennial Park, Sydney; 8. Augusto Pinochet; 9. A sweatshirt with a hood; 10. His neighbour; 11. Trial and error; 12. Sugar; 13. *Lonestar*; 14. 116 years; 15. An earthquake; 16. France

The Bumper *PUB* Quiz Book

QUIZ 106

1. England; 2. Andre Agassi; 3. 20; 4. Isaac Newton; 5. Four metal arms on his back; 6. Juneau, Alaska; 7. 1997; 8. Tequila; 9. Alternating current; 10. *Q & A*; 11. 6-pack; 12. Mexico; 13. Pussy Riot; 14. Africa; 15. Martin Cruz Smith; 16. Egypt

QUIZ 107

1. UNICEF; 2. Feelings; 3. Chief Executive Officer; 4. Hawaii; 5. Gabriel Garcia Marquez; 6. Vivacity; 7. Loss of property; 8. Biting off its head; 9. Swift, narrow ocean current; 10. Greyfriars Bobby; 11. Gyoza; 12. Rascal Flatts; 13. Hobart Zoo; 14. Pope John Paul II; 15. Italy; 16. North America

QUIZ 108

1. Population; 2. John James Audubon; 3. Esters; 4. Spain; 5. Japan and Germany; 6. 2004; 7. To care for his dying dad; 8. The Rentals; 9. 1809; 10. Violet; 11. Ari Emanuel; 12. Onion; 13. 1850-1851; 14. Lavender; 15. The Bahamas; 16. Queensland

QUIZ 109

1. WikiLeaks; 2. Melbourne, Victoria; 3. 5th Avenue; 4. Shrubs; 5. Recycling; 6. Upper Nubia; 7. Favouring peace; 8. Conservation; 9. *Freaky Friday*; 10. Heir; 11. Robinsons; 12. George Washington Carver; 13. Dino; 14. *Dirty Faces*; 15. A cat lover; 16. 42

QUIZ 110

1. East London; 2. Mary Shelley; 3. Keith Moon; 4. Netherlands; 5. 1898; 6. Reservoirs; 7. Tulip; 8. Rocks And Cacti; 9. Bill Condon; 10. Nile; 11. 1900; 12. A sweet cake; 13. Heights; 14. SARS; 15. Dark, medium-sweet sherry; 16. 2006

The Bumper *PUB* Quiz Book

QUIZ 111

1. A candle; 2. Papua New Guinea; 3. Bread and cheese; 4. Ham;
5. Paul Weller; 6. Veal; 7. *The Asphalt Jungle*; 8. *A Fortunate Life*;
9. Hybrid; 10. Less; 11. Bermuda; 12. Moderately slow and flowing;
13. His rug; 14. Camouflage; 15. The Atomic Bull; 16. Qunu

QUIZ 112

1. Germany; 2. Eight; 3. Shamrock; 4. Professor Snape; 5. James
McAvoy; 6. 500; 7. May; 8. 1958; 9. Algeria; 10. The triangle;
11. Burgundy; 12. Tyrion Lannister; 13. Fake fur; 14. Signal to other
crabs; 15. Actinium; 16. Bangui

QUIZ 113

1. Florence Nightingale; 2. .swf; 3. *Ace Ventura: When Nature Calls*;
4. *Sirius*; 5. Asia; 6. 76 years; 7. His father; 8. 1453; 9. Emile Zola; 10. A
cattle enclosure; 11. Adhesion; 12. Beach wear; 13. 10; 14. Grapes;
15. Frida Kahlo; 16. John Howard

QUIZ 114

1. Six; 2. Rebecca Jordan; 3. Fe; 4. Lebanon; 5. 1959; 6. Brown;
7. 63 days; 8. Anne Enright; 9. step dance; 10. Brunei; 11. 64
AD; 12. Minnesota; 13. Calcutta; 14. A pixel graphic; 15. Natural
carbonation; 16. Iago

QUIZ 115

1. Two per cent; 2. Foggy; 3. iPad; 4. Venezuela and Brazil;
5. Christmas Island; 6. Fox; 7. Andy Roddick; 8. *The Alexandria
Quartet*; 9. Magnesium; 10. Sixth Coalition; 11. Microsoft; 12. Nicholas
Grimshaw; 13. Black, red and yellow; 14. Sicily; 15. Your head;
16. *Can't Buy Me Love*

The Bumper *PUB* Quiz Book

QUIZ 116

1. Fewer nutrients are destroyed; 2. Cultural Anthropology; 3. *Wish*;
4. Natalia Ishchenko and Svetlana Romashina; 5. Castor and Pollux;
6. Maisie Williams; 7. 1992; 8. Twine; 9. David Fleay; 10. Messenger of
the gods; 11. Alfred Stieglitz; 12. Pork; 13. Griffith; 14. 1916; 15. The
Western (or Wailing) Wall; 16. Metre

QUIZ 117

1. 5 hours 25 minutes; 2. Short Circuit; 3. Henri De Tonti; 4. Edith
Wharton; 5. Molonglo; 6. SSRI; 7. Karl Lagerfeld; 8. Omega; 9. Dido;
10. Andes; 11. Saskatoon, Saskatchewan; 12. Zn; 13. Henry VIII;
14. Romanian; 15. Lime juice; 16. Mexico

QUIZ 118

1. Isotherm; 2. Horseradish; 3. First Canadian-born Prime Minister;
4. MTV; 5. Nitrogen; 6. 11; 7. 1901; 8. Paulie Gatto; 9. Hooligan;
10. Hair; 11. Anguilla; 12. Democratic Republic Of Congo; 13. Arpanet;
14. Vampires; 15. 9.1m (30ft); 16. Ocean of wisdom

QUIZ 119

1. 37; 2. 1973; 3. Patch of Heaven; 4. Justin Bieber; 5. 49; 6. Mexican;
7. Sue Charlton; 8. Light reflecting off the retinas; 9. October 29th,
1969; 10. Moirae, or Fates; 11. Oak; 12. 323 BC; 13. National Fire
Prevention Association; 14. Please; 15. Vienna and Budapest; 16. Title
deed

QUIZ 120

1. Alfred Hitchcock; 2. Neptune; 3. Mould; 4. Egypt; 5. AIDS;
6. Chiwetel Ejiofor; 7. Dynasty; 8. Ossicles; 9. Crete; 10. A half moon;
11. Kirsten Dunst; 12. Macau; 13. Chile; 14. Cavity; 15. Fledgling
pigeon; 16. *Clement*

The Bumper *PUB* Quiz Book

QUIZ 121

1. Eleven; 2. Georgia; 3. MC Breed; 4. 2001; 5. Tropic of Capricorn;
6. Inspector Todd; 7. Ra(dio) d(etection) a(nd) r(anging); 8. John Surratt;
9. Ctrl + left arrow; 10. Bobsled; 11. Faraday; 12. Oliver McCall;
13. Indian Ocean; 14. Herman Melville; 15. Limestone; 16. 1986

QUIZ 122

1. Shanghai; 2. 90; 3. Sandra Brown; 4. Skunk; 5. Front teeth;
6. Pheidippides; 7. Mount Bogong; 8. Alicia Silverstone; 9. Ginger;
10. James I (also known as James VI of Scotland); 11. The Moon;
12. Lionel Messi; 13. Tattarrattat; 14. Paprika; 15. Cheviot; 16. Demand

QUIZ 123

1. Denmark; 2. Steel or aluminium; 3. Fuse; 4. Sir Walter Raleigh;
5. Doux; 6. Tim Berners-Lee; 7. A computer hacker; 8. Central African
Republic; 9. Set theory; 10. Liechtenstein; 11. Manchester; 12. Jeremy
Irons; 13. 1983; 14. Ne-Yo; 15. Apathy; 16. 1989

QUIZ 124

1. Global Positioning System; 2. Genioplasty; 3. 2; 4. A woman;
5. None; 6. Brandy; 7. Allido Records; 8. A Parisian nightclub; 9. Asian
tsunami; 10. Daniel Gabriel Fahrenheit; 11. Bahrain; 12. Soviet Union;
13. Brazil and Mexico; 14. Laika; 15. Thistle; 16. Impressionism

QUIZ 125

1. The *Titanic*; 2. Four; 3. Tiny hairs; 4. Africa; 5. Peregrine falcon;
6. Smelly; 7. Wide, lace collar attached to the top of a dress; 8. Felipe
Massa's; 9. Albania; 10. *The King's Speech*; 11. 11th century;
12. American Standard Code For Information Interchange; 13. Sugar
cane; 14. Italy; 15. Conditioning; 16. Ravel

The Bumper *PUB* Quiz Book

QUIZ 126

1. Edinburgh; 2. 1999; 3. Pineau De Re; 4. Robert Metcalfe; 5. Shelly Winters; 6. Fairmont Hotel, San Francisco; 7. A childhood respiratory disease; 8. Joseph Swan; 9. One million; 10. The White Tower; 11. Thoth; 12. Coors; 13. Norway's; 14. Loss of the sense of smell; 15. Heracles; 16. Interphase

QUIZ 127

1. Sangria; 2. Richard Hakluyt; 3. Colombia; 4. Atlas Mountains; 5. An ancient Celtic alphabet; 6. Kate Beckinsale; 7. Tempera; 8. Carol Ann Duffy; 9. 89 years old; 10. Jessica Rabbit; 11. Decanting; 12. Ireland; 13. Lead; 14. Kare Kare; 15. 1990s; 16. *Agadir*

QUIZ 128

1. Uncle Vernon and Aunt Petunia; 2. Winston Churchill; 3. South; 4. Timbaland; 5. Pathway to peace; 6. Burkina Faso; 7. Lease; 8. 1960; 9. Nick Watney; 10. Seven; 11. Bartholdi; 12. Second; 13. Tropical; 14. Sloth; 15. Japan; 16. Japan

QUIZ 129

1. Game point/break point; 2. Event Horizon; 3. Coco Chanel; 4. Adelaide; 5. South Africa; 6. Cymru; 7. Plane; 8. Andy Serkis; 9. 1970s; 10. BSE/Mad cow disease; 11. Komodo dragon; 12. A watercourse; 13. Leonid Brezhnev; 14. Julia Louis-Dreyfus; 15. 3; 16. All-grain

QUIZ 130

1. Mark Cavendish; 2. 1974; 3. Makeup; 4. Kenya; 5. Being touched; 6. 1955; 7. High salt content; 8. Solomon Islands; 9. 1965; 10. Turkey; 11. Mark Zuckerberg; 12. Split Enz; 13. Erwin Rommel; 14. *Cutthroat Island*; 15. *Sirius*; 16. Joseph Conrad

The Bumper *PUB* Quiz Book

QUIZ 131

1. Electromagnetic Interference; 2. Argentina; 3. William; 4. 31;
5. £500; 6. Bhutan; 7. William Claude; 8. Hulk Hogan; 9. A circular
tent made of skins; 10. Aluminium pull-tab cans; 11. Czechoslovakia;
12. Noctiphobia; 13. Nationalism; 14. Paul Ehrlich; 15. Dupleix;
16. Flour, water, yeast and salt

QUIZ 132

1. Tegucigalpa; 2. Bull; 3. Peter Kurten; 4. Me?; 5. Zero; 6. Doves and
hawks; 7. Outhouses; 8. Roman Catholic; 9. Persian; 10. Hong Kong;
11. 1903; 12. Egg-shaped, of a leaf; 13. Vitamin D; 14. In the mountains;
15. 10; 16. Bowler

QUIZ 133

1. Israel; 2. Cocoa; 3. His wife; 4. Robbie; 5. Red; 6. Earlobes;
7. Ramesh Sippy; 8. Boris Yeltsin; 9. It died; 10. Hola; 11. Mary
Robinson; 12. Dallas; 13. Let's Go Crazy; 14. *Safari*; 15. Acceleration;
16. Forecast

QUIZ 134

1. 24 Hours; 2. 111; 3. Nubia; 4. Italy; 5. Tetrahydrocannabinol;
6. Europe; 7. Tennis; 8. His father; 9. Believe they are in front;
10. November 1963; 11. A Japanese family badge or crest; 12. Bitters;
13. Four; 14. Scholasticism; 15. Andromache; 16. Newton

QUIZ 135

1. Black; 2. Five sections; 3. Elephant; 4. Marry a divorcee; 5. A lightly
armed Irish foot soldier; 6. Quito; 7. Birmingham; 8. 1689; 9. 2005;
10. African grey parrot; 11. Coney Island; 12. 1954; 13. Patrick Stewart;
14. Sir Arthur Wellesley; 15. Nigeria; 16. Margaret Atwood

The Bumper *PUB* Quiz Book

QUIZ 136

1. Washington Monument, Washington DC; 2. Stairs; 3. Detroit; 4. War of Spanish Succession; 5. Seaweed; 6. Darth Vader; 7. *Atlantis*; 8. True; 9. Hydrogen and helium; 10. China; 11. Greece; 12. Cabbage family; 13. Central African Republic; 14. Match referee; 15. Rhododendron; 16. Four

QUIZ 137

1. *Iron Man 3*; 2. Basenji; 3. Translucent; 4. Chile; 5. You; 6. Covered with browned breadcrumbs; 7. Lorde, for *Royals*; 8. Park Geun-hye; 9. 78; 10. *The Colour of Money*; 11. Black, white, brown; 12. Starry Night; 13. General People's Congress; 14. Muslim; 15. London, United Kingdom; 16. Chimpanzee

QUIZ 138

1. 763mph (1,228km/h); 2. Frank Lampard; 3. Emperors; 4. Riyal; 5. The oceans; 6. Carol Ann Duffy; 7. *Fireworks*; 8. George Clooney; 9. Cleopatra, Queen of Egypt; 10. Keep the cauliflower white; 11. Robert de Niro; 12. 2011; 13. Helen Mirren; 14. Africa; 15. 1972; 16. Olive oil

QUIZ 139

1. Ultrasonic; 2. 8.1; 3. Cuban; 4. Bond Street and Stratford; 5. Tom Cruise; 6. Play quietly; 7. Cassius Clay; 8. Perry; 9. Harald Fairhair; 10. *I Know Where It's At*; 11. Atmosphere; 12. Norway; 13. Quidditch; 14. Jumps; 15. White; 16. Dubai

QUIZ 140

1. Doldrums; 2. Wages; 3. Czech Republic; 4. Taiwan; 5. 12; 6. The Triple Alliance; 7. *Cats*; 8. Chile; 9. Yann Martel; 10. Portugal; 11. Toupee; 12. *The 13th Warrior*; 13. Donald Faison; 14. Yesterday and Today; 15. Bowfin; 16. Doctor

The Bumper *PUB* Quiz Book

QUIZ 141

1. 23; 2. 1967; 3. *The Day the Earth Stood Still*; 4. Producing or bearing shells; 5. Hungary; 6. Hummingbird; 7. Joan of Arc; 8. Mexican; 9. Sensei; 10. Clog; 11. Tanzania; 12. Brazil; 13. Brazil; 14. Whale; 15. 1918; 16. 28

QUIZ 142

1. Gordon Brown; 2. Winchester; 3. Domestos; 4. Gizzard; 5. Frolian Gonzales; 6. Baguette; 7. Red; 8. *War*; 9. Prestwick; 10. Six; 11. Tap Clogging; 12. Ctrl + right arrow; 13. *Badger*; 14. Sir Henry Arthur Blake; 15. Arthur Balfour; 16. *The Godfather*

QUIZ 143

1. Cascading Style Sheet; 2. New Zealand; 3. Keira Knightley; 4. Juno; 5. Douglas; 6. Myanmar/Burma; 7. Spread it out for drying or bedding; 8. Arthur Ashe; 9. The ZX81; 10. A potentially dangerous fish delicacy; 11. Aldo Moro; 12. Lady Murasaki; 13. Scorpion; 14. 1649; 15. Sashimi; 16. Nose

QUIZ 144

1. Edinburgh University; 2. Clinique; 3. Bladder of a fish; 4. April; 5. Canada; 6. Osric; 7. Drawn out; 8. *Praying For Time*; 9. 22/7; 10. Michelle Obama; 11. Michael Landon; 12. They dilate; 13. Toothbrushes; 14. 1974; 15. *Romeo and Juliet*; 16. High city

QUIZ 145

1. 8; 2. Cartography; 3. *Can't Nobody Hold Me Down*; 4. Katie Holmes; 5. Death Valley, California, USA; 6. 40.5 miles; 7. Tom Watson; 8. Bruce Joel Ruben; 9. Matt LeBlanc; 10. Chess; 11. Italy; 12. *Creative Cloud*; 13. Asian; 14. French; 15. Seppuku; 16. Laces

The Bumper *PUB* Quiz Book

QUIZ 146

1. Garbage; 2. 1966; 3. 1997; 4. Ethics; 5. Charlotte Amalie; 6. Cyprus;
7. 1970; 8. Must; 9. Romania; 10. Asia; 11. Bones; 12. Scarlett O'Hara;
13. Michael Jacobson; 14. Muscle pain; 15. Iraq; 16. 43

QUIZ 147

1. 32; 2. Lake Poopo; 3. Pacific; 4. A dog; 5. Paris; 6. Lotus;
7. Hydrogen; 8. Lillehammer, Norway; 9. Angelus; 10. George
Handel; 11. Activate a nearby hydroelectric dam; 12. Monica Seles;
13. *Masterpiece*; 14. A method of preserving food by heat; 15. Vintage;
16. Without sorrow

QUIZ 148

1. C; 2. 72; 3. Earth writing; 4. Three; 5. Paramaribo; 6. Aaron Wills;
7. 4; 8. Papillon; 9. 176; 10. A semi-synthetic textile; 11. James
II; 12. Trickery; 13. Puffer fish; 14. Patio Diet Cola; 15. Hollywood
Roosevelt Hotel; 16. Pectoral fins

QUIZ 149

1. Yellow; 2. 32; 3. Jellyfish; 4. 1996; 5. Salvador Dali; 6. Russia,
Bulgaria, Romania and Turkey; 7. Sri Lanka; 8. 1976; 9. Golf; 10. A new
dog, Odie; 11. The Great; 12. In the ear; 13. Olive-Ann Burns; 14. Nancy
Green; 15. Saffron; 16. Fishing village

QUIZ 150

1. Campbell's Soup; 2. Burj Khalifa, Dubai; 3. Matavai Bay; 4. Legs;
5. Melbourne; 6. Augustus; 7. 15 seconds; 8. Mohammad Naguib;
9. A blow to the head; 10. Chile; 11. Egg, larva, pupa, adult; 12. Adam;
13. University Of Texas; 14. Dinglehopper; 15. Dust storms; 16. Thank
You and Goodnight

The Bumper *PUB* Quiz Book

QUIZ 151

1. Chickenpox; 2. John Travolta; 3. Silicon Oxide; 4. 1953; 5. 1981;
6. Mob; 7. *Chuyo*; 8. *A Moment Like This*; 9. Robert A. Heinlein;
10. Antwerp; 11. *Iron Man*; 12. Alligator meat; 13. Occipital lobe;
14. The Albert Memorial; 15. Tuvalu; 16. Holyrood

QUIZ 152

1. Horror; 2. Greenwich; 3. 0.75; 4. 1937; 5. Pomegranates; 6. Below
the surface of the earth; 7. Buttocks; 8. His childhood; 9. To illuminate;
10. Montana; 11. Republic of Ireland; 12. 7-year-old twins; 13. Babur;
14. Standard & Poor's; 15. Apron; 16. 12

QUIZ 153

1. Diuretic; 2. 36; 3. 2525; 4. A large arch; 5. Christmas yule log;
6. Dried or withered; 7. Cindy Jackson; 8. Golden-coated horse; 9. Mid;
10. Business district of La Defence; 11. Jamaica; 12. N'djamena;
13. Virginia Woolf; 14. Two; 15. Beryllium; 16. 35

QUIZ 154

1. Diamond engagement ring; 2. Iran; 3. Flower buds; 4. Gave to
slaves; 5. Tazo; 6. Yolanda; 7. John Galsworthy; 8. Bull; 9. RUF;
10. Sainsbury's; 11. Ruby; 12. Radon; 13. Athens; 14. Scarf; 15. 860;
16. Ukraine

QUIZ 155

1. *War Of The Worlds*; 2. Ecology; 3. Of a yellow tint; 4. 1551;
5. Sissy Spacek; 6. Normandy; 7. Olof Palme; 8. Barcelona, Spain;
9. Queensland; 10. Mars and Jupiter; 11. Mary, Queen Of Scots;
12. Blake; 13. Slander; 14. Niger; 15. Metering; 16. Canada

The Bumper *PUB* Quiz Book

QUIZ 156

1. Former Mexican President; 2. JavaScript; 3. Alan Rickman; 4. Chihuahua; 5. A process of mountain-building; 6. No Doubt; 7. Montevideo; 8. Jay-Z; 9. Mayonnaise; 10. Uranus; 11. *Bring Up the Bodies*; 12. Inflammation; 13. 1885; 14. Sean Connery; 15. Seoul; 16. 22

QUIZ 157

1. European Union; 2. Bechamel sauce; 3. Guy Fawkes; 4. Beginner's; 5. Baghdad; 6. Dalmatian; 7. Cucumber; 8. Elizabeth I; 9. Tasmania; 10. 1988; 11. A Paper Heart; 12. Tobacco syrup; 13. Our Nige; 14. Black; 15. Christian Bale; 16. Rwanda

QUIZ 158

1. JAVA; 2. Plums; 3. A woman who is proficient in yoga; 4. Dutch braid; 5. An alcohol; 6. 17; 7. Papyrus; 8. Billy Preston; 9. Henry VIII; 10. Archduke Franz Ferdinand; 11. Nickname of a small US torpedo; 12. Cowardly behaviour; 13. Owl's; 14. West Africa; 15. Summer; 16. Coughing and wheezing

QUIZ 159

1. Alsace; 2. An urgent need or demand; 3. Costa Rica; 4. Fidel Castro; 5. Eiffel Tower; 6. James I (also known as James VI of Scotland); 7. Its wavelength; 8. Jean-Claude Carriere; 9. Sucralose; 10. A still life; 11. 1912; 12. Two; 13. Cheetah; 14. George V; 15. DP World; 16. 90

QUIZ 160

1. 4; 2. 25; 3. Sony; 4. Electromagnetic Radiation; 5. Gulf of Aden; 6. Red; 7. Richard Trevithick; 8. Halle Berry; 9. Mexico; 10. Delta; 11. The god of marriage; 12. Paul Scholes; 13. Michelangelo; 14. Ghana; 15. Dionysus; 16. Cardinal Wolsey

QUIZ 161

1. Malta; 2. Turkey; 3. 1997; 4. Doppler radar; 5. Famine; 6. Triceratops; 7. Libreville; 8. A computer game; 9. Segway; 10. Baltimore, 1962; 11. Italy; 12. 5-7 years; 13. Neutral; 14. Bubba Watson; 15. Elk; 16. Chrome

QUIZ 162

1. 26; 2. *Apollo 11*; 3. Doris Lessing; 4. Vin Diesel; 5. Larry King and Jerry Seinfeld; 6. 4; 7. Bath; 8. Cats; 9. Sierra Leone; 10. Cliff Richard; 11. To infringe; 12. Nike; 13. St David; 14. With yeast; 15. Dogs; 16. 1923

QUIZ 163

1. Moving Picture Experts Group; 2. Hungary; 3. World Featherweight; 4. Model; 5. Andromeda; 6. 1272; 7. Jodi Foster; 8. Oceans; 9. Two; 10. Christopher Lloyd; 11. Fluorine; 12. Naan; 13. Addis Ababa; 14. A medieval full-face helmet; 15. The Globe; 16. Eric Bana

QUIZ 164

1. *Who Framed Roger Rabbit*; 2. Panama; 3. Central Nervous System; 4. Nunavut; 5. Henri Rousseau; 6. Mermaids; 7. Borodino; 8. A hula hoop; 9. Bird; 10. The feather of a phoenix; 11. Dublin Castle; 12. Albania; 13. Kenya; 14. Bad Meets Evil; 15. Ray Mancini; 16. Captain Hanson Gregory

QUIZ 165

1. 1985; 2. Rachel Carson; 3. Epoch; 4. Hydrogen; 5. It had a drainage system; 6. 1940s; 7. 'Not or'; 8. 1994; 9. Khrushchev; 10. Dr. John Styth Pemberton; 11. Golden Shoe; 12. Steve Reid; 13. Peru; 14. Italy; 15. Tirana; 16. Allonym

The Bumper *PUB* Quiz Book

QUIZ 166

1. American Airlines; 2. Zaire; 3. Uruguay; 4. 2; 5. Kahlua; 6. The main unit of currency; 7. 'Unsinkable' Molly Brown; 8. Fireplace; 9. 100; 10. Actress; 11. His Blackberry; 12. All Saints Day; 13. Blowfish; 14. Glucose; 15. P; 16. 1993

QUIZ 167

1. Leopard; 2. 1978; 3. *Queer as Folk*; 4. London; 5. In Paris in 1895; 6. Denmark; 7. Tissues; 8. Denmark; 9. Nathaniel Hawthorne; 10. A peasant or commoner; 11. Hendrik Van Houten; 12. William Wegman; 13. 500 million; 14. Semitic; 15. Furniture salesman; 16. Jimmies

QUIZ 168

1. 23.5 Degrees; 2. William Harvey; 3. Baku; 4. Dysplasia; 5. USA; 6. Playing cards; 7. A tree; 8. Haku; 9. Veronese; 10. Vesta; 11. Russian wolfhound; 12. Palatinate (Pfalz); 13. Monkey; 14. Montreal; 15. Hurricanes; 16. Amber Hill

QUIZ 169

1. 10 times; 2. Damascus; 3. Rakhee Thakrar; 4. Sweetcorn; 5. A. Escoffier; 6. 4.5 mph; 7. Beefeaters; 8. Arthur Miller; 9. 1974; 10. North America; 11. 29; 12. Afghanistan; 13. An eloquent orator; 14. 1821; 15. Abu Dhabi Grand Prix; 16. *Star Wars*

QUIZ 170

1. Famicom; 2. France; 3. Albania; 4. A genie or fairy.; 5. Tell the future; 6. Tart; 7. The narrator confesses; 8. *War*; 9. Koppen system; 10. The Tudors; 11. Weasel; 12. A causeway toll booth; 13. Saint-Denis; 14. Henri Matisse; 15. Morocco; 16. James I (also known as James VI of Scotland)

The Bumper *PUB* Quiz Book

QUIZ 171

1. Cranberry; 2. Nectar squeezed on the eyes; 3. Anti-aliasing;
4. Conger eel; 5. 13-14; 6. San Marino; 7. 1966; 8. Frank Oz;
9. Marathon; 10. Richard Nixon; 11. Comoros; 12. Bright, golden
auburn; 13. Index fossil; 14. Al-Aqabah; 15. Franz Joseph Haydn;
16. Third Geneva Convention

QUIZ 172

1. Vampire Bat; 2. 48; 3. The Dust Bowl; 4. Robert Laird Borden;
5. Gwen Stefani; 6. Johann Tetzel; 7. Purple and black; 8. Antananarivo;
9. The Soviet invasion of Afghanistan; 10. Death of Joseph Stalin;
11. White; 12. Kelsey Grammar; 13. Small, edible Japanese fish;
14. Tunis; 15. London; 16. Mali

QUIZ 173

1. Egypt; 2. Paly; 3. Argentina; 4. 17; 5. Gustav Klimt; 6. Bacon;
7. Straw bale; 8. Violeta Chamorro; 9. Dante; 10. Scanning electron
microscope; 11. Ethiopia; 12. *The Endeavour*; 13. Buck's Fizz; 14. eBay;
15. Earth; 16. 2

QUIZ 174

1. True; 2. The Southern Hemisphere; 3. Zero; 4. White and red;
5. Kir Royal; 6. Anwar Al Sadat; 7. *Motion*; 8. Canada; 9. *Overloaded*;
10. John Goodman; 11. Edinburgh; 12. 1937; 13. Mark Twain; 14. A
policeman; 15. Italy; 16. John Higgins

QUIZ 175

1. 20; 2. 36; 3. 81; 4. A large German railway gun; 5. Adenine, Cytosine,
Thymine, Guanine; 6. Ham and cheese; 7. *Stan*; 8. *Argo*; 9. The
Gilbert Islands; 10. Virginia Woolf; 11. 1275; 12. Suppresses coughs;
13. Greece; 14. First; 15. Lactase; 16. Dead skin cells

The Bumper *PUB* Quiz Book

QUIZ 176

1. Indonesia; 2. Tropic of Capricorn; 3. Ostankino Tower, Moscow;
4. Acorn Proton; 5. Thranduil; 6. Almond; 7. Formal rulings; 8. A Colt
.45; 9. All-Ireland Amateur; 10. Cardiff; 11. Ureter; 12. E. B. White;
13. 1962; 14. Alchemy; 15. 1923; 16. 8 hours 10 minutes

QUIZ 177

1. 10cm (4 inches); 2. Manhattan, New York; 3. Madagascar;
4. Armadillo; 5. *Pathfinder*; 6. Musicians; 7. Three; 8. Carbon
dioxide; 9. Jamie Foxx; 10. *The Wrestler*; 11. Of a single colour;
12. Constellations; 13. 59; 14. James I (also known as James VI of
Scotland); 15. John Steinbeck; 16. Devon

QUIZ 178

1. Canine; 2. The marriage of Peleus and Thetis; 3. Stone age, bronze
age, iron age; 4. Cray; 5. To belch or spit; 6. Mitch Albom; 7. 1707;
8. 15; 9. *Fahrenheit 9/11*; 10. Lack of appetite; 11. Coca-Cola; 12. Saudi
Arabia; 13. Munich; 14. Six; 15. Deafness; 16. Simon Bowman

QUIZ 179

1. CN Tower, Toronto; 2. Aberforth; 3. Alain Prost; 4. The Bible; 5. Swiss;
6. Marlin; 7. China; 8. *Explorer 1*; 9. 21st Century Tower; 10. Bathing;
11. Elizabeth II; 12. London Heathrow; 13. Lulu; 14. Leafy greens;
15. Popocatepetl; 16. Ruddervator

QUIZ 180

1. Ringing; 2. Michael Faraday; 3. Vladimir Nabokov; 4. Cameroon;
5. Pitch; 6. Winter solstice; 7. Make an easy living; 8. *Good Will
Hunting*; 9. Alcoholism; 10. David Bradley; 11. 66; 12. Stop-go penalty;
13. Carbon; 14. Rhine; 15. 41 AD; 16. *Audition*

The Bumper *PUB* Quiz Book

QUIZ 181

1. Whitehorse; 2. Dennis Ritchie; 3. 19; 4. Joe Simpson; 5. Iraq;
6. Immunity; 7. Goldeneye; 8. Clarendon Palace; 9. Washington, DC;
10. Medicine; 11. None; 12. Tequila; 13. A pond-dwelling salamander,
such as a newt; 14. Bock; 15. Pigwidgeon; 16. A tree

QUIZ 182

1. 365 days; 2. Londinium; 3. 1843; 4. Steinlager; 5. 22 months;
6. Soviet Union; 7. Hesiod; 8. *Madame Butterfly*; 9. His uncle and
aunt; 10. Boeing 727; 11. Switzerland; 12. Ostrich; 13. Turquoise;
14. Bladen'kerst Baenre; 15. Ronaldo; 16. Todd Wagner and Mark
Cuban

QUIZ 183

1. *Under the Net*; 2. Washington, DC; 3. Baja peninsula; 4. Indian;
5. Silver; 6. Sister and brother; 7. Blue and yellow; 8. Cows;
9. Maybelline; 10. Morocco; 11. 1547; 12. Adam Scott; 13. Fin whale;
14. *Smooth*; 15. Algorithm; 16. Chiffonade

QUIZ 184

1. 1989; 2. House of Hanover; 3. Won two gold medals; 4. France;
5. *Sister Act*; 6. Free; 7. 1974; 8. France; 9. Access control; 10. *Mylo
Xyloto*; 11. Mylo; 12. Croydon, London; 13. Hubert Raudaschl; 14. L;
15. 1940s; 16. Projectile vomiting

QUIZ 185

1. Groundhog; 2. 2514; 3. Eton College; 4. Afghanistan; 5. Holly Hunter
and Anna Paquin; 6. Security/anti-virus; 7. Major Boothroyd; 8. A former
unit of radiation dosage; 9. General Motors; 10. Six; 11. A Chinese
dish of seafood and chicken; 12. Red, black and green; 13. Iceland;
14. Valentina Tereshkova; 15. Victor Hugo; 16. Neville Chamberlain

The Bumper *PUB* Quiz Book

QUIZ 186

1. 1990; 2. Violin; 3. Lacoste; 4. A puppet; 5. Lilongwe; 6. USA; 7. To build and maintain body tissue; 8. Cooler than sun; 9. Jonathan Swift; 10. Black rot; 11. 'Go away!'; 12. 80 miles (129km); 13. Italian; 14. Mata Hari; 15. Roberto de Vicenzo; 16. 6

QUIZ 187

1. Jordan; 2. Audio; 3. Ursa Major; 4. Jack; 5. Red; 6. Make it Happen; 7. Lockheed SR-71 Blackbird; 8. Pita bread; 9. Beryllium; 10. Daryl Van Horne; 11. Managua; 12. *Julius Caesar*; 13. A twin crystal; 14. Margaret Thatcher; 15. F.W. de Klerk; 16. William Henry Fox Talbot

QUIZ 188

1. Mexican leather-thonged sandals; 2. Abu Dhabi Golf Championship; 3. Zed's; 4. Venus; 5. Caipirinha; 6. 1980-1988; 7. 50; 8. Euripides; 9. John Glenn; 10. Italy; 11. Sandal; 12. Romania; 13. Egg temperature; 14. Potato; 15. Wilhelmshaven; 16. 5 weeks

QUIZ 189

1. Former Mexican President; 2. Carbon monoxide; 3. Cardiologist; 4. Cauliflower; 5. Lyndon B. Johnson; 6. 38 minutes; 7. Head; 8. 1991; 9. *Gladiator*; 10. Japan; 11. High-Definition Multimedia Interface; 12. Complete public disgrace; 13. Longstanding illness; 14. 3,624 miles; 15. Miguel de Cervantes; 16. Nou Camp and Olympic

QUIZ 190

1. Vietnam; 2. Greenland; 3. Lizzy Calvert; 4. Pablo Picasso; 5. Removes the dampers so notes continue sounding; 6. Phobos; 7. Polio; 8. Russkaya Pravda; 9. Art, gold and other valuables; 10. Eric Jupp; 11. Jonathan Pryce; 12. Sleep Apnea; 13. 2006; 14. Triplane; 15. Cordon; 16. Anne

The Bumper *PUB* Quiz Book

QUIZ 191

1. 61; 2. Belgium; 3. *Pon de Replay*; 4. Giraffe; 5. Paper; 6. 25 - 30 years; 7. The Great Barrier Reef; 8. Egg yolks; 9. 1908; 10. Mark Edmondson; 11. 2G; 12. Relating to engraving; 13. Umberto Eco; 14. Root; 15. Japanese acupressure; 16. Nara

QUIZ 192

1. 4; 2. Nestor Carbonell; 3. Nixon's 'Western White House'; 4. Belarusian ruble; 5. A sigma bond; 6. 1810s; 7. Tapas; 8. Mohs scale; 9. An elephant; 10. Yang; 11. Nearby lightning strike; 12. Venice; 13. Gymnastics; 14. India; 15. Peppermint; 16. Saint George

QUIZ 193

1. Decorative handwriting; 2. The race or session has ended; 3. Circumference; 4. Silverbacks; 5. Budapest; 6. Eli Wallach; 7. Nine; 8. Dormant; 9. Zaire; 10. 11th century; 11. Basilisk; 12. Gareth Gates; 13. Guernica; 14. Australia; 15. Brandy and Kahlua; 16. 22

QUIZ 194

1. Cat; 2. Model A and Model B; 3. Vertebrae; 4. *Jack Frost*; 5. Mark Prada; 6. 1952; 7. Flow lines; 8. 14m (45ft); 9. Concerto; 10. The Hume River; 11. Leeds; 12. 1959; 13. Tunney Hunsaker; 14. Downing Street Declaration; 15. Stout; 16. Hg

QUIZ 195

1. Franz Beckenbauer; 2. Charing Cross; 3. Robert J. Waller; 4. Los Angeles, California; 5. Thailand; 6. Uranus; 7. North Korea; 8. Fergie; 9. *A Captain's Story*; 10. Jean Grey/The Phoenix; 11. Fermentation; 12. Iceland; 13. Amphibian; 14. Six; 15. Robert Goddard; 16. Cherries

The Bumper *PUB* Quiz Book

QUIZ 196

1. Valletta; 2. 1939; 3. Dallas; 4. Tomato and feta cheese; 5. Poland and Ukraine; 6. *Jumping Jack Flash*; 7. Packaging material; 8. Henry John Temple, Viscount Palmerston; 9. St. Leger Gould; 10. Hans Oersted; 11. Angelina Jolie; 12. Budapest, Hungary; 13. Ctrl + z; 14. Newt; 15. A woody climbing plant, found in rainforests; 16. Euler

QUIZ 197

1. Dominica; 2. New Caledonia; 3. Brother; 4. Poetry; 5. O2; 6. Vine; 7. *Blue Juice*; 8. Mendel; 9. USA; 10. Mexico; 11. Team name or emblem; 12. Longbow; 13. Apical meristem; 14. Mario Puzo; 15. Mosaic; 16. Cola

QUIZ 198

1. Denmark; 2. *Harry Potter and The Sorcerer's Stone*; 3. South Africa; 4. Clams; 5. Length; 6. White Anglo Saxon Protestant; 7. 1307; 8. Songhay; 9. Lead; 10. Pandora; 11. Lamprey; 12. Zeebad; 13. 63; 14. A nation of shopkeepers; 15. A crab that has discarded its shell; 16. 4.5 Volts

QUIZ 199

1. Warner Huntington III; 2. Religion; 3. In her mouth; 4. That it is, or is served with, a white cheese sauce; 5. Jenny; 6. Queen Victoria; 7. Wiltshire; 8. Moldova; 9. White truffle; 10. Atlantic Ocean; 11. 2004, 2005, 2009; 12. Enya; 13. Prints; 14. Yitzhak Rabin; 15. Eel; 16. 9

QUIZ 200

1. Juan Ponce de León; 2. Vatican City; 3. *Oracle of Seasons* and *Oracle of Ages*; 4. A large salamander; 5. God Is Great; 6. Valencia; 7. 100,000; 8. Luanda; 9. George Orwell; 10. Kate Bush; 11. Before birth; 12. Monotremes; 13. Peter III; 14. Soup; 15. George Lazenby; 16. The south-east

The Bumper *PUB* Quiz Book

QUIZ 201

1. Red cross; 2. 2000; 3. Guinea-Bissau; 4. Kneecap; 5. 5; 6. Otho;
7. A Shetland viol; 8. Laguna; 9. Myanmar/Burma; 10. Valkyr; 11. Nose
and prostate; 12. No problem; 13. Rye; 14. French Guiana; 15. Stag;
16. Ronnie O'Sullivan

QUIZ 202

1. 21; 2. Fianna Fail; 3. *Gravity*; 4. Heart specialist; 5. The
hypothalamus; 6. Oyster pails; 7. The Congo; 8. Joe Haldeman;
9. Its perimeter; 10. Europe; 11. 70 years; 12. A huge railway gun;
13. Brussels; 14. Battery; 15. Nursemaid or maid; 16. ALU

QUIZ 203

1. Candlemas; 2. Freddie; 3. In space; 4. 1.5 million tons; 5. Tyra Banks;
6. Lance Armstrong; 7. 1899; 8. H.G. Wells; 9. A Japanese savoury
pancake; 10. 1968; 11. 9 miles (14.5km); 12. Turtle; 13. Tanzania;
14. The Birth of Venus; 15. Muscat; 16. Port

QUIZ 204

1. Ariel Sharon; 2. 5 to 6 years; 3. Good evening; 4. London Bridge;
5. Andy Warhol; 6. Cheetah; 7. Dante Alighieri; 8. She broke up with
a band member from her band; 9. Egypt; 10. Seize Bolivia's water
supply; 11. Barnwell Manor; 12. Rocket; 13. *I Love To Eat*; 14. Thomas
Brisbane; 15. Bathurst 1000; 16. 1993

QUIZ 205

1. An Asian blend of spices; 2. 1958; 3. Osborne; 4. Angola and
Mozambique; 5. 2 months; 6. Per Pale; 7. Bit; 8. *Some Like It Hot*; 9. A
painter; 10. Meja; 11. Anchovy; 12. Portugal; 13. Zeus; 14. 4; 15. Jack
Davey's funeral took place; 16. Yellow

The Bumper *PUB* Quiz Book

QUIZ 206

1. Jamestown, Virginia; 2. Long-sightedness; 3. In five sacred canopic jars; 4. Montreal; 5. Silverchair; 6. Liver; 7. Mammals; 8. Nouveau; 9. 276 years; 10. Amethyst; 11. A narrow, jagged mountain crest or ridge; 12. Egypt; 13. Great Barrier Reef; 14. Henry VI; 15. Fault or crevice; 16. The Iari

QUIZ 207

1. Free radicals; 2. Former Socialist, industrial states; 3. Playwright; 4. 1982; 5. Qatar; 6. Massachusetts Institute of Technology; 7. 2004; 8. 1972; 9. 3; 10. Fourth; 11. Alton Brown; 12. Sleigh bed; 13. *Casino Royale*; 14. Slade; 15. Eris; 16. 5

QUIZ 208

1. 27; 2. Vilnius; 3. Her brother; 4. Beefeater; 5. Lucian Freud; 6. John Carpenter; 7. Student; 8. *The Knight's Tale*; 9. Trapezius; 10. A land mine; 11. Hyoid; 12. Rome; 13. Pauleta; 14. Lira; 15. *Evergreen*; 16. Wisdom teeth

QUIZ 209

1. 6; 2. 28; 3. Altair; 4. Taipei 101; 5. Pyroxidine; 6. Noble gas; 7. Quentin Tarantino; 8. Five; 9. Greenland; 10. Yin; 11. New Zealand; 12. Rome; 13. Mead; 14. *Breaking Bad*; 15. Jenny Lind; 16. Virginia Woolf

QUIZ 210

1. Methane; 2. Sweetcorn; 3. Cones; 4. Covered lizard; 5. Henry VIII; 6. It has an unusually high alcohol concentration; 7. Putter; 8. 1958; 9. North-West Africa; 10. Port Stanley; 11. *FX*; 12. Yellow, plum-like fruit; 13. Africa; 14. LEGO; 15. Romania; 16. Nero

The Bumper *PUB* Quiz Book

QUIZ 211

1. Elizabeth Tower (the bell is Big Ben); 2. Bye For Now; 3. Will Ferrell;
4. Evelyn Waugh; 5. Submariners; 6. Plucking with their fingers;
7. Shapes; 8. John Rabe; 9. New; 10. A galah; 11. Myanmar/Burma;
12. Barley bread; 13. Implanted; 14. Organic; 15. Asian Tour; 16. Two Pi,
One Sigma

QUIZ 212

1. 0 degree line of longitude; 2. Ultraviolet; 3. Chris Froome;
4. Argentina; 5. Spain; 6. Small, decorative, open sandwiches; 7. Skein;
8. Nicholas Aaron; 9. Mount Olympus; 10. Canton; 11. The Raconteurs;
12. Uma Thurman; 13. A way to quickly assess the health of newborn
children immediately after birth; 14. Hong Kong; 15. 1836; 16. Poaching

QUIZ 213

1. Aperture size; 2. Guernsey; 3. Bloc Party; 4. Maradona; 5. Mjosa;
6. Coral; 7. 1916; 8. Cassie; 9. Tequila Sunrise; 10. Ghana; 11. Churchill;
12. Vienna; 13. A theme park to the south of Barcelona; 14. William
Shatner; 15. *A Death In The Family*; 16. 15

QUIZ 214

1. Light fiction; 2. Indian; 3. Leonard Cheshire; 4. Flea; 5. India; 6. Nick;
7. Les Fauves; 8. Charles de Gaulle; 9. Caribbean Sea; 10. 1974;
11. Minister of the Interior; 12. Cassandra; 13. Charles I; 14. Dyslexia;
15. 83; 16. Saffron

QUIZ 215

1. Erratic boulders; 2. Ikra; 3. Panama; 4. Achilles; 5. Ezzard Charles;
6. Amal Alamuddin; 7. 1923; 8. 3363; 9. Kent; 10. *A Thousand Splendid
Suns*; 11. Masters and Johnson; 12. Nuerburgring; 13. Murray river;
14. Monsoonal; 15. 1924; 16. 10

The Bumper *PUB* Quiz Book

QUIZ 216

1. Cabin; 2. Frequency Modulation; 3. Winston Churchill; 4. Danger;
5. Binary star system; 6. Pope Leo II; 7. Mongols; 8. Sun spider;
9. John Kennedy Toole; 10. The World Health Organization (WHO);
11. Lightweight; 12. New Orleans; 13. *InDesign*; 14. Wax; 15. All I Want;
16. Portuguese

QUIZ 217

1. *Grace Kelly*; 2. Rory McIlroy; 3. China; 4. A magician; 5. 13.7m
(45ft); 6. Starve herself; 7. Amber; 8. Finland; 9. Saffron; 10. Singapore;
11. Barack Obama; 12. Shiwalik; 13. Two, Anne of Cleves and Catherine
Parr; 14. Jakarta, Indonesia; 15. Abba; 16. Italian Screwdriver

QUIZ 218

1. Zorro (South American fox); 2. Stuart Appleby; 3. Mercury and Venus;
4. Prague; 5. Al Pacino; 6. 1911; 7. *A Red Letter Day*; 8. Peking duck;
9. Athens, Greece; 10. Israel; 11. A quarter note; 12. Alexander Pushkin;
13. Dzhokhar Dudayev; 14. Jew's ear mushroom; 15. Bahamas;
16. Australia

QUIZ 219

1. Northern Ireland; 2. 56; 3. Killer whale; 4. HSBC; 5. Taiwan; 6. Vienna;
7. *Walk*; 8. Momentum; 9. Aung San Suu Kyi; 10. England; 11. A Da
Vinci notebook; 12. Maine, US; 13. Tracy; 14. Turkey; 15. 2; 16. Victor
Hugo

QUIZ 220

1. Epidermis; 2. Rhetoric; 3. Washington, DC; 4. Five; 5. Immac;
6. Permafrost; 7. Asia; 8. *Slumdog Millionaire*; 9. Pete Sampras;
10. Blood; 11. Blind, cave-dwelling amphibians; 12. Australia;
13. Trained specialists; 14. 18; 15. Robert A. Heinlein; 16. A battery (a
voltaic pile)

The Bumper *PUB* Quiz Book

QUIZ 221

1. Central African Republic; 2. 22; 3. Tungsten; 4. 0C (32F); 5. The common grape vine; 6. 1941; 7. Mozambique; 8. Halifax; 9. Martina Navratilova; 10. Red carnation; 11. Yggdrasil, a giant ash tree; 12. Harrison Ford; 13. Syria; 14. Paul; 15. Vladimir Putin; 16. number10. gov.uk

QUIZ 222

1. Capelli d'angelo; 2. Sound; 3. John L. Sullivan; 4. A dogsbody or lackey; 5. Phil Mickelson; 6. None; 7. Breakfast; 8. Blind-worm; 9. None; 10. Kolleru lake; 11. Maryland; 12. Peter Sellers; 13. Argentina; 14. 20 years; 15. Himalayas; 16. Rum

QUIZ 223

1. Io; 2. Sherlock Holmes; 3. Prime Minister; 4. 360; 5. Dermatological; 6. *Killer Queen*; 7. In the Atlantic between Canada and Greenland; 8. Oil; 9. Switzerland; 10. Chicago; 11. A White Russian; 12. *The Truman Show*; 13. South Sea; 14. West; 15. The central boss; 16. Five

QUIZ 224

1. Yuan; 2. The Kid; 3. Donna Karan New York; 4. 44 BC; 5. Tim Allen; 6. Cannae; 7. Vincent van Gogh; 8. A tropical evergreen verbena shrub; 9. Third; 10. Roll; 11. A dodgy moneylender; 12. 1804; 13. Sir Charles Lyell; 14. Free radicals; 15. Republic; 16. Skewered meat in peanut sauce

QUIZ 225

1. Joseph Smith, Jr.; 2. Series Circuits; 3. Accelerating; 4. Hydrogen; 5. Azerbaijan; 6. Eris; 7. Nineteenth hole; 8. Blondie; 9. Portugal; 10. 2.01m (6ft7in); 11. Apples; 12. Lake Taupo; 13. Breeds bulldogs; 14. Vaclav Havel; 15. Sylvester Stallone; 16. *Dick Tracy*

The Bumper *PUB* Quiz Book

QUIZ 226

1. G.I. Jane; 2. Equatorial Guinea; 3. Paul Biya of Cameroon; 4. 1936; 5. Sharpeville Massacre; 6. Brick red; 7. Sommelier; 8. Cytoplasm; 9. Cruz Cape; 10. A railing to help with balance; 11. 1999; 12. In his bedroom; 13. Australian football league; 14. 0; 15. 10; 16. 28

QUIZ 227

1. US Virgin Islands; 2. 1976; 3. Frankfurt; 4. Chicken coops; 5. Kimono; 6. Valkyries; 7. Creating a garden that needs little moisture; 8. Lois Maxwell; 9. Toronto; 10. *Concert*; 11. Replace; 12. Serfs; 13. A garment worn over armour; 14. Reduction; 15. 12; 16. Flow

QUIZ 228

1. Memory; 2. Borrowing a car to go and repair his bike; 3. *A Beautiful Mind*; 4. A chickpea; 5. Hans Holbein the Younger; 6. Edward the Confessor; 7. Nile; 8. France; 9. A tufty, velvety yarn or cord; 10. Neutron Star; 11. New Zealand; 12. Platinum; 13. *Oliver Twist*; 14. San Sebastian Church, Philippines; 15. Australia; 16. 40000

QUIZ 229

1. 1653; 2. Yellow; 3. The Man Village; 4. Pinball games; 5. North America; 6. 57,285; 7. *Waiting for Godot*; 8. *Always Where I Need To Be*; 9. Paella; 10. Leonard Lower; 11. 22; 12. James I of England; 13. Rob Glaser; 14. 35mm; 15. Bermuda; 16. December

QUIZ 230

1. Frank Bryce; 2. Bank Of Italy; 3. A solid swelling of clotted blood; 4. Trill; 5. Adult yellowtail; 6. *Million Dollar Baby*; 7. Pete Best; 8. Anthony Zimmer; 9. An Aboriginal rite of passage; 10. Placido Domingo; 11. A helium nucleus - two protons and two neutrons; 12. Bernardo O'Higgins and Jose De San Martin; 13. Pacemaker; 14. Two; 15. Switzerland; 16. Skunk

The Bumper *PUB* Quiz Book

QUIZ 231

1. Cardiff; 2. Unix system programming; 3. Communism; 4. Insider trading; 5. 1986; 6. France; 7. 2013; 8. Research In Motion Limited (RIM); 9. Angiosperms; 10. Sir Georg Solti; 11. *Syriana*; 12. Weathering; 13. Nagano, Japan; 14. 1999; 15. Japan; 16. Mel Gibson

QUIZ 232

1. *Say Goodbye*; 2. Florida; 3. *Chicago*; 4. A portable machine that records heartbeats; 5. Tolar; 6. St Matthew; 7. Metallic cricket used by paratroopers; 8. Modena; 9. Teeth; 10. Crashed it; 11. Warren Buffett; 12. Jack Grout; 13. Daedalus; 14. Debt relief; 15. Chickens; 16. Chile

QUIZ 233

1. Computerized Axial Tomography; 2. Beth Gibbons; 3. USA; 4. 5; 5. Tropical depression; 6. *Proxima Centauri*; 7. 1900s; 8. New York; 9. A craving to eat unsuitable substances; 10. Augustus; 11. Absolute Pressure; 12. Windsor Castle; 13. Carson McCullers; 14. Glamorgan; 15. Feijoada; 16. College of William & Mary

QUIZ 234

1. First Triumvirate; 2. East Africa; 3. Zepto; 4. A state of weariness; 5. 7; 6. Hypokalemia; 7. Lee Teng-Hui; 8. Seychelles; 9. Pimiento; 10. Ali Wilder; 11. Nick Bolletieri; 12. The Honeydrippers; 13. A flood plain; 14. A human skull; 15. 1943; 16. Rotation through a full circle

QUIZ 235

1. 66; 2. Seventh; 3. Cook Islands; 4. Milligram; 5. Jupiter; 6. Natalie Portman; 7. Mexican; 8. Fondue; 9. Surrealism; 10. Tunisia; 11. *Hyper Music*; 12. Somalia; 13. Anne; 14. Stop Worrying and Love The Bomb; 15. Bill Clinton; 16. Sydney, Australia

The Bumper *PUB* Quiz Book

QUIZ 236

1. Don't Talk About Fight Club; 2. Wide-Angle Lens; 3. Absolute;
4. Lebanon; 5. 1950; 6. *The Heart Of The Matter*; 7. He tunnelled out;
8. New York; 9. MTV Video Music Awards; 10. The Napoleonic Wars;
11. Satellites; 12. The Army; 13. A sweet bread; 14. Caligula; 15. Rand;
16. 23.5 Degrees South

QUIZ 237

1. Ten; 2. Cornwall; 3. Nitrogen; 4. Missouri, US; 5. Early morning;
6. Hen; 7. Soap salesman; 8. The Amazon; 9. Beijing; 10. Rampant;
11. Leo Tolstoy; 12. Emulsification; 13. Xerxes; 14. Sugar; 15. Jamaica;
16. A governor during the Mogul empire

QUIZ 238

1. Saudi Arabia; 2. Denmark; 3. Margaret Thatcher; 4. 1825; 5. Cystic
fibrosis; 6. *Dangerous Minds*; 7. Fear of death or dying; 8. Intifada;
9. *Aneurysm*; 10. Mike; 11. Phlegethon; 12. Doug Nicholls; 13. IEEE;
14. Bacon; 15. 1969; 16. He secretly married her maid

QUIZ 239

1. *Happy Days Live*; 2. Forgiving; 3. A bearded collie; 4. Istanbul;
5. Etna; 6. Three; 7. Albert Lake; 8. A fast-beating heart; 9. It has an
audio track in the DTS format; 10. Mikhail Gorbachev; 11. CMOS;
12. Sahara Desert; 13. Duluth; 14. Crucified them; 15. Luxembourg;
16. Optics

QUIZ 240

1. Hops; 2. Vodka; 3. 8.65m (28ft 4.5in); 4. Long-sightedness;
5. Corebar; 6. Tetrodotoxin; 7. Hyrax; 8. Sally Field; 9. Greek;
10. Bedding; 11. 1949; 12. Aristotle; 13. NATO; 14. Australia;
15. Silverstone; 16. Germany

The Bumper **PUB** Quiz Book

QUIZ 241

1. Eclipse; 2. 1st July 1961; 3. White and red; 4. *Jurassic Park*; 5. Dry sherry; 6. Upper Volta; 7. Chongqing; 8. May 1802; 9. Downpatrick; 10. Royal; 11. The Hitman; 12. Burger King; 13. Polka; 14. Poet Laureate; 15. Disco; 16. William Lyon Mackenzie King

QUIZ 242

1. 27; 2. Aeration; 3. Foot And Mouth Disease; 4. Google; 5. Musk ox; 6. Dr. Peter Venkman; 7. Cambodia; 8. Luke Pritchard; 9. Sir Chrisopher Wren; 10. 5; 11. *La Boheme*; 12. Nikita Khrushchev; 13. Lebanon; 14. Budweiser; 15. The Lion; 16. New York Mercantile Exchange

QUIZ 243

1. Heart rate; 2. 8; 3. Cabbage; 4. Sally; 5. Methane; 6. The Eiffel Tower; 7. Australia; 8. *Call It Sleep*; 9. 1910; 10. Conakry; 11. A type of numeric crossword; 12. Apollodorus of Damascus; 13. Shin of veal; 14. Yitzhak Rabin; 15. Luis Suarez; 16. Decibel

QUIZ 244

1. Cardinal points; 2. Gertrude Stein; 3. Nine; 4. An essential oil distilled from the flowers of the Seville orange; 5. *The Bubble*; 6. Their tongue and their feet pads; 7. Versailles; 8. Yemen; 9. Four; 10. Asp; 11. Seafood stew; 12. Four; 13. 1902; 14. Organelles; 15. A million; 16. Panzer Armee Afrika

QUIZ 245

1. Forehead; 2. Egypt; 3. *A.I. Artificial Intelligence*; 4. 87; 5. LHR; 6. Edoras; 7. Shivering; 8. Sage; 9. November; 10. Spain; 11. 88; 12. A person's duty; 13. Contra dance; 14. *We've Got it Goin' On*; 15. Miso; 16. 36

The Bumper *PUB* Quiz Book

QUIZ 246

1. 5; 2. Appellation d'origine contrôlée; 3. Hyundai; 4. 1998; 5. Fevered;
6. Neil Robertson; 7. None; 8. Capri; 9. 37; 10. *The Body*; 11. Boss;
12. *Android*; 13. 100; 14. *The Next Best Thing*; 15. Guadeloupe;
16. Asia

QUIZ 247

1. 4; 2. Dick Button; 3. Molasses; 4. Stephen King; 5. Kent; 6. Germany;
7. Blackout; 8. Onement; 9. *Nexus*; 10. Lebanon; 11. Kampala;
12. Yellow; 13. Boxing Day; 14. Sushi; 15. Ferdinand and Isabella of
Spain; 16. Casino War

QUIZ 248

1. Four; 2. Seven billion; 3. Frankie Muniz; 4. Shampoo; 5. South-East
Asia; 6. 0.01; 7. A root vegetable such as potato; 8. To smell; 9. Luffield;
10. India; 11. *Nimbus 2000*; 12. 19 Years; 13. A tailless, small black dog;
14. Ant; 15. Cory Monteith; 16. 7

QUIZ 249

1. Germany; 2. 2003; 3. Mongolia; 4. IBM; 5. 1953; 6. Steve Harris;
7. The Inquisition; 8. An introductory psalm or antiphon sung
during Mass; 9. True; 10. Water cycle; 11. Mexico City; 12. Green;
13. Augustus, born Gaius Octavius; 14. Michael Jackson; 15. *Malicious
Intent*; 16. Houses of Parliament

QUIZ 250

1. A separate living space attached to a house; 2. Yamanashi
prefecture; 3. The German Army; 4. Elbe; 5. Afghanistan; 6. *A View To
A Kill*; 7. Leg warmers; 8. Ginkgo biloba; 9. Continental Drift Theory;
10. Brussels; 11. Koba Gogoladze; 12. She is petrified; 13. Apathy;
14. Adlerian; 15. 1054; 16. Matt Smith

The Bumper *PUB* Quiz Book

QUIZ 251

1. 340; 2. 5%; 3. Celine Dion; 4. Michael Bergin; 5. Four; 6. 1999;
7. Red and black; 8. Backwards twirl; 9. *Mrs Doubtfire*; 10. Stratford-upon-Avon; 11. Anise; 12. Antibiotic; 13. Lilangeni; 14. Major Thomas McGuire; 15. Antarctica; 16. His horse

QUIZ 252

1. FujiFilm; 2. Alexander II; 3. Hunter S. Thompson; 4. Aspartame;
5. Kenya and Tanzania; 6. Bow-tie pasta; 7. Fear of beautiful women;
8. Sweden; 9. Wes Craven; 10. *Danzig III: How the Gods Kill*;
11. Nicaragua; 12. Brazil; 13. Six; 14. Venus; 15. Glacier; 16. Moderately fast

QUIZ 253

1. Apple; 2. Tomato; 3. Pixie-bob; 4. Poland; 5. 1990; 6. Red-green colour blindness; 7. International Business Machines; 8. *Rolling In The Deep*; 9. After World War 1 General Joffre; 10. Neon; 11. North Korea;
12. Six; 13. Ahmad Shukeiri; 14. Charlie Hunnam; 15. Jessie; 16. Paris

QUIZ 254

1. Epidural; 2. Sony; 3. Sounder; 4. Colin Firth; 5. James Connolly;
6. Blue and white; 7. Beer became legal to sell again; 8. Mahmoud Ahmadinejad; 9. Trenches; 10. Honiara; 11. Los Angeles; 12. Prisoner exchange at the end of the war; 13. Trajan; 14. Bissau; 15. Fire; 16. *The Open Boat*

QUIZ 255

1. 1974; 2. Y; 3. Basenji; 4. Paul McCartney; 5. 1940s; 6. India;
7. Portugal; 8. It becomes denser; 9. Origami; 10. Snorkasaurus;
11. Malabo; 12. Cinnamon; 13. 2500; 14. Santa Claus; 15. Joe DiMaggio; 16. Electrical Engineering

The Bumper *PUB* Quiz Book

QUIZ 256

1. Barometer; 2. Argentina; 3. Violin; 4. Stanmore; 5. Imagine Entertainment; 6. *WinZip*; 7. Alec Douglas-Home; 8. Dresden; 9. Maine Coon; 10. Hyperkalemia; 11. Guatemala; 12. 17th; 13. Charles II; 14. 1; 15. Kensington Palace; 16. The season of Spring

QUIZ 257

1. Venezuela; 2. 77; 3. Eleven; 4. 9; 5. Lamb; 6. A long ridge of glacial deposits; 7. Scipio; 8. Cnidarian; 9. The Bahamas; 10. 4; 11. Mr Potato Head; 12. Gobbler; 13. *The Velvet Underground & Nico*; 14. Dave Matthews; 15. The Guggenheim; 16. Monopoly

QUIZ 258

1. 22; 2. Before Christ; 3. Barbados; 4. Return to the previous speed; 5. Fredericton; 6. Less than 24 per cent; 7. Hades; 8. Beverly Hills Cop; 9. Wayne Rooney; 10. 1831; 11. Ellen Johnson-Sirleaf; 12. *Sputnik I*; 13. A sweet-flavoured sugar-syrup drink; 14. Still life; 15. Mach 1; 16. Panache

QUIZ 259

1. Formosus; 2. 18th; 3. Mexico City; 4. Alyson Hannigan; 5. Amman; 6. 53; 7. Pluto; 8. Squash; 9. Blue; 10. Mammoth; 11. Lamb; 12. West Africa; 13. 1912; 14. India and Pakistan; 15. Farm tractors; 16. Union

QUIZ 260

1. Echolalia; 2. Genghis Khan; 3. Colombo; 4. Diamond; 5. Pete Doherty; 6. Herbert Asquith; 7. Cloudy; 8. Toad; 9. Rhombus/diamond; 10. Speed; 11. Yell words of support to your team during a game; 12. 4/4; 13. New York City; 14. Lenin; 15. 1976; 16. French

The Bumper *PUB* Quiz Book

QUIZ 261

1. Greenwich; 2. 8 Points; 3. 37; 4. Canada; 5. Barry Levinson;
6. *Microsoft Money*; 7. Barney Rubble; 8. Gin; 9. Distributor and
manufacturer; 10. Lover of wisdom; 11. Non-ferrous; 12. Reaction
agent; 13. 1961; 14. Iron; 15. Paris, France; 16. The Protectorate

QUIZ 262

1. Black; 2. Charles I; 3. 2; 4. Gamma rays; 5. World War 1; 6. *Link's
Awakening*; 7. Brunch; 8. Madrid; 9. Chetumal; 10. The longbow;
11. Russia; 12. A herbal tea; 13. John Malkovich; 14. Czar's decree;
15. Dr Cox; 16. Jeffrey Archer

QUIZ 263

1. Dodo; 2. Century; 3. Shanghai; 4. Farmer; 5. Fidel Castro; 6. Neon;
7. 1957; 8. American Cantonese; 9. Moscow; 10. Alaska; 11. A listless
feeling of boredom; 12. 1966; 13. Whipped chocolate and cream;
14. The first-ever captain of the England national women's team;
15. The Notorious B.I.G.; 16. Vincent Vega

QUIZ 264

1. Gavrilo Princip; 2. Falkland Islands; 3. Four; 4. Kimi Raikkonen;
5. Like a man; 6. An Aztec god; 7. Kip; 8. One; 9. Frederick Banting;
10. Ice skating; 11. Off-Broadway; 12. *The Handmaid's Tale*; 13. French
Guiana; 14. Aeration; 15. A repeater; 16. 1969

QUIZ 265

1. 1996; 2. *Edward Scissorhands*; 3. Seurat; 4. New York; 5. Annette
Bening; 6. The Visigoths; 7. Ricotta; 8. Yemen; 9. *Love's Labour's
Lost*; 10. Argentina; 11. A meat substitute made of wheat gluten;
12. Parabola; 13. Vera Wang; 14. Cape Town, South Africa; 15. China;
16. Geologist

The Bumper *PUB* Quiz Book

QUIZ 266

1. A Cuban or Colombian soup; 2. A storey below a basement; 3. Peter Carey; 4. *The Monkey's Paw*; 5. A special US bomb; 6. A radio; 7. Stylus and clay; 8. Pina Coladas; 9. Siberian; 10. 2.2k Ohms; 11. Marie Curie; 12. Helena Bonham Carter; 13. Chile; 14. 1991; 15. United States; 16. *Witness*

QUIZ 267

1. World Wide Web; 2. Angola; 3. J.R.R. Tolkein; 4. 15; 5. Shermer High; 6. Scotland; 7. Ambivalent; 8. 54.6cm (21.5in); 9. A very hot green chilli pepper; 10. Great Charter; 11. A painter; 12. Robert Millikan; 13. Kestrel; 14. Johnny Mathis; 15. Honey; 16. Eight Hours And 10 Minutes

QUIZ 268

1. Crazy Horse; 2. Server; 3. Through the skin; 4. Iran; 5. No one is sure; 6. *Endeavour*; 7. Lu Chen; 8. Severn; 9. Dropsy; 10. 1982; 11. Germany; 12. Mark Twain; 13. Silkworm; 14. Excess fat around the stomach area; 15. To lightly sprinkle flour or sugar; 16. Ethiopia

QUIZ 269

1. Nepal and China; 2. 4; 3. Marcel Duchamp; 4. Pork lo mein; 5. Jean-Pierre Jeunet; 6. Roy Keane's; 7. Niacin; 8. Brazzaville; 9. Tartar deposits; 10. 9; 11. Toronto; 12. Carrot; 13. Kensington Palace; 14. Methane; 15. To march or tramp; 16. Chuck Palahniuk

QUIZ 270

1. 9; 2. iPod; 3. Lady Jane Grey; 4. Annuals; 5. Peasants; 6. 10; 7. Marc Antony; 8. Chad; 9. Slice; 10. Purple; 11. Two; 12. Pinot Noir And Chardonnay; 13. Endospore; 14. 19; 15. Laurie Lee; 16. Mrs. Jennings

The Bumper *PUB* Quiz Book

QUIZ 271

1. Francesco Totti; 2. Iron; 3. Spirit of the time; 4. 3G; 5. Monte Rosa;
6. The resistor; 7. Alton Towers; 8. An Inspiral Carpets tour poster;
9. Fievel; 10. Louis Braille; 11. Mao Zedong; 12. A cypress tree with
valuable timber; 13. 55%-65%; 14. Root; 15. Vietnamese soup;
16. Diabetes, Thyroid disease, Androgen excess

QUIZ 272

1. *Hell's Kitchen*; 2. Athena; 3. Colin Montgomerie; 4. Vincent Price;
5. Five; 6. It expands; 7. Chamomile; 8. 1965; 9. Dung beetle, or
sometimes a cockchafer; 10. Basseterre; 11. James Watt; 12. Tony
Blair; 13. *The Artist*; 14. *Watchers*; 15. Saint Vincent and The
Grenadines; 16. *Hansard*

QUIZ 273

1. Claudio; 2. Three; 3. Australia; 4. Mexico; 5. Dylan; 6. Amount
of energy in food; 7. Stamens; 8. A cropped sweater; 9. Peninsula;
10. Havana; 11. Maybelline; 12. 250; 13. Henry VII; 14. *Four Swords
Adventures*; 15. Neapolitan; 16. *Titanic*

QUIZ 274

1. 1907; 2. *The Murder of Roger Ackroyd*; 3. Père Noël; 4. 1832;
5. Clinical; 6. Silver with a red trim; 7. *Charlie and the Chocolate
Factory*; 8. Nine; 9. *Always Where I Need to Be*; 10. Belgium; 11. Germs
or dirt; 12. A town or village; 13. Argentina; 14. David Cameron;
15. *Carcaradon carcharius*; 16. Six

QUIZ 275

1. Tennis; 2. Kenya; 3. Fortune Cookie; 4. 182; 5. Miley Cyrus; 6. Taipan;
7. Jimmy Carter; 8. Belgium; 9. Catheter; 10. Ford Maddox Ford;
11. *The Mothman Prophecies*; 12. Mantis shrimp; 13. Humpback whale;
14. Fear of the number 666; 15. Europe; 16. Cambium

The Bumper *PUB* Quiz Book

QUIZ 276

1. Florida; 2. Prince Harry; 3. *Glamorous Glennis*; 4. Ice caps; 5. Sirius Black; 6. Spring; 7. Llama; 8. Barbary ape; 9. Lion; 10. Burkina Faso; 11. Worst Dressed; 12. Viceroyalties; 13. The Cam; 14. *Powerpoint*; 15. Johannes Vermeer; 16. French

QUIZ 277

1. Antoine Fuqua; 2. Texas Instruments; 3. Turnip; 4. 1965; 5. Softens the notes; 6. 17 years; 7. Bird; 8. Tasuki and Chichiri; 9. 1558; 10. Lake Volta; 11. Aviation fuel; 12. J.M. Coetzee; 13. Canada; 14. Road Town; 15. Dr Pepper; 16. 9.58s

QUIZ 278

1. 5 Ohms; 2. Hologram; 3. Greece; 4. The height; 5. France; 6. Kill Me; 7. Goya; 8. *Rocky*; 9. Lubeck; 10. Gold medal; 11. August 22, 1485; 12. India; 13. James Baldwin; 14. Sylvester Stallone; 15. Ideal society; 16. India

QUIZ 279

1. Catalytic converter; 2. International Monetary Fund; 3. Kevin Costner; 4. Francis Crick, James Watson and Maurice Wilkins; 5. Schism; 6. Barley, hops, yeast and water; 7. *Tender*; 8. Sylvia Gore; 9. Suva; 10. Joseph Charyk; 11. 1625; 12. *The Adventure Of The Speckled Band*; 13. Birchard; 14. Vincent Van Gogh; 15. Aeneas; 16. Germany

QUIZ 280

1. First Western woman to teach yoga; 2. *Crash*; 3. Celta Vigo; 4. Yasmine; 5. 9; 6. Italian-American; 7. Macau special administrative region; 8. *After Effects*; 9. Vera Wang; 10. Respiratory; 11. Frankfurt; 12. Rovers Return Inn; 13. Bogota; 14. Relating to the cheek; 15. 1500 BC; 16. Clam

The Bumper *PUB* Quiz Book

QUIZ 281

1. 23; 2. France and Italy; 3. Majorca, Minorca, Ibiza and Formentera;
4. Teeth; 5. The Cure; 6. Disney; 7. The Alps; 8. Vermouth; 9. Fiji;
10. Acorn RISC Machine; 11. Grass; 12. Moroccan dirham; 13. Clinique;
14. Labour Party; 15. Cuckoo; 16. Greenhouse Effect

QUIZ 282

1. Its holes; 2. Edmund Blake; 3. South Korea; 4. Canada; 5. Dirtee
Stank; 6. *About a Boy*; 7. Sorbonne; 8. Diana; 9. Falun Gong;
10. Armada; 11. Lilac; 12. Griots; 13. By a causeway; 14. 1996;
15. Venom; 16. 32

QUIZ 283

1. Guy Fawkes; 2. 40%; 3. Czech Republic; 4. Statistics; 5. Athens;
6. Evian; 7. North Pole; 8. *Too Close To Hate*; 9. A1 Team Brazil;
10. Tundra; 11. 'This one time, at band camp...'; 12. To continually
harass; 13. Air pressure; 14. Logan Lerman; 15. Put mud on their face;
16. Ancient Egypt

QUIZ 284

1. 4.6 Billion Years; 2. Scottish; 3. Lewis Carroll; 4. Liberia; 5. Bermuda;
6. Constitutional Monarchy; 7. Greece; 8. A plot of land; 9. In Waves;
10. Palestinians; 11. Dolce; 12. She was rather mannish-looking;
13. London Heathrow; 14. *No One Knows*; 15. Nepal; 16. Edward
Hopper

QUIZ 285

1. Colin Montgomerie; 2. *That 70s Show*; 3. Ultraviolet; 4. Wiltshire;
5. Otoplasty; 6. Out of the ocean; 7. Gianni Versace; 8. Ontario; 9. 1899;
10. Belgium, Luxembourg and Netherlands; 11. 1565, St. Augustine;
12. Relating to the open sea; 13. Darlinghurst; 14. A stump, peg or nail;
15. The Hague; 16. Irrational

The Bumper *PUB* Quiz Book

QUIZ 286

1. 20; 2. 4kg (9lb); 3. 39C (102F); 4. Red Guards; 5. 156 people;
6. Seed; 7. Paris; 8. 1135; 9. French; 10. Antarctica; 11. *LA*; 12. 12;
13. Earth's tilted axis; 14. Tennis; 15. Red and white; 16. 10th

QUIZ 287

1. Vietnam; 2. An island prison; 3. Marsupial/kangaroo; 4. Nothing;
5. The Caterpillar; 6. Duck fat; 7. A malarial illness; 8. La Coruna;
9. 1962; 10. Jim Carrey; 11. Team; 12. America Online; 13. Rheinhessen
(Rhine-Hesse); 14. Albert Einstein; 15. Edict of Nantes; 16. A sacred
religious musical instrument used by Native Americans

QUIZ 288

1. CCD; 2. France; 3. France; 4. Pet Shop Boys; 5. A member of the
lowest Japanese class; 6. Ostrich; 7. Lakshmi; 8. Stick figures; 9. Frys.
com Open, San Martin, California; 10. Yasser Arafat; 11. Great white
shark; 12. Brunei; 13. East Germany; 14. Smoked haddock; 15. Edith
Wharton; 16. Mutation

QUIZ 289

1. Eight; 2. 1789; 3. Phrenology; 4. The Torah; 5. Andes; 6. Her Father;
7. 1954; 8. Photosynthesis; 9. Caligula; 10. Stamford Bridge; 11. Tommy
Hilfiger's; 12. Retrieving from water; 13. Protagonist; 14. Cyprus; 15. Let
the buyer beware; 16. Radio waves

QUIZ 290

1. Germany; 2. Spain; 3. Dover; 4. Pete Best; 5. Thiamine; 6. *Made in
Dagenham*; 7. Colt; 8. Saul Alvarez; 9. 5,895m (19,341 feet); 10. Cuticle;
11. Antimicrobial; 12. Chelsea; 13. Bill Clinton; 14. Ray; 15. George W.
Bush; 16. Its volume

The Bumper *PUB* Quiz Book

QUIZ 291

1. 78 gifts; 2. The Pleiade; 3. George Washington; 4. Asia; 5. The Chainsmokers; 6. No; 7. Jupiter; 8. One, in 1932; 9. The Scorpion; 10. Henry Fielding; 11. Papua New Guinea; 12. Charles I; 13. China; 14. 1982; 15. Wind flowing from the sea towards the land; 16. Summit Entertainment

QUIZ 292

1. Ukraine; 2. Fibonacci; 3. New Zealand; 4. Rafael Nadal; 5. Fleas (carried by rats); 6. *You Only Live Twice*; 7. *Hole in the Head*; 8. Magnum; 9. Internal; 10. Little peasant girl; 11. 20-35 per cent; 12. Kakapo; 13. 1942; 14. Sir Leigh Teabing; 15. ASDA; 16. Hind feet

QUIZ 293

1. Birmingham New Street; 2. *Die Hard*; 3. Blue Boy; 4. 1974, 1978 and 2010; 5. 1936; 6. Ares; 7. Frog; 8. Chickpeas; 9. Boxer; 10. Catherine Parr; 11. Smell; 12. Gerald Ford; 13. 1; 14. Kenya; 15. Intestinal; 16. Cherry blossom

QUIZ 294

1. 9.96s; 2. Fennel; 3. Kublai Khan; 4. Shinjuku Station in Tokyo, Japan; 5. Baby food; 6. Your torso; 7. Polar bear; 8. Louis Oosthuizen; 9. O'Malley's; 10. Bangladesh; 11. Scrambled eggs; 12. Glass-blowing; 13. An exact location in space; 14. Minas Anor; 15. Ganymede; 16. 0.37%

QUIZ 295

1. Electrocardiogram (ECG); 2. Thrown out of a window; 3. 2005; 4. Stanislaw Lem; 5. They were all the same person; 6. *Ocarina of Time*; 7. Sow; 8. Great Britain; 9. 13; 10. Stalingrad; 11. National Challenge Cup; 12. Oceanic crust; 13. Cotton or hemp; 14. Tyler; 15. 3 days; 16. Argentina

The Bumper *PUB* Quiz Book

QUIZ 296

1. 19; 2. Electron or positron; 3. Horned Toad; 4. England; 5. Sudan; 6. H.F. Verwoerd; 7. Combs; 8. Colm Meaney; 9. Alsace and Burgundy; 10. Carbohydrates; 11. South America; 12. The Angel's Share; 13. John Calvin; 14. 1846; 15. Evel Knievel; 16. *Borrelia burgdorferi*

QUIZ 297

1. Iceland; 2. Water lily; 3. The organic component of soil; 4. Paris, France; 5. 15.5 tons (14,000kg); 6. Mudgee; 7. A peasant farmer who was rewarded with a cottage; 8. It flows northward; 9. *The Minish Cap*; 10. Czech Republic; 11. Aztecs; 12. *The Artist*; 13. Pivo; 14. Producers; 15. Queens of the Stone Age; 16. Computer-Aided Design

QUIZ 298

1. Echo 1; 2. Lebanon; 3. Carbon dioxide; 4. Cosmetics; 5. *Rubyfruit Jungle*; 6. Journeying on foot; 7. Utah; 8. Mexican; 9. Triumph; 10. Idiopathic; 11. Ronnie O'Sullivan; 12. Artificial harbours; 13. Monaco; 14. *The Big Wedding*; 15. 1974; 16. Coromandel Peninsula

QUIZ 299

1. China; 2. 1190; 3. Vietnam; 4. iPhone 4S; 5. Stephen King; 6. Admiral Karl Doenitz; 7. A dwarf planet; 8. Transistor; 9. Raoul Silva; 10. A Christmas wafer; 11. Rubens; 12. The Coriolis effect; 13. Brandy Alexander; 14. Hatshepsut; 15. The Replacements; 16. 6

QUIZ 300

1. Silicon; 2. Carbonation/bubbles; 3. Isle of Man; 4. Peter Carey; 5. Extravehicular Activity/spacewalk; 6. Pigpen; 7. 1990; 8. The ultimate; 9. MSG (Monosodium glutamate); 10. Jamestown, Virginia; 11. *The King's Speech*; 12. Lake; 13. Five; 14. Glen Johnson; 15. The Philadelphia Museum Of Art; 16. Alexander II

The Bumper *PUB* Quiz Book

QUIZ 301

1. China; 2. Bubonic Plague; 3. Brown Pelican; 4. Italy; 5. 50 to 60 years; 6. Lie; 7. Africa; 8. Iota; 9. Two months; 10. Thyme; 11. Job search; 12. Bill; 13. Babyshambles; 14. Christianity; 15. Frances Burnett; 16. The Karun

QUIZ 302

1. Genghis Khan; 2. Jools Holland; 3. Caffeine; 4. Swimming; 5. Boiling water; 6. China; 7. Pound; 8. Jordan; 9. Rutger Hauer; 10. Anne Tyler; 11. Coelom; 12. 24601; 13. Wilhelm Wundt; 14. Pain; 15. About four million; 16. Macau

QUIZ 303

1. Bamako; 2. *Titanic*; 3. 1974; 4. Neoclassical; 5. The Pretenders; 6. Dry; 7. Cardiff; 8. Turkish Van; 9. The Caribbean; 10. Rice and wheat; 11. The Sumerians; 12. Pan Am; 13. Pleiades star cluster; 14. Rum; 15. Poet Laureate; 16. A Japanese, acupuncture-like therapy

QUIZ 304

1. The UK; 2. 3.75MB; 3. Mary II; 4. Roasted Pig; 5. Climbing; 6. Joseph Conrad; 7. 1660; 8. Crawl; 9. Camille Guerin and Albert Calmette; 10. Escudo; 11. 147; 12. Lowlands; 13. Peru; 14. Brad Pitt; 15. Aerosol; 16. 15

QUIZ 305

1. Estonia; 2. 80%; 3. Dutch; 4. The eye; 5. A custard dessert; 6. Naboo; 7. Cordons; 8. Tifosi; 9. 1024; 10. Santorini (Thera); 11. Crushed ice; 12. 1966; 13. Ribosomes; 14. Penelope; 15. Steve Emerson; 16. Eure-et-Loir

The Bumper *PUB* Quiz Book

QUIZ 306

1. South Korea; 2. Gotland; 3. Dermis; 4. Bush; 5. 1956; 6. Congenital heart defects; 7. Blue, red and white; 8. Mackenzie; 9. Kylie Minogue; 10. Atop the Acropolis of Athens; 11. Sharp or bitter; 12. Dr Doug Ross; 13. England; 14. Leonardo da Vinci; 15. French; 16. Coat it with oil

QUIZ 307

1. Sony; 2. 1954; 3. 18; 4. The mint; 5. Tom Ford; 6. Turning on their lights; 7. 1199; 8. Epilepsy; 9. Acetone; 10. Twice a day; 11. Comic book; 12. Suva, Fiji; 13. Jupiter; 14. Australian Grand Prix; 15. Nike; 16. 31st October

QUIZ 308

1. 400; 2. Tortoise; 3. Nepal; 4. Eastern; 5. Bitch; 6. The nose; 7. Russia's; 8. *Tom Jones*; 9. Snowy owl; 10. Cocaine; 11. Both represent other things; 12. Thomas Jefferson; 13. Germany; 14. Susannah; 15. Blue; 16. Gisele Bündchen

QUIZ 309

1. Socialist Party; 2. 2010; 3. Monica Keena; 4. Sweden; 5. Don Delillo; 6. Hindu Kush; 7. Lithium; 8. Permineralized; 9. *St. Elsewhere*; 10. Comet Hale-Bopp; 11. 1937; 12. Very fast; 13. British Virgin Islands; 14. Australia; 15. Dakar, Senegal; 16. Mackerel

The Bumper *PUB* Quiz Book

QUIZ 310

1. Grace Murray Hopper; 2. True; 3. B and C; 4. Amazon; 5. Kona;
6. 100th; 7. Fifth; 8. Losing; 9. Afghanistan; 10. Lion; 11. Per Cross,
or Quarterly; 12. Abel Xavier; 13. Bamboo shoots; 14. Amber Waves;
15. Aorta; 16. 1483

QUIZ 311

1. A painting by Penelope's father; 2. *State of Alert*; 3. Diane Von
Furstenberg; 4. *Meet The Fockers*; 5. Anne of Cleves; 6. Squid; 7. A
coarse-grained metamorphic rock; 8. A compressed image; 9. Charles,
Prince Of Wales; 10. Cote d'Ivoire; 11. Digger; 12. 650; 13. 2003;
14. Mansa Musa; 15. Greyhound; 16. Quesadilla

QUIZ 312

1. 7; 2. Solar radiation; 3. Aztecs; 4. Feet; 5. About 80; 6. Jacques-Louis
David; 7. Newcastle Brown Ale; 8. Mount Olympus; 9. Ace; 10. James
II; 11. Kuala Lumpur, Malaysia; 12. John le Carré; 13. Flatulence;
14. *Firefox*; 15. South Korea; 16. *3000 Miles To Graceland*

QUIZ 313

1. Tibet; 2. Worm; 3. Sheep's Stomach; 4. Jack Nicholson; 5. Interest;
6. Argentina; 7. Third; 8. Steven Bray and Patrick Leonard; 9. 3,000,000;
10. 4; 11. Mexico; 12. Hephaestus; 13. Cutaneous; 14. 1889;
15. Nitrogen; 16. Endodontist

The Bumper *PUB* Quiz Book

QUIZ 314

1. Ham; 2. Soldier's uniforms; 3. King Julian; 4. Andorra la Vella;
5. Superiorly; 6. Trio; 7. Janissaries; 8. Fierce Battle Areas In Stalingrad;
9. Robert Delaunay; 10. P.G. Wodehouse; 11. Asia; 12. A conglomerate
rock; 13. The human foot; 14. Anise; 15. Cote d'Ivoire; 16. Deer Lake,
Pennsylvania